CHARLES GOD

Aikins
of the U of T Medical Faculty

© 1998 Codam Publishers
ISBN 0-9684226-0-8

Codam Publishers
RR1
Madoc
Ontario
KOK 2KO

Printed by University of Toronto Press Incorporated

For Dylan

Acknowledgment

It is always difficult to give credit to those who have helped write a book of this nature. However, due thanks must be given the University of Toronto, Department of Archives; The Robarts Rare Book Library; The Archives of Ontario; and the Hannah Institute. Individual thanks must also be offered to Professors Michael Bliss, Ned Shorter, Jim Connor and Pauline Mazundar, Harold Averill of the University of Toronto Archives, Jon Smitz of the Ontario College of Physicians and Surgeons and Leon Walmsley of the Ontario Archives. A special appreciation is acknowledged to David R. Keane, who generously provided the research notes used in writing his DCB biography of Aikins. Miss Peggy Runacre and Ms. Judy Cardwell have been indefagitable in typing and correcting my script and of course, I must acknowledge to my wife, Margaret, the many hours she has foregone my presence so that I could work on this project.

Foreword

It is surprising that William Aikins has escaped the attention of scholars and historians. Some say that the Medical Faculty of the University of Toronto would not enjoy its current acclaim, if Aikins had not lived in the last part of the 19th Century. In those formative years the proprietary medical school was the norm. Although Britain and the United States were changing this practice, it is likely that the Toronto University would not have established a Medical Faculty in 1887, without the persistence of Aikins. A religious man, deeply committed to his faith, he also believed firmly in the proposition that doctors should receive their instruction at a university level, complete with a full range of subjects other that the traditional "trade" courses. In particular, he constantly demanded that science was the necessary ingredient in a physician's bag. Although he was busy fighting for science to be part of a student's curriculum, he also urged, and was the main proponent of, a professional association to maintain high standards in medicine – the College of Physicians and Surgeons.

All of these efforts took place against a background of the tremendous changes that transformed medicine from the heroic to the scientific age. Aikins led his students, and teachers, into the new concepts of disease and treatment and while doing so became the first Dean of Medicine at Toronto.

Charles Godfrey has traced the Dean's career from his undergraduate days through the tumultuous period of establishing a university medical school, that was destined to become a major force in the world of scientific medicine.

Professor Murray B. Urowitz, MD., FRCPC
Vice-Dean, Post-Graduate Medicine
Faculty of Medicine University of Toronto

Introduction

It was a magnificent occasion. The Chancellor, The Honourable Edward Blake, occupied the Chair. The platform was crowded with distinguished dignitaries, guests and professors of the University. Vice Chancellor William Mulock sat next to the Premier of the Province, G.W. Ross. Mulock, who had been such a vehement fighter for this moment often told the story of how, in 1859, he took his matriculation examination in the old Medical School "... which used to stand amidst a grove of pine trees, dark and secluded, one entrance facing east and the other, for students, facing west". Mulock, with the other applicants, wrote his examination on the old anatomy tables in Moss Hall, with the permeating smell of whiskey oozing from the pickling vat, which stored whole and partial cadavers. And now the wheel had turned full circle and he was officiating at the re-opening of the University of Toronto Medical Faculty. There was Daniel Wilson, the President of University College. He too was a link between the old University teaching faculty, which had been abolished. The President reminisced "When I entered on my duties as Professor in 1853, I was left that there was no doubt but the abolition of the Medical Faculty was largely due to the antagonisms between Rolph and certain professional rivals. Fresh as I then was from Edinburgh and familiar with the relations of the science departments to other branches of instruction in that University, I was strongly impressed with the beneficial influence which an efficient Medical Faculty exerts in stimulating and fostering all departments of science". Wilson had been a sturdy soldier in the battle for improved medical education.

In the second row was Dr. Abner Rosebrugh, the founder of the Toronto Eye and Ear Dispensary and an innovator particularly in the new field of medical electricity. Next to him towered the great Dr. William Canniff, the last Dean of Victoria Medical Faculty who, after its demise, transferred back to the Toronto School of Medicine. He had been President of the Canadian Medical Association in 1880 and now basked with his peers on the platform. Each of these prestigious persons paid tribute to one or another and to himself, Dr. William Thomas Aikins, the newly appointed Dean of the Faculty of Medicine.

They echoed the words of Mulock who had primed the engines which had built the medical school in 1883, when he said, "It is the duty that the Provincial University at the earliest possible moment establish a teaching Faculty of Medicine, instead of permitting that important branch of education to remain almost exclusively in the hands of private corporations ...". His zeal had stimulated Premier Ross who explained, "I had not the expectation, when engaged last session in preparing the Bill for the Federation of the Provincial University and other universities and colleges, that the provisions made for the establishment of the Medical Faculty would bear fruit so soon, but thanks to the broad-mindness of the Senate and above all thanks to the public spirit of the medical profession, we are permitted today to take part in the ceremony which very few could have expected would have taken place for several years to come".

Aikins' day was complete. Finally he could grasp the grail for which he had sought through many years. Not only had the speakers given praise to the University's foresightedness and to the excellent teaching staff of the new Faculty, but they had also set the tone for the future. "The theme of medical education which deals simply with the curative, neglecting the preventive aspects of medical science, is radically defective". Now, at last, after labouring for 34 years in the Toronto School of Medicine, struggling with the financial hardships, feeling the frustration of insufficient scientific apparatus, lacking the ability to call on other sciences such as comparative anatomy, sanitary sciences, chemistry and physiology, the first Dean of the University of Toronto Medical School could compose a new curriculum – one designed for the 20th century.

Aikins of the U of T Medical Faculty

Chapter One

The Student

The *King William IV* trudged through the lake and the heights of Scarborough Bluffs slowly flattened in the distance. William Aikins leaned on the rail gazing at the shore, comparing it with his father's lush farmlands just north of Cookstown, which he had left the previous day. To travel from Toronto to Cobourg by steamer was indeed an adventure. And when he reached the town to register at Victoria College and begin his matriculation studies, was the high point of his life. He would never forget, or be able to repay, the generosity of his father, James, for paying the tuition. Of course, for a family of devout Wesleyans there could be no other choice for schooling than Victoria. William followed his older brother James and preceded his younger, Moses Henry. The unacceptable alternative was to attend Upper Canada College, but that was an Anglican school under the direction of Bishop John Strachan and so was out of the question.

Although it was William's intention to complete his matriculation and go into commerce, he was not hard set on that course. He could return to the family farm which his father and mother, Ann Cox, had worked since emigrating to Upper Canada in 1816, with their neighbours John W. Montgomery and his family. They came directly to Upper Canada, but the Aikins went to Philadelphia. Montgomery prospered and wrote a glowing account of life in the British colony to James, who then took out a patent for 100 acres near Burnhamthorpe. He too became a successful farmer, and was able to send his children to secondary schools. William was born on the farm on the 5th of June 1827.

James Eakins, as he signed his name for the rest of his life (although his children adopted Aikins), had been a Presbyterian before leaving Ireland. In a letter written at a later date, William stated:

> This hasty sketch which you will please view in the same light as if it had been incidently elicited during a morning conversation in your papa's drawing room. Some thirty-four years ago owing to the pecuniary and the threatening of a greater damage from the incensed Roman Catholics, for the most part enmity against Protestants thus existed ... my parents left the north of Ireland for America. Two or three years they spent in Philadelphia and then left for Canada, purchased in Toronto township fourteen miles from Toronto and four east of Cooksville, where they have since resided. By their personal exertion making their home comfortable and endeavouring to provide for the future in the life of their family. The evening of existence is now settling upon them, my father being 70 and my mother 60, both enjoying good health, although the imperfections of age are slowly but surely encroaching upon this. Two daughters and four sons complete the domestic circle. The eldest daughter united to a plain but genuine farmer, the eldest son to a party formerly Miss Somerset, who lived somewhere near your papa's on the lot south of Proudfoot's, if memory is correct. The remainder, a sister and brother younger and myself, are single. A second son goes on his farm shortly. My parents family wished that young William would finish and go into business. He asked for greater time, gives his reasons and obtains his request. As to religion, the parents and those of the family settle down and are members of the Methodist church. William though not united to any church, yet enjoys, I trust, the blessings of a personal religion.

James set a high example for the family and was a trustee of the local Methodist chapel. In his obituary, the *Christian Guardian* printed his "piety and worth and weight of character marked him for remembrance".

The boat trip took seven and half hours and William noted in his diary:

> The day was cool, windy and snowy and in the natural consequence, the lake was rough. I was quite sick for two or three hours.

> I arrived at Cobourg about half past nine and then proceeded to the College.

However, it wasn't just the sea-sickness that gave him major problems. He reported later that he had visited the dentist the following day and his gum had been lanced in two places. A series of visits to the dentist began which continued over the next several months, with many applications of warm poultices of camomile or wormwood.

It was William's first venture away from home and he tended to stay on his own. While he recorded going to the sermons of some of the staff, including the redoubtable Egerton Ryerson, he avoided many of the student activities:

> A certain number of students purchased a barrel of cider, and carried it to a particular room, in which they seemed to enjoy all the pleasures of the cider.

At this time, Ryerson was a well known public figure, a strong Wesleyan and editor of the *Christian Guardian* who had been appointed to be the first principal of the College. He was also Head of the Department of Moral Philosophy and Rhetoric and had worked ceaselessly for a Methodist school. His forthrightness and obvious dedication to mankind's welfare plus an eloquent tongue and pen, had procured for him a favoured place with the decision makers of the province. Although he had parallel thoughts to the Reform party of the 1830's, he disagreed with them, particularly in that they wished to break from the British connection. Ryerson argued forcefully that remaining with Britain would lead inevitabily to a democratic government in Canada. On several occasions he voiced harsh criticisms of the Reformers, especially during and after the Rebellion. About the time of Aikins' arrival at school, Ryerson had published a series of articles vindicating the new Governor General, Lord Metcalfe, who had refused to make patronage appointments as had been suggested by the Reform cabinet. Ryerson was quick to point out that this was using patronage to promote the sway of the Reform party. In defending Metcalfe's actions, Ryerson became the target of much criticism from the Reform group. However, he was used to confrontation and remained adamant.

He was equally steadfast in religious matters and believed strongly in evangelical Christianity, having earned his spurs as a circuit rider in the Ancaster – Cobourg area. He showed his feistiness early in his career when he verbally attacked John Strachan, later a Bishop, who had written that Methodists were "ignorant American enthusiasts", with little knowledge of religion and were prone to disloyalty in politics. Ryerson's vehement denial and counter-attack marked him as a leader of the Methodist adherents. In addition to calling up the rhetoric of hell-fire when he confronted the Bishop, the principal was a vigorous preacher who never slackened in his zeal. When he spoke to the students at Victoria, he used the same suasive powers as he did at camp meetings of several hundred or as pastor of the Methodist Church on Adelaide Street in Toronto. He was always a strong vicar of John Wesley, and imprinted his passions on the seventeen year old William. The young student did well in his courses, but his psyche and soma were vulnerable. On Sunday, December 5th, 1844 William recriminated himself:

> much time has been spent idly and now I begin to think seriously about the evils of attending such a course. For some length of time I have been troubled with a toothache and feel rather dejected in spirits ... time flies rapidly and I appear to make but little progress in comparison to that which I should make.

There were thirty-three classmates and Aikins reported that they were boisterous and in good health, although over the next few months six had to leave school because of sickness. The curriculum included algebra, chemistry, philosophy and rhetoric and he recorded displeasure with his marks with his last recitation of the week in chemistry on the 24th of December. The Christmas holidays passed quietly with a cricket match on the pitch of the Cobourg Club. Christmas service at the Trinity United Church, a frame building which had been built in 1824, was a moving experience. The church was a tangible proof of the ability of the four denominations of Methodism in Cobourg – the Bible Christians, the Primitive Methodists, the Methodist Episcopals and the Wesleyan Methodists – to come together for worship. Although the name Trinity United had been chosen by the congregation, it became known as the "College Church" because the professors and student body filled its pews.

Cobourg was quiet at this time of the year, because the flood of Irish immigrants on their way to take up land in Peterborough County was over. More than one thousand residents supported twenty-five stores, three taverns, two schools, a post office, some mills and three surgeons. The bell from the steeple of the Church of England called a sprinkling of parishioners to service. Some of them grudgingly acknowledged the irony of the pushy Methodists ("levellers, you know") who had named their school the Upper Canada Academy (later Victoria College after Ryerson gained a charter and funds). They knew full well that the Church of England had an Upper Canada College in Toronto. But possibly the name was a sly riposte against the Anglicans who had sited the Diocesan Theological Institution in this modest Methodist "metropolis".

William's loneliness was somewhat relieved by a letter from his older sister, Eleanor, who wrote on Christmas Eve with news of the family. All were in good health except Ann Jane, his younger sister by three years, who had had a severe toothache for a week. Eleanor reported that: "the scarlet fever is quite bad in some places. The winter is very favourable for the cattle, but unpleasant getting about. There is no sleighing, nothing but mud ... James (her husband) and the children join me in love to you and wish you a Happy New Year."

The holiday season passed quietly, although some of the high jinks at school gave Aikins concern. At a party one of his classmates fired a pistol in celebration of New Year's Day, shocking the young student, who never used firearms. William, although in good health, had some worries and on several occasions required to be seen by either one of the Faculty or one of the local surgeons to be re-assured that he had no major problems. But his diary continued to show entries about his general well-being, with frequent reference to chronic toothache.

He found that the lecture material was interesting and carried out experiments with galvanism. Luigi Galvani and Alessandro Volta had published their work on electro-stimulation fifty years previously and clinicians were still searching for a use of the phenomenon. John Wesley had urged setting up a clinic to treat the poor with this technique at St. Thomas' Hospital in London. Electric shocks for various medical conditions had been administered for many years, however there had never been an accepted body of knowledge which suggested jolting was of value or desirable:

I received several of the shocks. Whether they will be useful or not I
cannot say. I cannot place my mind firmly and unceasingly on my
studies.

He also had lectures on magnetism and began some experiments by
hypnotizing his friends, including another student, John Howitt. Franz
Mesmer in Paris, had popularized "mesmerism" and the use of magnets for the treatment of a wide variety of conditions, after perceiving
the influence of the planets on man. From this he derived that the
human hand had a similar power. He touched his patients and peered
deeply into their eyes and gave directions which cured their illness.
Part of his therapy was to seat a patient beside a magnetic tub which
emitted healing electric currents. His book on mesmerism was published in 1779 after he was driven out of Vienna to Paris by a medical
commission set up by the Empress Maria Therese.

Although less then ten years had passed since the rebellion of '37,
there was little discussion of those events in Aikins' diary. Cobourg
had been a centre of loyalism and there had not been any difficulty in
raising a regiment which defended Toronto against Mackenzie and
his "army". One of the local heroes, Captain Macnab, who had per-
ished when he stumbled and fell upon the bayonet of a soldier in his
regiment, was still revered by the local citizens. But he was never the
subject of a discussion by Aikins and his group who were too young
to have much interest. There were occasional flurries of excitement in
the community as another rebel was denounced and brought up for
trial, but these incidents did not seem to stir the atmosphere in the
College. Nor was there any great interest over the political furor
which was caused by the continuing contest between the Reformers
and the Tory party. The resignation of the Reformers from the cabinet in 1844, did not affect William or his friends. In the same year, Dr.
John Rolph, one of the rebel leaders, was pardoned and returned to
Toronto.

What did interest Aikins were the activities of his schoolmates. Most
attended special Bible classes or the local Women's Mission meetings. It
was accepted practice that proper people attended at least one Sunday
service and frequently one or two prayer meetings during the week.
Methodism was an exacting religion. Some classmates enlivened their

academic lives by harrying their teachers and it was not unusual for
lecturers to be greeted with catcalls or applause. However one professor stirred up a rowdy element in the class. Students adopted "the
practice of firing off crackers", which irritated this instructor, who
responded by threatening to catch the culprits. He was countered with
a "cracker of more than ordinary size which was placed at the principal's door and a match applied to it. In a few moments it exploded,
causing the College to tremble". Ryerson's sermon on that occasion
was searing, and two boys left the school.

Such pranks were not unusual in most colleges. The Faculty frequently reported "insubordination and disrespect" but unlike the
events at King's College, Windsor, there was no reported abduction of
the President's pig. Rendering a professor's horse invisible by painting
it grey was another demonstration of student exuberance.

And so the first year passed at Victoria and Aikins, who had received
good grades, returned to the farm for the summer months. When he
left to return to school on October 29th, he wrote with deep feeling:

> I left home attended by my affectionate mother and brother. I must
> now pause for a moment and look at the face of my mother, kind as
> she was on former occasions, she appears to have more so now that
> tender affection. That sincere depth of love was fully manifested in
> her conduct towards me. Her advice with respect to the health of
> my body was excellent. When I took hold of her hand, to take my
> leave, the tears streamed down her faded and care-worn cheek.
> While she bade me to take care of my soul, to seek an interest in the
> blood of Christ, the soul-felt voice dropped upon my ear. Nor did it
> cease to be heard, but like the last toll of the distant church bell, the
> loving sound continued in my ears and gently died away.

During that fall, his diary shows much introspection on devotional
matters. The sermons of Dr. Ryerson and his colleagues had had great
effect. Aikins, like many of his contemporaries, was deeply concerned
with one's state of grace and life after death. He lamented that:

> I must confess before my God that I have not spent (Saturday) as I
> ought to have done and this day finds me with cold religion. My

heart is at a greater distance from my Creator and therefore in an unpleasing condition and uncomfortable status mentis.

By the New Year, he was seized even more deeply with moral matters:

The New Year is ushered in while the old one is now far away and in the realm of eternal shade, never more to return ... before my mind, in melancholy glow, the bygone year thus passes. While reason strongly speaks and conscience powerfully condemned, undone, undone would I now be, but for atonement and the cleansing power by Jesus made, which from all sin the guilty soul sets free. Then in humble form, His pardon seek. Nor shall I seek in vain. His word is sure, though Heaven and Earth away do pass and be no more, in that word his promise stands to save the erring soul.

This depth of piety had not been apparent until his return to school during the previous fall. It continued throughout the spring term and was manifested by an increased attendance at missionary meetings in the chapel and by more fulsome entries in his diary:

Oh glorious privilege. So kindly given to us that we may know not only where He is but also His will concerning us. By this means, He will enable us to prepare for a joyful passage out of this world and a happy entrance into the beyond. Oh thou adorable being, await I fly to thee, who has set His vast inexplicable machinery in motion and with thy goodness and atonement, I ever trust and confide so that when the time shall be no more, I shall remain uninjured, a living monument of the eternal goodness.

Although William's thoughts were frequently well above the clouds, he expressed many of the emotions held by young men of the day. His inspiration, Egerton Ryerson, had left for England. Nevertheless, the call of the great leader still echoed through the halls of the school. But it was necessary to pay attention to less lofty matters. Pencils and tacks for two pence. Writing paper for one shilling, eleven pence. Two pence towards "a lamp which the students purchased to light the upper hall," and also the bed rental to be paid to Victoria. His haircut was 4 shillings, 5 pence and soap was 2½ pence. He balanced the one shilling threepence he spent on a ticket to an evening party, with the same amount given to missionary causes.

His records of 1844–45 showed "received on leaving home two pounds ten shillings". This was supplemented by a further five shillings from home and he also sold one of his books for three shillings. Steamer charges from Toronto to Cobourg were barely above that of a hair cut – six shillings, three pence, which was possibly his most expensive personal pay-out – cutting, hair oil, shampooing of the head, all of which ate into his capital. Although he was careful about his spending, there were occasions when he "treated" himself. In February of 1846 he "bought six apples for 9½ pence, a pair of gloves for two shillings sixpence". His charities were few. However, he donated one shilling, three pence to form a cricket club in April and gave tuppence to the class in church, followed by another three pence.

But there was still money for books. Charles A. Lee's *Physiology for Use of Elementary Schools* came for five shillings (used) – published by the American Common School Society, 1835 and Blair's *Rhetoric* for two shillings. The physiology purchase was important, possibly an augury, as he continued to show fascination in body functions, stimulated by accounts of the Frenchman Rene Laennec, whose description of the heartbeat demonstrated the skill of the Almighty in creating man.

To satisfy his appetite, William enjoyed eating fruit and was able to buy oranges in May for seven pence halfpenny as well as apples, raisins and licorice. This may have accounted for his numerous visits to the dentist every two or three months. He was constantly recording payments of up to 18 shillings for tooth fillings. Between his teeth and his hair he was constantly reaching into his pocket.

But his source of funds was slim. He had received 7 pounds 15 shillings and 5 pence from his father in October of '45 and another 10 shillings from his mother and from James, his brother 5 shillings, but money was short by the time spring came and he had to borrow 1 pound 5 shillings from J. Beatty, a classmate. Steamer travel was cheap but Aikins had to pay several pence to have his trunks transferred to the residence or to the stage which took him to Cooksville. Stage fare was 1 shilling 10½ pence. During the summer he had to visit

Dr. J. Gilchrist in Cobourg whom he paid 3 shillings 9 pence for "medicine which included the doctor's fee".

Compared to the turbulent thirties, the 1840's were relatively stable in Upper Canada. Having completed its rebellion but with an aftermath of the trials and sentencing of rebels. Lord Durham's report, with the prescient statement, "I found two nations warring in the bosom of a single state", had been accepted in general and the "Great Ministry" of Baldwin and Lafontaine was giving sound legislation. One or two skeletons remained as serious bones of contention including the disposition of the Clergy Reserves and the matter of the Rebellion Losses Bill. Just as in the War of 1812–15 when everyone took one step forward to claim the Loyal and Patriotic Medal of Upper Canada, so after the rebellion, the applicants for compensation under the Bill almost outnumbered the number of inhabitants and caused rioting in Montreal. In Toronto a mob stoned the homes of MacKenzie and Rolph.

In the early part of the forties it was politically incorrect to speak of reform and those Reformers who had remained or returned under amnesty maintained a low profile. Relative peace and prosperity prevailed and Toronto became a bustling provincial centre. Fortunately there were no major epidemics until later in the decade to disrupt the burgeoning economy.

During the mid-thirties the medical profession began to feel that it was strong enough to govern itself and several Bills aimed in that direction were proposed. Physicians had been licenced by the Upper Canada Medical Board (UCMB) under an Act passed in 1818. This legislation provided certificates to candidates who presented with the appropriate qualifications. Anyone showing a medical diploma from any University or from the Royal College of Physicians and Surgeons in London, or a commission or warrant as a physician or surgeon in the armed services, could be granted the necessary licence. The Board examined candidates from various medical colleges in the United States, but there was no training facility in Upper Canada.

Even though there was a strong representation by the physicians for self-government, the action was opposed by the Royal College of Surgeons of London on the basis that their Charter gave jurisdiction over the colony. "An Act to amend the laws regulating the practices of Physics, Surgery and Midwifery" was passed in 1827 and remained in force until 1865. It permitted qualified candidates to practice medicine. However in the later years, the emphasis of the Board changed from just who should practice to attempts to control the study and practice of medicine. Homeopaths and eclectics, who were at constant odds with orthodox (allopathic) medicine, finally achieved their own separate legislative authority in 1859 and 1861.

Against this background there was a strong thrust by the leaders in government and medicine to establish a medical teaching centre. Originally, this had been desired to prevent young men who went to the United States to become doctors, from returning with a medical degree and a baggage of republican ideas. While some of this concern remained, the driving force was a desire for independence – from all off-shore agencies in all professions. Rolph had attempted to establish a proprietary school in St. Thomas in 1824, but it failed. On receiving his pardon, he repeated the attempt in the Toronto School of Medicine.

William's account of his days at Victoria are typical of the education of a middle class youth. The Aikins farm was prosperous and according to the *Christian Guardian*, 9th of March 1864, "no expense was spared in the education of his family". The choice of Victoria and its associated Upper Canada Academy, was natural as it was reputed to have a good pre-university level of instruction. Ryerson, who was Chair of the Department of Moral Philosophy and Rhetoric, was also editor of the *Christian Guardian* and wrote:

> ... by imparting to youth and children, the elements of a classical education and by preparing them to enter the halls of a college or university. The promoters of this measure, however, principally intend the contemplated Seminary to be a place of learning, where the stream of educational instruction shall not be mingled with polluted waters of corrupt example; where the public shall be guarded against the infection of immoral principles and practices; where a good English and Classical education may, with all possible facility, be acquired; where the rudiments of several sciences will be taught; where the habits of industry will be encouraged; where scholars of every Religious creed will meet with equal attention and encouragement; and where the terms will be made as moderate and easy as the circumstances of the Province will admit ...

While at Victoria College the Methodist philosophy was imprinted deeply on William's mind. This was not surprising as the search for salvation was an everyday voyage in the church-centered communities of Upper Canada. In the quest for the ideal that actual sinlessness was possible in this life, William was following in Wesleys' footsteps. However, his diaries, although full of pietism, contained little of the discussion current at that time about the various roads to the kingdom of heaven. Wesley who died in 1791, had stressed that each could choose a way of salvation. The Methodist families, particularly around Cobourg and the Bay of Quinte, took greater solace in their voluntary association which led to Holiness, rather than relying on the denomination. None of these considerations were voiced by William.

There is little doubt that in those formative years, William built a firm basis for his religious fervour which manifested itself continually during the rest of his life. In addition, he established a place in church circles which put him in frequent contact with the Methodist leaders of the community.

Most farm homes had a small collection of books – the Bible, hymnary and some medical works such as John Gunn's *Domestic Medicine* or William Buchan's *Domestic Medicine* or *A Treatise on the Prevention and Cure of Diseases, by Regimen and Simple Medicines*. In the Aikins home, John Wesley's *Primitive Physic* was the medical mainstay. He believed that profound spirituality was of greater significance than any religious dogma. When preaching to the poor and sick, he developed a deep concern with the healing of the body, as well as the soul, and urged many medical reforms, including the use of electrotherapy for the disabled. He preached that while by conversion you could enter the temple of God, at that same time it was paramount that care must be taken of the tabernacle of the body. On this basis of do-it-yourself, he built a system of care which he enshrined in *Primitive Physic*.

Aikins completed his education at Cobourg but did not matriculate. After returning to the family farm for the summer months, he enrolled in the Toronto School of Medicine (TSM) in the fall of 1846.

Entering medical school was a surprising decision as he had not mentioned a desire to become a physician in his diary, but it was compatible with his enthusiasm and general interest in the works of many of the philosophers who explained the wonders of the universe. The first half of the nineteenth century saw an intellectual epiphany through the works of Charles Lyell and Gideon Mantell which interpreted the terrestrial body as a manifestation of the glory of God, kindling appetites to learn more about the human body.

The efforts to found a school were finally successful with approval of a course at King's College. While he had been one of the main proponents of a "made in Upper Canada" medical school in the 1830's, Rolph was chagrined when the John Strachan was appointed as head. It was clearly an Anglican school and drew on funds generated from the Clergy Reserves. The college was shaped on the English model and, for its initial enrollment of two students, it was top-heavy with professors. This association of King's with the Reserves question constantly blistered Rolph's hide, as all Reformers felt other denominations should have a share. In addition, George Brown, through *The Globe* in 1844, warned readers "never forget that King's College will only be a hot bed of sectarianism". Brown's zest for this prophecy was heightened by his Wesleyan background. Even Robert Baldwin, the son of Dr. W.W. Baldwin, and himself a Church of England member, realized the inappropriateness of this arrangement. By 1846 the feelings of a large number of Reformers, in and out of the House of Assembly, led to a "great King's College meeting" where resolutions were moved opposing the continuing control by the Church of England over King's. It was a monopoly that should be broken. In addition, the meeting tackled the Clergy Reserve moneys urging that they should be distributed amongst various church colleges in other parts of Upper Canada.

To the young Aikins, given his strong Methodist belief, it was still unthinkable to go to an Anglican school, so Rolph's school was selected. Arriving in Toronto he began boarding at Langley's, a favourite of students. Toronto at that time was a busy place, far more active than Cobourg. The TSM advertised that it was "a self supporting institution, and as it draws nothing from the public resources or from the education resources of the country ... the lecturers confidently rely upon the continued patronage of the liberal and enlightened community ...". This Rolph strategy was deliberate, for his school was in direct competition with King's College.

The TSM was a different proposition to King's. The classroom was above the stable on the second floor in the rear part of Rolph's house.

He or an alternate lecturer sat behind a table and spoke while the students were on benches. There was no dress code as many of the students were "farm boys". In no way could they compete in style or manner with the students at King's College, a scant few blocks to the north, where teacher and student sat, properly gowned, at ornate desks.

Living in Cobourg was relatively cheap, however William's Toronto expenses for the first winter, 1846/7 were heavier. Amenities included a new umbrella at three shillings eleven pence, razor case and brush at one shilling, eight pence. His medical course was more demanding and he purchased the *Dublin Dissector* at seven shillings six pence and John Burns *Midwifery* at fifteen shillings. He paid more for anatomical work in December when he purchased lancets for two shillings and six pence and anatomical injection material for one shilling and three pence. He dissected a cadaver which was laid out on a trestle-table at the rear of the classroom directly above Rolph's cow and horse and stored in a formaldehyde mixture. The room was cooled only by nature. His scented water and hair oil, at one shilling tuppence, may have made the atmosphere more acceptable.

As he was having difficulty in his housing accommodation, he moved from Langley's house to another in January, but this lasted for only two months with the result that in March 1847, he took a room in the Rolph home. This began an association with Mrs. Rolph, with whom he had extensive dealings and correspondence over the next ten years. Grace Haines Rolph was an energetic 49 year old woman who knew how to run a house, keep the books for the TSM and in part supervise the behaviour of some of the medical students. Later in life she operated a school for girls. When William moved in, her first son John, was three years old and Sarah Francis was born in October just after Aikins arrival. Life at the Rolph home, a two storey building on Lot Street (Queen) with a privy, was not tranquil. The street was not paved and as it was a main thoroughfare there was heavy traffic. In addition to the school in the rear of the building, John Rolph conducted a busy medical practice from the downstairs living-room.

As a medical student, Aikins frequently accompanied his teacher on calls and, in rare cases, even consulted patients alone. In theory Rolph was required to be present, but the practice was that Aikins would see the patient and report to Rolph at a later time. In addition to the office and housecalls, Rolph admitted patients to the General Hospital.

Even though Aikins was a fervent church-goer and frequently gave money to the church, the Rolph family was not dedicated and Rolph himself varied between Methodist and Anglican services.

Aikins' room, as small as it was, had to accommodate his books including Thomas Watson's *Practice of Medicine*, Watt's *On the Mind*, Robley Dunglison's *Medical Dictionary* (1833) and John Hunter's *Treatise on the Blood, Inflammation and Gunshot Wounds* (1794). There also had to be space for the new surgical instruments and importantly, a stethoscope. Stethoscopes were not in common use and were not accepted by all physicans. Although Rene Laennec had first demonstrated their use in 1818, there was grudging acceptance by the medical profession. Part of this reluctance was the general opinion in the profession that the patient should be seen as a whole person, rather than to investigate simply the heart or other specific organs. A canard ran "I would rather look at a man with a telescope than a stethoscope." In spite of this view, Aikins bought one in May 1847 for eight shillings nine pence.

The board and room cost two pounds per quarter, and as he had no way of earning money, he continued to draw upon his family and during 1847 received fifty-two pounds, fifteen shillings. But all the expense was worthwhile. He was entranced by being a student in medicine and in particular enjoyed Rolph's lectures. On November 7th 1846, he took tea with Rolph and was introduced to Dr. Joseph Workman, one of the assistant lecturers," with whom I am much pleased." At that meeting, the schedule for classes was arranged and a timetable set out for the year. One of the most important subjects was anatomy. Diagnoses were made on the basis of a defective or injured organ, and since structure governed health and disease it was paramount to be a good anatomist. Although it was seen as a vital science, "It may become interesting hereafter, but it is dry at present. The bones of the pelvis first occupy my attention". On November 11th, he wrote:

> spent the evening with Dr. Rolph and his lady together with Drs.
> Morrison, Workman, Bull, Brown and my fellow students. It was
> spent agreeably on the whole ... became more intimate with Mr.
> Ogden ... oh may I ever feel grateful to my Creator for bestowing

such favours on unworthy me and may a scent of his goodness
leave me to make the proper use of those talents bestowed on me.

Workman had migrated from County Antrim, Ireland in 1829 and
had graduated from the McGill University in 1835. Arriving in Toronto
in 1836, he decided not to practice medicine, as it was difficult to make
a living, but rather went into the ironmonger business. Even though his
thesis on graduation had been "Asiatic Cholera", which qualified him
well to fit into the Toronto medical scene because of three terrible epidemics of cholera in the preceding five years, he felt business offered
more opportunity. But Workman kept up his medical reading and in
1846 restarted his practice of medicine, and became a teacher. In addition he wrote many political articles and had been associated with
Rolph before the rebel had fled to the US.

Toronto had grown considerably since Workman's arrival. In 1837
there had been a population of 9,200 which generally lived south of
Queen Street between the Don River and Spadina Avenue. However
ten years later, the city had spread north to Bloor and west to the garri-
son region on the Humber River. In addition to the size, the political
climate in the city had changed. There had been a ferment of discontent
which created much uncertainty. After the rebellion and the severe
punitive measures that had been taken by the Tory government, the
city had regained some stability. Although the threat of an armed
revolt had passed, there remained serious political questions with
regard to the disposal of the Clergy Reserves and the status of King's
College.

These were heady times for young people in Upper Canada. In 1849,
the Canadian Institute was organized in Toronto and a continuing flow
of papers on Natural History provided much food for speculation. The
works of Charles Lyell in 1830 had been succeeded by Robert Chambers' *Vestiges of the Natural History of Creation* and Hugh Miller's *The
Footprints of the Creator* in 1847, which all gave cause to heated discussion. The word "science" was in the air and, to the young students, provided a lodestone for their vocations. To Aikins, with his deep spiritual
feelings, the study of medicine offered an opportunity to be a scientist
and still be close to the Creator.

Rolph's annual initial lecture was a major social event for the town.

Since the public could attend, at times it had to be moved to the Mechanics Hall on Market Street, because of the large audience. Even though he had been a leader of the rebellion, he was well accepted by many of the townspeople. Others to whom the word "Reformer" had remained an anathema, coldly ignored the proceedings. But the lecture was reported in the newspapers and although the content varied little from year to year, there was always sufficient new interest to warrant attendance. Rolph's delivery was greatly appreciated for he could call down fire and thunder or speak in a dew-like tone with thespian ability.

It was said that where Rolph was, there was medicine. Certainly he imprinted his students with a love of learning and a great sense of the vast field of knowledge which was opened to medical students. Aikins was bowled over by Rolph's words. In his diary, he proclaimed that the "Introductory to the Study of Medicine" was:

> Decidedly the best lecture I have ever heard. His views are transcendentally comprehensive, embodying the most extensive with the most sound philosophy and reflection, not only tracing in Her benovelent provision for the necessities of man and for the preservation of Her whole self, but like a wise philosopher, directs, the attention to the mighty benevolent origin of them. To attempt his choice in proper language, I will not endeavour, but merely give a synopsis of the those parts which I recollect.

The content of the speech ranged from allusions to Roman and Greek philosophers through the vulcanist and neptunist theories of creation. It described the glories of Nature as displayed by recent scientific discoveries and urged dedication to study and service to fellow-men.

In contrast with current theories of the world's origin, there was little scientific basis in any of the medical lectures. Aside from a few special treatments such as the use of digitalis for dropsy, cinchona for fevers, or mercury for many types of illnesses, there were few specifics available to the physician. The advanced state of knowledge gave no concept of the cause of diseases and although J.B. Morgagni's work *On the Sites and Origins of Disease*, which had appeared in 1761, correlated symptoms with anatomical abnormalities, there had been little further effort to expand this to describe the aetiology of disease. In the York cholera epidemics in 1832 and 1834, seven different causes had been postulated – sol-lunar, cometary, geology, miasmatic, meteoratious, contagion and animalacular – each with its proponents. Although surgery could have a more direct effect upon the patient than medication, the use of anaesthesia had not become common, and rarely did the surgeon venture into the abdomen. Small pox could be prevented by vaccination, however in many cases the lymph material which was used was of varying strength and resulted in the recipient developing small pox rather than an immunity. Therefore, the basis of most of the lectures was empirical with emphasis on what had been effective previously.

Although Aikins had purchased a stethoscope, the Billing's type which was a 5 inch tube with a flare at each end, there was little agreement as to the interpretation of the sounds that were heard. In spite of Morgagni's work it was still difficult to relate physical findings to the pathology. Leopold Auenbrugger had demonstrated clearly the difference in the sound elicited on tapping the chest of a patient with lung disease. However, though Laennec claimed that increased breath sounds were associated with consolidation of the lung, there was denial of these basic findings by many clinicians. For example, Jean-Nicolas Corvisart, physician to Napoleon, never listened to a chest and those who did use Laennec's invention argued endlessly as to the meaning of the heart sounds. Was this snap the closing or opening of the valve, and of which valve? Even with the experiment reported by J. Rouanet in 1832, *Analyse des Bruits du Coeur*, when he pumped water through a cadaver heart, there was still speculation as to the cause of the first and second sounds of the heart. James Hope, who studied in Paris, the centre of physiological discoveries, wrote of his experiments on donkeys in which he opened the chest wall of an animal which had been stunned and listened to the heart directly. He was able to state definitely the origin of the heart sounds, but his work was not believed.

On November 9th, Aikins recorded the different types of cellular tissue:

> The cellular membrane is that portion of cellular tissue which developes the muscles and passes between the vassillae, accompanying

blood vessels and nerves. Not as glutineous expansion as many supposed, but consists of elementary fibers composed of albumin, fibrin and some water and is capable of sustaining life ... resembles a spider's web ... it secretes a fluid to lubricate the parts in which it resides. It is vascular and nervous because pain is felt when it is in place. It possesses absorbents. It has the power of contracting on the application of stimulus.

Many of these lectures took place between 7 and 8 a.m. and opened the day to a series of classes which could continue until 8 p.m. Subjects included anatomy, physiology, materia medica and therapeutics, with the necessary knowledge of chemistry, medicine, midwifery and diseases of women and children. According to Walter B. Geikie, when he was Dean of Trinity Medical College at the end of the century, "The Medical School stood so high that it's tickets were received everywhere, and its students were exceptionally successful in passing their examinations before the Medical Board".

Other lecturers taught:

Adipose tissue is situated in the subcutaneous, and internally around the lower parts of the heart and kidney. It is not in the brain, for it would be the cause of apoplexy, nor in the lungs or it would cause laborious breathing. Not about the uterus, it would not expand sufficiently easy. Not in the scrotum because it would cause a great size. Not in the penis for reasons easily known. It is situated in no place where it would not be needed nor absent from any place where it is needed. Where a hernia might take place it is secreted in abundance. About the nates and pudenda of some females, it is found in great quantities. In the camel's hump, or protuberance not much. Not much in birds for it would render them too heavy, their bones being filled with air. Its use – it may serve for protection from the cold, fat being a poor conductor of heat. And a certain padding as in the orbit of the eye, soles of the feet, ends of the fingers, its practical benefit may be more easily perceived in the buttock, on the flesh or a covering of the tuberosities of the ischium. The lean man sitting very uncomfortably and vice versa.

He went on to quote work done by Sir Astley Cooper, as passed on by Rolph, who had found that a fat hog covered in the snow, had remained alive at the end of six weeks, but by that time was quite lean. *The Principles and Practice in Modern Surgery* by Robert Druitt of Philadelphia was recommended strongly by Rolph, and was a necessary part of any student's library in the TSM.

In the proprietary medical schools, as opposed to King's College or the University of Toronto, the fees of the students paid for the teacher's stipend. Aikins paid the TSM five pounds, five shillings three times per year. He noted his total expenses for his first year at the TSM were £45, part of which was spent on books.

The fall term passed quickly. He had little time for social life in Toronto and on January 1st 1847 entered in his diary:

> The old year has now passed and a moments reflection of its flight may not be useless with respect to myself during its escape ... I was much affected with melancholy which I now believe to have been from a peculiar state of the nervous system, which I then thought resulted from the influence of religion which in a major part explained the cause of some solemn and warning expressions given at that time; a condition of mind and body laid the foundation ... of my feeling and health during the greater part of the year and consequently of my actions. I am not going to philosiphize at present on various feelings nor my success either mentally or morally; suffice it to say I have become more acquainted with my own nature and that of mankind in general. I see in a greater space my own consistency out of faithfulness in the daily service of my God. It is my present determination by the Grace of God to live differently during the next year and to adapt as my motto "Fly from the very appearance of evil" and rely on the atonement of Christ alone for salvation.

The following weekend Aikins attended Sunday school and consented to act as teacher. Preaching in the morning was by Rev. Sanderson and Sunday school and preaching in the evening with Mr. Crofts.

In the spring term, he attended the christening of Sarah Francis, the infant daughter of Grace Rolph. It was fitting that he should be present for a birth ceremony as he was beginning clincial duties:

Sat up with Mr. E.B. Palmer, he departed this life about half past five in the morning. He died very easily, fully composed and resigned and his spirit as capable of enjoying happiness or suffering in a separate state from the body. I believe it to be in the condition of the former.

The following morning Aikins attended his first post-mortem. He reported that he had felt many symptoms of approaching apoplexy with giddiness, headache, hot scalp, "the forehead very hot", muscle weakness and a reluctance to move. He felt that his vision was impaired with a mist and there was a slight nausea with mental confusion and inability "to keep his mind". He wrote that his memory was greatly affected in the lecture room in the evening and he forgot questions as soon as they were asked:

Probably resulting from deep thinking while I was observing my friend depart.

Boarding at Rolph's home gave Aikins great opportunities for an intensive exposure to medical problems. On May 8th he observed:

A tall, stout, working man, a farmer, I believe, came into the surgery about 25 minutes after 1 o'clock and informed me that he had poisoned himself having taken arsenic at 11 o'clock. He since then had drank some beer (I know not how much, nor whether he drank anything else) about two hours after taking the poison he vomitted (according to his own statement) when I saw him, he complained of a pain in his stomach. I gave him some warm water which continued his vomitting. The perspiration was rolling off him and he was becoming weak very fast. I felt rather uneasy but was soon relieved by the appearance of the doctor. He now refused to drink the water, perspirated copiously – was very weak, pulse 120 per minute. He was taken to the hospital when the stomach pump was promptly used. During the operation, I left and have not since heard with what success it was attended. He procured the arsenic under the pretence of poisoning rats. He was subject to slight mental aberrations. I asked him why he took it. He replied he had no peace in the world. I asked him if he thought he would be in the next world after acting the part he had. He said he did not know. His health apparently seemed to be improving during the two past days which were bright, warm and very pleasant.

After barely six months in the medical school, it is obvious that he was learning a great deal. Taking the pulse and describing it, showed that he was developing some clinical skills. As with other students and graduates it was remarkable how quickly they became engaged with seriously ill patients, and that they were able to respond in some fashion. While much of the lecture material was inaccurate, mis-leading and sometimes quite erroneus, the students were acquiring medical ability. But there were many questions about the efficacy of treatment. *The Toronto Mirror* stated:

> One half the cases admitted into the hospital have been simple, mild cases, which would have recovered under simple, mild treatment. Why should the remainder under wine and brandy be now in the graveyard? And should 800 out of 2,000 be still in jeopardy? Is medicine really but a humbug and the Faculty but a league of charlatans?

On May 23rd, still feeling very much depressed, Aikins went to hear John Roaf, a charismatic Congregational minister, who established the Zion Church in Toronto in 1840. His evangelist enthusiasm was fired by a hot conviction that there should be no connection between church and state, thus allying himself with Reformers, such as John Rolph and Egerton Ryerson. He disagreed with Ryerson on the issue of free school teaching and was a strong opinion on many public issues. In the evening, Aikins heard the great evangelist, John Saltkill Carroll, whose text of Psalm 104, "Let the sinners be consumed out of the earth, and let the wicked be no more", burned into the heart of the young student. Carroll was one of the most eminent and eloquent of the circuit-riders who had fashioned a strong Methodist church in the province. The next day after Sunday school, Aikins took a walk up Yonge Street to College Avenue, then down to Queen Street. However, he found Queen to be:

Too public, every variety of character has to be found in it. And it appears to be impossible when there is such numbers going to and forth and walking up and down to spend this time either in profitable conversation or uninterrupted meditation. Second, the effect of example which encourages thousands of the unfaithful persons to pursue a light course in collecting together all manners of evil results in smoking, intemperance, swearing, evil conversations, etc., etc. Now if the situation was required of a person either alone or with a suitable companion might spend an hour or two amid the beauties of nature with much pleasure and advantage improving his moral and intellectual and physical powers. At the same time, honouring his Creator by mentation and conversation on His works. Remember the Sabbath to keep it holy.

He continued his introspection over the following week and recollected :

While viewing the children collected at only a short distance from me, I was struck with the suggestion of my deceased friend, E.B. Palmer, viz how I feel that many I see will never arrive at the age of 25 – or how many will be cut off even before they reach my own age – it is a serious thought ... Will my actions comprising my look, voice, conduct and instruction press down the balance in favour of eternal ruin for there is not a ray of light or of heat? Not the gentlest whispering of the soft gale or the slightest drop of the morning dew, but what exerts an influence even so, there is no movement of the countenance nor a tone of the voice, but what it exerts in influence, where perceived or not ... I have enjoyed many precious seasons of the presence of God during the last week. Yet not as many as I thought I might have had. The fault is all my own, for I feel fully convinced that although I am of myself an imperfect, yet if I would come to the throne of Grace believing the righteousness of Christ is sufficient to render me acceptable to God and its merit sufficient to procure the choicest blessing.

As he acquired more medical knowledge he began to think of the future of young children and his role in maintaining their health. Death at any early age was a common fact. Rolph lectured:

> The study of medicine embraces the whole art of being – before we can heal anything we must become acquainted with its nature – plants cohabit as well as animals and thus recreate their species. The animal and vegetable kingdoms are mutually dependent on each other, preserving the atmosphere and the state of purity – without either of which the other would perish. The carbonic acid given off by animals would soon deteriorate, the atoms rendering it destructive to themselves, without the benevolent assistance of the vegetable kingdom and vice versa. The power of the vital principle resides in and resists the laws of chemical affinity and preserves its temperature in whatever situation it may be placed. The degree of heat at which man's system functions at his greatest is between 80 and 100 degrees and during life, it is kept at this temperature. It has the power of producing heat and cold, not now understood. Several insects and animalacules have been taken out of their natural sphere (the fluid) and may appear lifeless like dust. Yet sprinkling on a little water, they become a living being ... insects and other living things have been discovered in flint after its pulverization and in rocky form in which it existed probably for ages. Why may not this be a case for the revivication of man's body at resurrection?

Rolph was alluding to some of the current investigations that reflected interest in calculating body heat and other physical aspects which were intriguing researchers who were beginning to make measurements. As yet there was little comprehension of any relationship between the workings of the body and any disease process. When he spoke of the power of the vital principle he referred to the work of Johan Reil who taught that there was a force flowing out of matter which determined health. Underlying much of the lecturing was the necessity to make congruent medical science with religious convictions, hence the reference to re-incarnation and life everafter, a basic of the Christian faith.

Other lecturers maintained this general theme. Workman spoke of:

> The dignity of the profession – is a work of benevolence. We should

duly appreciate the greatness and superiority of our profession, without which no man may expect to succeed in whatever calling he has engaged ... the doctor should be regarded as a friend – his smile cheers the house of sorrow. He should confidentially preserve all those little secrets entrusted to his honour by his female patients.

In truth, Workman was laying the ground for increased professionalization of the medical profession through staking out a specific area in the humanities, akin to that held through the confessional privileges of the priest.

The occult thought in this particular lecture continued the concept of previous centuries that in order to be a physician it was necessary to be in a state of Grace with God. Aikins knew that while he might not be in full Grace, he was moving in that direction. He continued his religious studies through a wide choice of places of worship. The British Methodist church at Richmond Street west of Yonge; the Primitive Methodist church at Bay south of King; the African Methodist church at Richmond Street west of York; the British Methodist chapel, at Queen west of Peter; the Brick Church (Canadian Wesleyan Methodist) at Adelaide corner of Toronto or the Methodist chapel in Yorkville – all proffered the word of God. That word could be heard also in the five Episcopal churches, two Roman Catholic, Church of Scotland, Presbyterian or Baptist churches which were scattered throughout the city.

On some occasions Rolph lectured on animal experimentation. He reported on a study he had performed to observe the process of dying:

> First the left ventricle ceases to contract. The stomach and intestines cease 45 to 50 minutes afterwards, followed by the bladder. In an hour the right ventricle ceases ... the right auricle of the dog was found to contract eight hours after death. The tonicity of muscles was the result of an act of nutrition going on.

In addition the students received instruction in birthing. They were warned that the shoulder presentation was the most dangerous and were given direction on the handling of a breech presentation according to the eminent authorities, Dr. James Douglas and Sir James Simpson of Edinburgh. In spite of their eminence, obstetrics was not taught in English schools.

During the summer months his diary showed continuing enthusiasm for the Sunday school and the preachers. He heard Edward Ryerson, the brother of Egerton; and Egerton himself on several occasions, and called again on Carroll. In the week of Sunday the 29th, he attended two services in the morning and evening and spent Tuesday evening walking and discussing with Mr. Sanderson. On Wednesday he called on Mr. Woodhouse and again on Carroll. On Thursday he called on another student Uzziel Ogden and then on to his sister Mrs. Austin. His life was full with his devoutness competing for his attention with his urge to be a physician.

Although engrossed in his studies, he was able to take some leisure. However, at no time did he mention the severe epidemic of typhus or ship-board fever which struck Canada, and particularly Toronto, in 1847. About eight hundred Irish immigrants died in Upper Canada from a disease caused by massive crowding and lack of sanitation. The affliction, which was spread by a louse bite, had been described by Girolao Fracastoro in 1546 who identified the specifics which caused the infectious nature of the disease. Surprisingly, this vector was unrecognized by the physicians in York and did not form part of the undergraduate curriculum at the TSM.

No other deaths were recorded amongst medical personnel in Toronto, but on the 9th of September Aikins wrote:

> Quite unwell, pains in the right hypochrondrium, the right lumbar region. Became more easy about bed time.

He had some cause for concern. The previous week he had received a report that his mother was recovering from dysentery and that Aunt Jane had a painful neurological condition in the face while Moses, his younger brother, had a severe eye infection, which seemed to have been passed on from Father.

William's physical complaints were only a minor concern. On Saturday, the 11th, he noted:

> The week has passed. I must say I have achieved but little. This will

not do. The farmer to become rich rises early, works hard during the day and retires weary to rest. The merchant is equally assiduous and others the same. Will not I put forth some effort to acquire knowledge of any profession, not that I hope that knowledge will be spent nearly enough in obtaining ... Our knowledge is not transitory, but immortal, but my candle is expiring.

The studies continued and early in February he recorded:

Paracentesis abdominis was performed by the doctor on Mrs. Thompson. Five years since the first child born. Nine months after incomplete paralysis of the lower extremity, what caused it I know not. For more than three years, abdomen has been gradually increasing. She has been under the care of many medical men, by some she was diagnosed pregnant, treat (the fetus) as dead and accordingly they attempted to induce labour ... but like the mountains of Aesop, the labour brought forth nothing ... .

She had been for sometime under the doctor who considered it an ovarian dropsy – the trocar was introduced under the umbilicus, but the fluid was so thick it did not run down the cannula. It was then introduced above the umbilicus. Three gallons were withdrawn at first, having the appearance of honey, afterwards mingled with sanguinous fluid. The cannula was left remaining for about a pint daily was discharged. After retching for 36 hours, she died.

Although he mentioned a post-mortem had been done, he did not enter the findings.

Beginning in July, Aikins seem to take greater interest in matters other than medicine. At least his diary recorded that Emperor Louis Phillipe of Spain was dying of carcinoma of the stomach and the Queen of Spain had been performing a novena that the Holy Virgin may grant her a safe delivery. He also visited Parliament a number of times and listened to the discussions.

On one occasion he reported:

Pain in the anterior part of my right hypochondrium region. Severe

on Saturday night, less so on Sunday, til the evening, still continuous catching on taking full inspiration ... Dr. John Phalen called
upon me. Employed dry cupping to the side. Excused myself from
C.W. Flacks party.

Dry cupping was a half-way measure of bleeding a patient. During
the first half of the century, bleeding was a commonly accepted means
of treating many disorders. However, by 1850 it was less popular with
some physicians. Rolph taught that with different types of inflammation, it was more desirable to use sedatives, stimulant gargles of the
throat and astringents such as opium and lead. But:

> bleeding is an excellent remedy. General bleeding is taking the
> blood from all of the body, local bleeding is taking blood from the
> part. You may bleed to produce sedation, that is to lessen the flow
> of blood from the heart ... if you have congestion of the brain and
> not time to administer drugs you should necessarily bleed.

Yet there was a growing body of feeling that advocated either wet or
dry cupping, using a heated "cup" or bulbous shape glass which was
applied to particular areas of the body. With wet cupping a scarificator
produced a series of scratches on the skin and as the warm air inside
the glass cooled, blood was sucked from the abrasions. Dry cupping
did not break the skin, but the blood collected beneath the end of the
glass which caused a bruising. In both cases it was asserted that this
local bleeding was as effective as the general bleeding. In Aikins case, it
did have a beneficial effect as he reported a few days later that he was
feeling much improved. Post hoc ergo propter hoc!
    The controversy over bleeding was not settled for many years. Gei-
kie, when a senior teacher of Victoria, read a paper to the Canadian
Institute in January 1870 in which he reviewed the indications. He
began with a quotation:

> By bleeding the marrow cometh heat
> It maketh clean your brain, relieves the eye;
> It mends your appetite, restoreth sleep,
> Correcting humours that do waking keep

All inward parts, and senses also, clearing –
It mends the voice, touch, smell and taste and hearing.

He then reviewed the great physicians who had used the lancet as their weapon – Dr. Dover, Dr. Cullen, Sir William Blizzard, Marshall Hall and others.

He quoted extensively from James Gregory in his *Practice of Physic*, who claimed that bleeding was far superior in the treatment of inflammation than any other effort.

A more balanced argument was put forward by Dr. Joshua Flint, Dean of the Kentucky School of Medicine. He deprecated the extent of its use, but he was inclined to think that the reaction against it might prevent the use in the few cases where it might be of real service. He advised "so using the remedy as not to abuse it". In Geikie's opinion where the inflammation was "exceeding acute", cautious bleeding should be used seldomly and never to excess. Where the disease was less acute, he felt there was improvement without, rather than with blood letting "... shews a far lower mortality than the followers of King Lancet ...".

In the third class, which he stated was too numerous, were all the cases where no depletion was called for, as it would destroy the lives of the patients. [1]

Aikins continued to note the course of various patients. "Gastric formation of gas in the girl Caulfield ... Mrs Webb very ill. Disagreement in diagnosis ... called away to attend Mrs. Higgins". He also reported that cholera was raging in Cincinnati with some cases in Pittsburgh, but not in Toronto. On June 5, 1848, he recorded the death of James Smith, a patient in hospital for some time who had been treated for debility. Aikins took part in the post-mortem:

> pleura in upper part especially, and also in the posterior and inferior part, was firmly adherent. A portion of the non-united pleura covered by organized lymph. No fluid in pleura. The lungs – right side – upper lobe in the state of grey hepatization. The smaller bronchii still pervious, but the air cells, as well as the intercellular tissues completely filled with this grey orangized matter ... that I have seen on a former occasion in a hepatized lung – very crepitant under pressure, was said by Mr. Ogden to be emphysematous.

The pericardium of the heart was:

> ... nearly full of fluid of greenish hue. Heart much enlarged, arch of
> the aorta much dilated, especially the ascending portion. Specific
> deposits in arch and thoracic aorta and also in the commencement
> of the abdominal. I did not trace it any further. These deposits not
> found in the valve of the aorta; their sinsuses behind the valves
> were dilated ... the stomach, I am sorry to say, I did not examine.
> The symptoms were copious mucus expectorations slightly increas-
> ing in later state – vomitting on taking food – *the two natural sounds
> of heart present – respiratory murmurs diminished, mucous rales.*

He performed many autopsies and in some cases co-related physical
signs with post-mortem findings.

> Clark, right lung fully interspersed with blackish and yellowish
> tubercles of the size of pinheads – left lung a much worse condition
> some of the tubercles the size of little fingertips – which were
> undergoing softening – pleura – left adherent to posterior. Pericar-
> dium nearly full of serum ...

On June 6th, he reported on the case of Jane Ramsey:

> ... age 28, married, complained of palpitations since an attack of
> rheumatic in Ireland, almost incessant coughing, lately edema of
> lower extremities and right arm. A very uneasy sensation in cardiac
> region. Impulse of heart much increased – a broad blowing sound
> as almost to entirely absent of the natural sounds – on examination
> higher up the sound signs much more distinct; but over the aorta
> the second sound appeared to be absent, not so with the pulmonary
> artery – a very uneasy apprehensive state of mind, after being in
> the hospital a few weeks, she died on the 6th. She had indulged
> much in liquor.

He was able to do a follow-up and at the autopsy:

> ... lungs – right – posterior part of upper lobe adherent to pleura –

and middle lobe hepatized. The other side no tubercles – liver, dark coloured and congested, some serum in abdomen ... heart surface indicated bygone peritonitis ... Heart enormously enlarged, completely engorged with blood, also in its cavities as much as a small teacup full of lymph ... I have not yet seen the interior of the heart as it is to be sent to the university museum. Happening to introduce the finger into right ventricle and carrying towards the bottom of the septum, it readily passed into the left ventricle, and indeed the passage would also admit two or three fingers. Colour of the skin did not truly indicate the circulation of the venous blood ...

His clinical findings, particularily the "blowing sound" suggest aortic valvular disease and his mention of passing his finger from right to left is consistent with a septal defect caused by a higher pressure in the left ventricle. The physical examination was excellent. On July 11, he gave a history that:

... Margaret Kerr came into the hospital sometime ago, very weak with pain in the precordial region, palpitations, edema of the right side and afterwards general edema relieved by scarification about the ankle. (A very improper place). Treated with diuretics.

Her physical examination showed pulse did not correspond in force to the action of the heart. From these principally I considered and stated that pericarditis existed with effusion. At first examination I considered the pulmonary valve safe, but a condition of the aortic valve producing a murmur but accompanying which sound I forget.

Had an examination a few days prior to death, I could not perceive anything abnormal in either sound, but a sound which I considered was produced by disease of the aortic valves, nor did I perceive so much difference between the pulses and the impulses as formerly. The patient asked how she was and I told her, the sounds of her heart were much improved, although she was weaker.

Aikins noted at her autopsy that the "pleura adhering to the pericardium throughout. Three or four ounces of fluid in the pericardium, adhesion between the heart and opposed pericardium".

On December 9th, he conjectured:

> examples of sympathetic action tending to health or producing dis-
> ease. First irritating particles or effluvia fall upon the living mem-
> brane of the nose, the diaphram, muscles of the velum, the glottis,
> and abdominal muscles are suddenly called into action; what a
> quick excitor of impression! How is the irritation conveyed from
> centre of pain to the origin of the phrenic? A fixed number of
> actions take place.
>
> A second initiation of teething exciting convulsions – deranged
> or abnormal circulation ... is the irritation owing to presence of the
> spinal nerve supplying the mucous membrane which excite the
> reflex motor action, but how is the irritation conveyed from origin
> of the 5th to the whole spinal cord? Is it the presence of the sympa-
> thetic fibres which causes and modifies through circulation? How
> is irritation conveyed from one ganglion to another, are they con-
> nected together by white or grey fibres, irritation is conveyed along
> white to grey, why not also from grey along white to grey?
>
> ... third, irritation of a few fibres and in tetanus throwing whole
> spinal cord into action; question as before – in this may we not
> ascertain how many of the voluntary muscles are also supplied
> with spinal nerves?
>
> "Fourth, irritation of compound fracture of leg, giving rise to the
> following in 24 hours, pain in the lower extremity, of the cord, pain
> in the head; restless, anxious. Tongue, first day, though coated with
> whiteness first as symptoms increase with a yellowish one – lastly a
> thick brown one – irritability of stomach and anorexia, nausea,
> vomitting – stools white – pulse quick, heart irregular, alternately
> intermittent.

These observations, considered naive in later years, demonstrated
attempts to co-relate symptoms, clinical signs and autopsy findings.
They awaited further physiological and bacteriological facts before a
clear line of cause and effect could lead his enquiring mind to the modern concepts of scientific medicine.

In addition he listed social calls. He excused himself from "Miss
Patterson's picknick" but he did spend an evening with F.L. As a matter
of fact this lady was mentioned several times:

"note from Miss F.L., prompt attention and an interview ... I intended to call upon F.L, a visit of her friends prevented ... clear views of Miss F.L. concerning the duty of man, the danger of being hurried along in a common current, and then in a few years occupying the same position which we now condemn in others. It is not behind the dignity of irrational being to devote all of his energies of soul and body to accummulate that which, however necessary in society as an article of exchange, can never yield happiness as much as the mind. By a favourable calculation one half at least of life will soon be over and how melancholy the prospect of the other half is to be spent in the same unthoughtful irrational, undutiful manner; must we bow to the iron laws under which mankind seems to live ... her displeasure at the customs of society with the constant indulgence in light and unimproving conversation ... endeavors to deduce something useful from every remark, however trivial and to render the actions of mankind to great moral laws on principle – how rapidly life flows out! 11 p.m.

These meetings were the first mention of any social contact with women, aside from church events. The discussion with Miss F.L. stirred Aikins deeply so that he next wrote:

Oh heavenly Father give me clear views of my duty and energy sufficient to accompany it..may I think and live for a nobler end than merely to be "very rich" ... and this is really life? Can it be that I know I live. Impossible!

However he was not devoting all his attention to Miss F.L. Shortly after Aikins had tea with Miss Osborne and called upon Miss J.R. Agnes for a "familiar tete-a-tete". It was apparent that the young doctor was an eligible bachelor.

Dr. A. Rosebrugh reported to the The Ontario Medical Association(OMA) meeting in 1888 of his days as a student in 1849. "In the old hospital on King Street, Toronto, there were no clinics given and there were no interns. Students were not required to take a hospital course. Only rarely did a senior student visit the hospital. The maternal mortality was high and there were no trained nurses. The medical students were usually of a rough type with little concern about study. Great improvements have taken place since those days."[2]

Some of these improvements resulted from observing other exemplars.

Dr. Oliver Wendell Holmes, who was credited in America with discovering the contagiousness of puerperal fever was an author, poet and wit. Born in Cambridge, Masschusetts, he graduated from Harvard Medical School under the direction of Dr. James Jackson. In 1838 he was appointed Professor of Anatomy at Dartmouth College. Prior to that he had been a physician to the Massachusetts General Hospital. In 1842 he published "Homeopathy" which was a brilliant exposition given by an opponent of homeopathy. His essay, *Of Puerperal Fever*, pointed out that it was frequently due to contamination conveyed by the hands of the physician from one mother to another. His views were opposed by the leading obstetricians of his day, but gradually became accepted. His essays were in advance of the reseach of Semmeweiss. In 1847 he was appointed to the Harvard Medical School. Dr. D.W. Cheevers wrote about Holmes as a teacher, and described a scene akin to that in Toronto: "it was near one o'clock, and the close work in the demonstrators room becomes even more hurried and eager as the lecture hour in anatomy approaches. Four hours of busy dissection have unveiled a portion of the human frame, insensate and stark, on the demonstrating table. Muscles, nerves and blood vessels unfold themselves in unvarying harmony, if seeming disorder, and the 'subject' is nearly ready to illustrate the lecture ... the room is thick with tobacco smoke. The winter light, snowy and dull, enters through one tall window, bare of curtain and falls upon a lead floor ... there is nothing to inspire the intellect or imagination, except the marvelous mechanism of the poor dead body, which lies dissected before us, ... some complex and delicate machinery, whose uses we seek to know ... He asks 'What have you for me today?' and plunges, knife in hand, into the depths of the subject. Time flies and a crowd of turbulent Bob Sawyers push through the halls and begins a rhythmical stamping, one, two, three and a shout and a pounding on his lecture room doors. A rush takes place; some collapse, some are thrown headlong, and three hundred raw students reciprocate themselves into a bare and comfortless ampitheatre. Meanwhile the Professor is running about, now as nimble as a cat, selecting plates, rummaging the dusty museum for specimens, arranging microscopes and displaying bones. The subject is carried in on a board; no automatic appliance, no wheels with pneumatic tires, no elevators, no dumbwaiters in those days. The cadaver is decorously disposed on a revolving table in a small area, and is always covered, at first, from the curious eyes by a clean white sheet. Respect for poor humanity and admiration for God's divinest work is the first lesson and uppermost in the poet lecturer's mind. He enters, and is greeted with a mighty shout and stamp of applause. Then silence, and there begins a charming hour of description, analysis, simile, anecdote, harmless pun, which clothes the dry bones with poetic imagery, enlivens a hard and fatiguing day with humour, and brightness to the tired listener, the details of a difficult though interesting study ..." (David William Cheever, who began the study of medicine in 1854 and was one of Holmes students.)

Although Holmes was outstanding as a teacher, he was not unique. Toronto, too, had lecturers who could elucidate, inspire, amuse or irritate. And they could also evoke the poetry and magic of dealing with God's divine creation. While at Jefferson Medical College, Richardson wrote to Aikins deploring that Rolph was not present to hold on equal footing with the cream of Jeffersonians.

At the middle of the century, the major purpose of a physician was to intervene – to do something to check the progress of disease. This was almost a moral imperative, rather than the result of rational professional thought, as frequently it could not be demonstrated that the patient benefitted from the intervention. It was vital that the physician have confidence in his practice which resulted from his special education. However, anatomical or physiological knowledge was not the prime requisite. Experience, the observation of the patient, and the use of judgement, would lead to a specific remedy for each individual. With these particular agents the doctor could change the symptoms of the patients. This type of unique treatment for an individual meant that each patient could be treated in a different manner. There were few general diagnostic labels which would lead to a uniform therapeutic regimen.

Part of this philosophy stemmed from the teaching of Dr. James Jackson Sr. now of Jefferson. In an 1832 letter to his son, James, he wrote, "I almost think that a man may learn so much before he begins to practice as to prevent his doing well. Too much knowledge of the dangers and difficulty tend to paralyse ones' powers." This approach was echoed by Dr. John Ware in an article *Success in the Medical Profession* when he asserted that the physician "... had to apply this knowledge with the wisdom which is sometimes altogether beyond that which merely high attainments in science can confer ... His wisdom could come only through experience and the application of good judgement, rather than the results of any scientific learning ..."

Although to practice successfully in the 18th century, it was necessary to be in Grace, this gradually devolved about the time of the French Revolution and the ascendancy of the Paris medical school, so that by the middle of the 19th century, a high moral standing was sufficient (and necessary) to be a good physician. This was drummed constantly to the students in the introductory lectures of their classes, reports to medical societies and journals. The emphasis was on a sense of responsibility, duty and judgement – and the necessity to "cure" the patient by action. It was not until later that science replaced this ethic.

REFERENCES

All quotations from letters are from holograph reproductions in the Academy of Medicine collection at the John Robarts Library, University of Toronto.

No corrections have been made to any of the original material which has been used in this book.

1. Geikie, W.B. A Few Observations on the Past and Present Employment of Bleeding in the Treatment of Fever and Inflammatory Diseases. Canada Medical Journal 1865; p 16.
2. Ontario Medical Review October 1963; p 662.

Chapter Two

The Graduate

"I now leave for the land of freedom." wrote Aikins. Armed with his diploma from the Rolph School, he took a cabin passage to Rochester for three dollars in October, 1849. He had cash on hand of $202.45, which was necessary as his expenses mounted. The fare to Albany was $7.55 and he went via New York, where he stayed for three days. While there he bought a $13.00 suit and then went to Philadelphia.

The Jefferson Medical College in that city was a traditional place for Canadian physicians to take further training. It had been founded in 1825 by Dr. George McClelan who, among other accomplishments, distinguished himself by removing the parotid gland from one of his students. Ten years later, student J. Collins Warren described a class by Dr. Samuel Gross:

> ... The lecture room was a large, well shaped ampitheatre into which the class poured tumultously; it held four or five hundred students and was always well filled ...[1]

This was a period when hundreds of graduates from medical schools in the U.S. were flooding the market. In Toronto classes were rarely above 30. While the certificates from the TSM were recognized by McGill, they had little coinage in other areas. Jefferson offered the opportunity to achieve an advanced standing at a relatively small cost as the matriculation fee was $55.00, followed by a $30.00 deposit with a thesis. But Jefferson was worth it with such medical giants as Druitt, Dunglison and Pancoast.

Many medical men had an impact on the TSM students. While there were no medical journals published in Upper Canada before 1851, cases were reported frequently in the newspapers and some journals did appear from the US or England. The professors at Jefferson, where a number of young Upper Canadians attended, were greatly respected. Robley Dunglison had studied in London and Edinburgh and had received his medical degree at the University of Erlangen. He published *Human Physiology* in 1832 and *The Practice of Medicine* in 1842. Naturally students attending from Upper Canada were required to study his works including a case of chronic hereditary chorea (Huntington's).

Joseph Pancoast made surgery his specialty when he began practice in Philadelphia and later was appointed professor at Jefferson. He devised many new operations including soft and mixed cataract removals; an improved type of plastic suture, used extensively in rhinoplasty; an operation for empyema and in the 1860's demonstrated an operation for division of the 5th cranial nerve for the treatment of tic douloureux. He published a revised edition of Dr. Caspar Wistar's *System of Anatomy for the Use of Students* (1844). Aikins frequently quoted from Wistar, who in addition to his brilliant surgery, was instrumental in combining the University of Pennsylvania and the Medical College of Philadelphia into one organization.

Henry Ingersol Bowditch was a pioneer who specialized in diseases of the chest and developed examination by auscultation and percussion. He devised a method of thoracentesis (aspiration of the chest) and a system of detecting the probable predisposing causes of pulmonary tuberculosis. In addition to a brilliant medical career, he was a strong proponent of the abolition of slavery and took part in much auxillary work in Massachusetts until slavery was abolished. His treatment for pleuritic effusions, with opening of the chest wall by surgical incisions, was opposed by medical men of the highest reputation, but in 1850 he was able to demonstrate the success of the procedure using a trochar and cannula connected with a suction pump. This led to a book, *On Pleuritic Effusions, and the Necessity of Paracentesis for the Removal*.

While Aikins was at Jefferson; he received lectures from Charles Delucena Meigs who was one of the first authors of the *North American Medical and Surgical Journal*. He published several works on midwifery and drew special attention to cardiac thrombosis as a cause of the sudden deaths which occurred after delivery. Some of his peers writing at a later date, stated that he had "... just escaped the honour which is now and will be hereafter given to Virchow for a great pathological discovery ...". He felt strongly that a physician and other professionals should retire before they lost their ability to judge their own fitness for practice and resigned from Jefferson at the age of 67. However following that he blossomed in many areas, including blacksmithing, carpentry, drawing and painting.

Jefferson, like many other teaching institutions attracted highly talented professors. John Kearsley Mitchell had made three voyages to China and the East Indies as a ship's surgeon before being appointed to the Chair of Theory and Practice of Medicine. In addition to a book on malaria, he published a volume of poetry. One of his major works was on the *Parasitic Etiology of Disease*. His son, S. Weir Mitchell followed his footsteps in the publication of poetry and novels and was the most acclaimed neurologist in North America, in the latter part of the century.

There was an enormous wealth of talent in the medical men of that era. Poets, explorers, soldiers, journalists, scientists – all were present in these eminent physicians and surgeons. It is uncertain whether the practice of medicine called forth unusual talents or whether the reverse was the case. It is certain that to be a student in the classrooms of these giants was an inspirational experience.

Aikins had other matters on his mind, apart from his medical studies. During the summer and fall of 1849, he had become acquainted with the Piper family. Hiriam Piper lived close to the Rolph home and had two charming daughters, Louisa Adelia and Lydia Ann. In the normal social life of the city, Louisa attracted Aikins' attention, and there began a long series of letters between them. Some were never sent, or mailed at a later date.

September 11th, 1849

Miss Piper,

Please pardon the unwarranted and unrequested liberty I assume in now addressing you. By reputation as well indeed as by a limited observation, I am pecularily pleased with some unusually

interesting and desirable features in your character, a further
acquaintance with which I would, with your approbation, be very
happy to cultivate.

These sentiments not being from the impulse of the moment,
together with my present departure and future temporary absence
from the City afford the only shadow of an excuse which I can now
offer for my strange conduct. If on reflection you should deem it
proper to answer this a few lines directed Cooksville P.O. will
reach a remembering friend.
W.T. Aikins.

It was some time before a reply was received.

To qualify for the advanced standing in medicine it was necessary to
have a good reference library and William purchased in short order the
Atlas by John K. Mitchell and Justus von Liebig's *Chemistry*. Von Liebig
was rapidly becoming an outstanding researcher in the German science
era, which reached world-wide pre-eminence in the second half of the
century. In order to expand his other studies Aikins purchased William
Paley's *Views of the Evidence of Christianity (1794)* and Bishop Joseph
Butler's *Analogy of Religion, Natural and Revealed, to the Constitution and
Course of Nature*. Paley had seized the imagination of the community
with the convincing logic of his arguments for the presence of God
which were based partially on Butler's rationalist demonstration of the
existence of the Deity. It was re-assuring for Aikins to have this solid
basis during a time when new findings were challenging old faiths. The
addition of a rational proof to the elixir of faith was a heady wine for
the young doctor.

It was also necessary to buy James Miller's *Principles of Surgery*, and
the 1849 publication by John K. Mitchell, *On the Cryptogamous Origin of
Malarious and Epidemic Fevers*; C.D. Meigs', *Obstetrics, The Science and
Art* and Sir Astley Cooper's *The Practice of Surgery*.

And there were other expenses – or indulgences. His diary was
sprinkled with outlay of "six cents on fruits", a gold pen and case
($1.00), a cravat buckle and a pair of red gloves for $1.00. In addition he
required a French/English lexicon and a grammar and Testament, in

French. All in all, the outlay from October, 1849 to March, 1850, when he received his certificate, was $297.00. He estimated that the books had cost $44.00, including Sir James Simpson's *Work on the use of ether and chloroform* and a volume of poetry for $1.50.

Finally, an answer arrived from his first letter to Louisa.

8 November, 1849

Dr. Aikins:

You have perhaps thought me cold, calculating that I thus required so much time for reflections. But it is that forcibly have I been stricken with the unhappy consequences of friendships of this kind being formed too hastily. When though perhaps both parties were equally praiseworthy characters, yet eventually sympathies proved entirely different; that I was fearful lest we too might be among the unfortunates, and an intercourse indulged be in the end, alas, a source of regret to both.

The "risk" you generously remarked "was all on my side" but permit me to say, it is not so. A larger acquaintance might develop many incongerfialities of temperaments habits of thinking, etc.etc.

That I have been favourably impressed, the candour due to one whose high bearing in this I cannot but admire, requires me to acknowledge our correspondence may then continue though it would seem advisable that the length of time should be determined by the views entertained on either side when a farther intercourse has unfolded the peculiar features of each character.

In conclusion, one favour I most urgently desire – that should your opinions, consequently your regard, change, you will immediately acquaint me for on no account would I, that influenced by principles of honour you should continue these communications, when feeling has expired. In this, I pray you as you value your happiness – mine – be candid.

With sentiments of highest esteem yours, etc.

Louisa A. Piper.

Little time was lost in responding to this open and inviting note.

Philadelphia, 20th November 1849

Miss Piper;

In due time your kind favour was welcomed by me, gratified to believe that you have considered me worthy of regard.

No, Miss Piper, if I never more neither saw or heard from you, yet would I not for a moment imagine you "cold calculating' – wisdom requires that you (that we) should act with prudence and caution but coldness in not implied in such.

I clearly see the uncomfortable, I might say painful position in which you are placed, or in deference to your liberal assertion, in which "we" are placed ...

It is nearly five years since I had the pleasure of being introduced to you, with whose person and conversation I was very agreeably entertained. We were both young. Time called and circumstances threw us into different localities, me into different pursuits – old associations were broken; new ones formed–But neither time, circumstances, nor associations removed from my mind those early and youthful impressions.

My studentship in Toronto being now completed; I was honoured with a second introduction, which served only to deepen my former and growing conviction of your worth.

About to depart from Toronto for the winter and probably longer, and not being endowed with prescience, it remained for me to choose one of two courses – either leave in silence, or adopt the alternative and address you upon the subject. The latter I pursued.

I am FULLY aware that you are unacquainted with my character, disposition, etc. and many other facts necessary to be known ... I hope that a little time may overcome some of this unfavourable state of affairs ... As for the coming summer, I propose spending it in Toronto.

The winter after I should like to spend in some foreign country, but where, I am not sure as yet.

The justness of your subsequent remarks I admire and hope I fully appreciate. Cordially do I join with you in believing that rashness here has been the cause of much unhappiness and misery; nay, farther, that it must always produce such results, except in casual cases. I pray Heaven that we may not belong to this class of unfortunates. There will yet be time, sufficient I hope, to allow of making a wise conclusion and which, of course as you remark, will determine the propriety or impropriety of a further correspondence.

In answer to your request allow me to observe, that when my views of your intrinsic superiority shall wither and fade then shall a deeper change have taken place in my own nature, if I do not immediately inform you of it.

I am pleased that I came here instead of going to Montreal, Philadelphia is a lovely city, though I may say more immoral than I had anticipated. Thus far we have enjoyed a very agreeable temperature though not quite so bracing as you find that of Toronto in your morning walks. I hope your Mamma's health continues to improve, that your own is still good and your time passing happily. I feel mine passing very rapidly, probably owing to the pleasing and instructive variety in our duties.

In pleasing hope I shall wait to hear from one whose kind nature has already favoured me so highly.

Aikins did not have the money to return home at Christmas, and he had a thesis to complete. On January 26th he wrote:

I am happy to hear that the commencement of the New Year has been so conducive to your enjoyment.The remainder of its course though it may not be marked by so much excitement will I hope not be less liberal in its contribution to thy beings ends and aims.

How spent I my holy days? We had only a week-end that was about five days too long, for when away from home I scarcely ever enjoy them. The mind released from duty flies back and dwells on distant friends clustering around them yet not yielding the pleasure their presence had been wont to supply ... so that only for an unavoidable duty, it would have been long as a child's week to me.

The monotony was broken by the unavoidable duty of preparing my thesis, also by visiting some places of interest. As for New Year's Day, it was very richly spiced with variety, tea, butter and bread for breakfast, butter, bread and tea for dinner, and bread and butter and tea for supper.

New Year's Day calling in Pha. as in Toronto. I am not an admirer of the system unless confined to the reception of friends. For to me it has appeared that the day as it rolls along is loaded with the rites of mass formalities and polite falsehoods.

... Expect we shall be able to leave on the 11th of March.

Yours faithfully,   W.T. Aikins

Aikins had some interesting observations of his class-mates, which he passed on to Louisa:

There is more truth than poetry in your remark about the morality of medical students as a class. My chum and I frequently remark that as far as external appearances at least are concerned, the tone of moral feeling is not as low here as among the Toronto students in proportion to the number of students there, being less drunkeness, less profane and impure language. You take a peek at our class during lecture, all wearing their hats, three or four chewing tobacco, it seems indispensible, the southerners wearing cloaks, rings and costly watches. The lecturer is cheered on entering and retiring and occasionally during the lecture, not "viva voce" but with the feet.

On his return to Toronto, he sent a letter to Louisa, who was now at an academy in Hamilton:

My amiable friend, indecision is accompanied by anxiety. At least that has been so in my case for the last five weeks, with the most confused feelings. I took the pen to answer your kind and sympathizing favour, but laid it down at the commencement of this page ...

Although their romance was on paper only, there was an obvious warming of feeling to the "Kindred spirit" with the common ideas and

religious convictions there was a growing together and two weeks later
he wrote:

> ... last evening I went to the Diorama of Jerusalem ... and while I
> gazed on the small representation of those lovely scenes, I sincerely
> wished thee by my side to behold with pleasure also.
>
> If it should go through Hamilton before you leave, a visit will
> richly repay you for the time spent in seeing it – as I arrived rather
> late, I purpose going again.

William was proud of his chosen vocation, but there was a loud negative chorus from many others who were disenchanted with the poor
record of success in medical practice. In many instances, "orthodox"
medicine was under continuing fire from the alternate practitioners. In
1846, J.G. Rosenstein published *The Comparative Merits of Alleopathy, The
Old Medical Practice and Homeopathy, The Reformed Medical Practice*,
which preached the merits of homeopathy. This sect, which had been
founded by Dr. Samuel Christian Hahnemann in Germany, maintained
that orthodox physicians overdosed and overdrugged their patients.
Homeopathy used miniscule amounts of medication and claimed that
it achieved better results. A short time after, *A Medical Essay, Or the
Nurse and Family Physician*, was published anonymously which lauded
the system of medicine propounded by Dr. Samuel Thomson, an American physician, who had implicit faith in lobelia and steam. It opened
with John Wesley's essay on the *Ancient Practice of Medicine*, which
stressed self-help. Thomson had published a *New Guide to Health* in
1832 in Hamilton, which attacked the medical profession and became a
household "bible". He proposed that all men were born free and equal
and that the medical profession had taken over the health of the people
improperly, a philosophy re-iterated by the Rev. Schuylar Stewart in
1851 who published *The Canadian Herbal* in Hamilton. Its main emphasis was on health and religion. But the greatest impact came from
Domestic Medicine; a Treatise by William Buchan, which appeared in
many editions published in Canada and was the vade mecum of many
Upper Canada households.

Another powerful voice against allopathic medicine was *The Unfettered Canadian*. This was a pamphlet published regularly beginning in

1849 and presented Thomson's medical treatment under the name of the Canadian Eclectic Medicine Society. The pamphlets were eagerly read and were major forces in the shaping of public opinion on medical matters. The author, Baptist minister, Robert Dick, frequently distributed the material along with his evangelical preaching duties. These papers supplemented a flood of flyers and other print which sought to sell patent medicines and many other health aids.

Opposition to regular physicians was not confined to the competing schools of the root, the miniscule or the herbal sects. Hydrotherapeutics became a major health movement at the turn of the century. This was associated with the crusade for pure water, the exposé of the causes of cholera in 1849 by John Snow and the popularization of pure water by Charles Kingsley in *The Water-Babies* (1863).

All this resulted in a popular social reform campaign in North America which espoused the American Hydropathic Movement. In Kingston, a public demonstration by John Langtree in 1855, with admission of 5 shillings, exposed the imposters of allopathy and homeopathy while singing high praises of the hydropathists. Readers of the St. Catharine newspapers were urged to buy Dr. Russell Trall's *The Illustrative Hydropathic Encyclopedia, A Complete System of Hydropathy and Hygiene in One Large Volume*. This publication, written in simple terms, was intended to be a guide for home treatment or domestic practice. A Scottish-trained physician, Dr. J.E. Rankin, published a remarkable cure for chronic spinal irritation. This consisted of directing a stream of cold water up and down the spinal column. According to the directions, it took two sessions only for the patient to state that he felt much stronger and within five sessions could forward bend without pain.

In Markham, a treatment house was used by Dr. Robert Hunter and his junior colleague, Dr. Reid, who stated "it is high time that the medical profession was purged of that dark mysticism which obscures us of otherwise noble principles, which, when rightly understood had no other object that the investigation of truth, for the purpose of relieving human misery".[2] He reported remarkable recoveries. But there was a revenue problem in that the citizens saw little need to pay good money for ordinary water. However, mineral water was another matter and spas at London, Ancaster, Cambridge, St. Catharines, Kingston and Ottawa were a thriving business. The Sandwich Mineral Springs, which were tapped while drilling for oil, led to the building of a hotel and commodious bath house. Dr. Theophilus Mack, one of the founders of the St. Catharines Marine and General Hospital, established his own spa at Springbank, London.

The spa movement, like electrotherapy, attracted many female doctors later in the century. It became popular after the work of Vincenz Preissnitz, a German advocate of cold water pressure packs. After being run over by a loaded wagon, he shunned regular medical care for his own treatment. He had an excellent response and became an advocate of ingestion and ejection of copious amounts of cold non-mineral water; hot and cold baths; sweating and plenty of fresh air and exercises. His therapy was based on the humoral pathology that a "materia peccans" was expelled in sweat and eructions. He constructed a cure house and reaped a great profit from thousands of clients. His theories were adopted by Trall who opened a hydropathic institution in New York in 1844.

Aikins was approached by Dr. J.J. Furinvall from Woodstock, in a letter on October 30th, 1854, when he suggested:

> Success would attend the attempt to introduce in Toronto a modified system of hydropathy or rather caloropathy ... you know the success it has had of late years everywhere and I am of the opinion a few advertisements with prospective uses detailing the function of the skin in its striking activity and the consequences of stoppage of the pores of various causes ... the curative power to be derived from various baths; warm showers, baths of warm water, vapour and medicated baths, etc., if under proper advice would bring many a person to our establishment – I hope you will join. I would live at the place, attend to the patients and take the whole trouble on myself ... but to carry out this plan money must be forthcoming. I have it not – you ought not to furnish it, if you have wherewithal it would be requisite to find persons who would join in our scheme, by furnishing money on certain terms, to be agreed upon ... do you think you know any such persons?

The proposal was not accepted.

While most of these publications were aimed at the general public, the regular medical profession wrote primarily for their colleagues, and ignored the flood of negative comment. The first textbook in Upper Canada did not appear until a year before Confederation and was by William Canniff – *Manual of the Principles of Surgery* – which was not likely to be read by the man in the street.

Although Aikins and other zealots pursued excellence in the teaching of medicine and the improvement of the medical profession, their philosophy was frequently well in advance of the general public, including its elected representatives.

The lead editorial in the *Upper Canada Journal of Medical, Surgical and Physical Science* on July 1851 decried that several members of the Provincial Legislature considered the medical profession "as a noxious part of the community, whose extermination is to be accomplished at any hazard". This statement was made during a stormy parliament session which questioned why new legislative restrictions on the healing arts should be adopted, and extended the discussion to press that the old barriers should be repealed.

> Who would de facto legalize the murder, by rendering its detection impractical. If we examine the bearing of the arguments put forth by these champions of charlatinism, we shall find resolveable into the following general axioms:
> 1) that the practice of medicine is as much a trade as any other mechanical persuits of life ... and therefore ought to be as free and unfettered in its exercises as they are
> 2) that the criminal law of the land is sufficient protection against the evil consequences of ignorance and malice ...
> 3) that every person ought to be as much at liberty to employ their own *doctor*! (save the mark) as they are to select their own parson or lawyer.

The article continued and stated "we say it is wise, it is right, it is necessary, that the Legislature *should interfere* to protect the lives, the interests and the physical happiness of the people."

But the strength of the argument was lost by attributing certain qualities to the "educated and licenced practitioner" which were denied to the others – "when danger threatens his patient, it is required by a sense of moral obligation, by custom in the rules of his profession, to call in the aid and seek for the advice of one or several equally or more experienced than themself, to counsel him in a difficulty which exists, to collaborate his opinion ...".

The Bill, which caused this out-pouring, proposed to limit the provision of medical care to orthodox physicians who had graduated from an incorporated school. This raised great objections from the irregular practitioners and also some citizens in the province. The *Examiner* avowed:

> it incorporates all the half-educated and immoral practitioners throughout Western Canada who would adhere to the purge and lancet mode of treatment and Canada empowers them to destroy by fine and imprisonment all who prefer the more natural botanic system or the simple but efficient treatment by cold water. It is quite notorious that there are licenced physicians in this province to whom no man of judgement would confide the care of his sick dog while there are botany and cold water physicians, etc., etc.

The editorialist had several other items on his agenda. He did not fail to invoke freedom of choice, promotion of the dedication of doctors other than the allopaths; and succor to down-trodden unincorporated schools. However, it espoused a mixed marriage in the diatribe against the incorporated University medical school, by bedding the irregular physicians with John Rolph.

> Like its predecessors in former Sessions, it comes with a professedly benign intention, but in reality it is designed and calculated to confer vast powers upon an incorporated monopoly ... this Bill is intended, however, to deprive the people of the right of choosing their own physicians ... cases have frequently come to our knowledge where patients have been lingering for a long time and finally abandoned to die under the care of licenced ignorance or brutality, which afterwards, terminated favourably – almost, indeed miraculously – under the care of a botanic physician – a hydropathist – or perhaps some experienced neighbour. The Bill is framed as to prevent the people from seeking relief in cases of this

kind, or at least to punish with fine or imprisonment the individual who shall dare to afford it. Is this indeed the character of our boasted modern Legislation?

... another obvious design of this measure is to crush all schools of medicine not incorporated by law, and to give to a monopoly of medical education to the lancet and camomile physicians ... we want the aid of Cruickshanks and Punch to depict the scenes which would follow the passing of such a Bill! A gathering of the beagles of the medical corporations prior to hunting down all the unincorporated; the whole in full chase; and the coming in at the death of the last of the unprotected, would form three such scenes ... to raise the standard of education by free and generous rivalry and emulation, it proposes to crush all who differ with them, as to the philosophy of disease and cure and to destroy if possible the Toronto Medical School and all similar instructions, which are not incorporated and may outshine the University. This school, it is well known, is under the efficient management of Dr. Rolph, aided by other professors and has ordinarily enjoyed an equal (if not a larger) share of public patronage than the University itself – as heavy and cumbersome a staff of professors not withstanding, and has turned out a class of students, who have, in many cases taken rank with respect to solid professional requirements above those educated in the College. To get rid of Dr. Rolph's school, we presume, they supposedly would place the profession on a more respectible and efficient footing. Their light would shine to more advantage and profit if his could be put out. Messieurs Baldwin, Hincks and Price, nay add Mr. Cameron of Cornwall and his friends in creating two of the most despicable monopolies which could be inflicted upon the country – a monopoly of the practice of physic, surgery, etc. and a monopoly of medical education.

On leaving Jefferson, Aikins equipped himself for a medical practice. A walking stick cost 1 pound 3 pence, a pair of shoes 12 shillings and 6 pence. By September he was seeing patients and his first accounts show eight billings. In October, this increased to twelve, most of whom were females. Meanwhile; he continued his book purchases with the *London Pharmacopoeia*, Kehn's *Chemistry*, *Anatomy* by Gwynne and

Shoope, Robert Lee's *Clinical Obstetrics, C. Matteucci's Lectures*, and R.B. Todd and W. Bowman *Physiological Anatomy and Physiology of Man*. Bowman published several works on microscopy of the kidney and of striated muscle. Although the text did not preach as much Christian morality as did its predecessor by W.S. Carpenter, *Principles of Human Physiology*, the Bowman message was that all these magnificent activities that could be observed through the microscope, were part of God's grand design. With these acquisitions, Aikins assembled one of the best medical libraries in Canada West, including works on medical practice, surgery, chemistry and some physiology.

The second half of the century marked an end to the under-graduate life. On his return to Toronto, Aikins took out a partnership with Rolph and was appointed to the staff of the TSM. The school was having some difficulty. In 1850, Reverend Strachan, responding to the dis-establishment of the University of Toronto into "godless institutions," founded the Upper Canada Medical College. This institution was based on allegiance to the Queen and required a swearing of the statement: "I do willingly and heartedly declare that I am truly and sincerely a member of the United Church of England and Ireland". The faculty, which included Drs. Halliwell, N. John Bethune, James Bovell, E.M. Hodder, Henry Melville and Frederick Badgley, was a political powerhouse which threatened the enrolment of the TSM. In addition, by providing alternative arrangements for those students who might have difficulty in subscribing to the Thirty-nine Articles, it was possible under the acceptance process to enrol without the necessary vows, thus providing a wider net for the clergyman to act as a fisher of medical souls. Bovell made a special arrangement with Queen's University at Kingston to grant Medical Degrees to those who could not sign the required Articles. Eight Trinitarians took advantage of entering the world of medicine via this detour.

Aikins rapidly became the right-hand man in the TSM. This was a wise move on Rolph's part as he knew he would be leaving soon to take his seat in Parliament. His return to the political fray saw another figure enter the arena – George Brown. He and his father, Peter, moved to Toronto in 1843 and began publishing *The Banner*, a newspaper dedicated to upholding Presbyterian interest and Reform principles. The paper was successful in attracting a group of prominent Toronto

Reformers, who provided sufficient capital for the Brown's to publish a larger paper, *The Globe*, beginning in 1844. The paper began a long history of exerting pressure in the community and, by the time of Aikins' return, was a major mover in provincial politics.

His dissertation for the degree of Doctor of Medicine was titled: "Osteology, It's beauties and utility". Although he had stated previously that he found anatomy to be a dull and boring subject, when advanced standing was at stake, he breathed life into the skeleton by use of the "Divine architect". Throughout the whole of the paper, he used biblical allusions and, drawing from Paley's works, evoked the presence of God and declaimed "our intellect bows in humility to the wisdom of He who created this magnificant structure". The delicate articulations; beautifully symmetrical muscles and convolutions of brain and gut, all bore testimony of a divine designer.

In the TSM, he joined Drs. Workman, Thomas David Morrison and James Langstaff. Morrison was a longterm friend and admirer of Rolph and had joined him as an exile in Buffalo following the abortive rebellion. Langstaff was a recent graduate of the TSM, and his position was to accept apprentice students in his office on Yonge Street. Aikins moved into his old room in Rolph's home at 53 Queen Street West.

Rolph showed great foresight in partnering Aikins, for the younger doctor was able to direct the school, especially while the older was in Quebec City, one of the alternating seats of Parliament. Indeed, Rolph was spending less time with his medical practice and his teaching duties because of a heavier involvement with government. This involvement eventually led to a cabinet post, and to his teaching duties being shouldered by Aikins and accounting duties by Grace Rolph. She and Aikins got along easily, possibly because Aikins usually bowed to her opinion and requests. There was a constant stream of assignments for Aikins to carry out while the Rolph family was in Quebec, including buying an overcoat and shoes, as well as the more mundane matter of collecting the money which was owed to Rolph by some of his patients.

By September of 1851, Rolph was deeply immersed in his continuing battle with regard to the disposal of the Clergy Reserves. It was not enough that the Tories were constantly attacking him, but George Brown, through *The Globe* had begun a lasting feud with the doctor. Brown was always suspicious of Rolph's professed principles and repeatedly suggested that principles would bow to the practices of power acquisition in the long run.

As he began his professional life, young Aikins had to consider certain tasks – both immediate and long term.

First he had to earn a living. His family had spent large sums supporting him over the past decade. Even though the home farm had been prosperous, there had not been enough money to set William up on a farm and establish him in the agricultural business, however there was enough to manage a modest farm for his younger brother. To earn a living, the new doctor required a practice and a hospital appointment. Most doctors in the city could admit to the Toronto Hospital, but there was much contention, particularly from the Trinity physicians, as to who should have control of the beds. Rolph arranged Aikins' staff appointment through his friendship with Dr. Christopher Widmer, a founding member of the Toronto General Hospital, and the acknowledged doyen of the Upper Canada medical establishment.

The second job was to maintain and expand the TSM. Pressure was mounting on the school. The wisdom of altering the King's College situation was recognized by John A. Macdonald who introduced a University Bill proposing a radical change.

However, anticipating events, Strachan organized funding for the Upper Canada School of Medicine, which later became the medical school of Trinity College. In doing so, he presciently divined that Francis Hincks, the new leader of Government in 1852, would recognize developments in the major United Kingdom universities and separate the function of the University from teaching activities, reserving to it the degree granting rights. Not surprisingly, Rolph had written to Aikins on at least two occasions advising that he should "spread the word" amongst influential contacts that the teaching of medicine should be reserved for individual schools. Rolph's role was recognized in *The Patriot* which editorialized that the "wily old chief, the oily old doctor ... had we not long since called attention to some of the doings of this disinterested patriot; had we not kept his actions constantly before the eyes of our readers; had we not paraded his conduct before the public, as uniformly as a regiment of red coats are paraded before the eye of their commanding officers, the probability, if not the certainty, is that all his schemes of self aggrandizement, would have been received from others as reform, and would not have passed readily through the public mind".

The Upper Canada Medical College was transformed within the next year to Trinity Medical College, which offered considerable attraction to medical students, particularly for the sons of the upper classes in Toronto and surrounding regions. Students paid directly for their education and the lecturers received a proportion of the fees. Without sufficient paying students, the TSM would be in serious trouble while Trinity Medical College could draw on resources from Trinity itself, and not be entirely dependent on earned fees.

As well as teaching and maintaining the viability of the TSM, Aikins was immediately concerned with the quality of graduates. Although he had not matriculated from Victoria College, he immediately began a campaign to raise the levels of entrance to the medical schools. He was aware that in many cases students had difficulty in reading and writing. He also had knowledge from reports from the United States that students were frequently totally illiterate. Many examples were cited at various educational meetings of investigators between 1850-90, who had written deliberately unintelligable letters to Registrars, and who then received a letter of acceptance into the school. The same letter included the approximate price of graduating as a physician in a seductive few months time.

This enticement was not practiced in Upper Canada. Queen's College required all applicants to have completed a matriculation. King's required completed matriculation in theory, but in practice was not rigid in its application. However, graduation could not be given unless the matriculation was passed. In truth, matriculation was difficult to acquire in many parts of the province, as the student was required to have a knowledge of Greek and Latin, English grammar, history and geography, arithmetic, algebra and geometry. The simple fact of the matter was that there were not sufficient teachers in the province who could lead the class in all these subjects, which meant that students in rural areas where this grade of tutition was not available, were barred from applying, unless the rules were flexible.

A matriculated, or "under graduate" was one who was recognized by the College authorities as having passed a prescribed program of studies in a grammar school, leading to graduation. The matriculation examination was set by the Faculty in which the student was registered or to which a new student sought to be admitted, and corresponded to the entrance examination. Each college had varying levels of difficulty. These standards were set arbitrarily and might not be equivalent in each institute. The general curriculum included the Greek and Latin languages, English grammar, history and geography, arithmetic, algebra and geometry. A candidate for admission had to be of a certain age and have testimonials to a good moral character. Non-matriculated students were called "specialists" at Victoria College and "Matriculants" at University College. Generally they would write a special matriculation examination after one or two years study. Those taking a course but not proceeding to graduation were called occasional students or partial students.

A significant minority of the province's medical students attended McGill in Montreal, rather than schools in Toronto or Kingston.

Daniel Wilson, professor of history and later President of the University College (1880-1892) said "the true test of the efficiency of a college is its progress in the number of matriculated students".[3] But there were problems here because many of the secondary schools were religious and had priorities other than higher education.

A letter to Egerton Ryerson, when he was Chief Superintendent of Education from Rev. J.M. Bruyere, Rector of St. Michael's Cathedral, Toronto, protested Ryerson's suggestion that the Clergy Reserve funds should be used to provide library books, maps and apparatus to the common schools, thus enriching their curriculum. Bruyere objected to providing "Godless schools, from which religion was banished, with elegant School apparatus" while one third of religious schools were denied:

> ... a Catholic parent, who values his faith above all wordly advantages, and who rightly considers Religion as the basis of all education, would rather doom his child to the horror of the most degrading ignorance, than to permit him to drink in the Common Schools the poison of infidelity, or heresy, along with the pure draught of useful knowledge. These convictions are likewise shared by a large portion of the Members of the Church of England. Talk to us not of your superior training, splendid school apparatus

and highly qualified teachers. If these advantages, great as they may be, are to be purchased at the price of our faith, we value them not; we don't want them; we spurn them; and fling them back in your face.[4]

In such a climate it was difficult for anyone to raise entrance levels, but Aikins persevered.

His own qualifications were from the "commercial" department of Victoria, where he had completed his English and mathematics, but he also took Latin, physiology and chemistry, which were considered necessary to enter an academic stream. His experiences at Jefferson, however, convinced him of the necessity of setting a high entrance level in order to produce a well-trained physician. This could be ensured by a stringent matriculation qualification. Although Jefferson had low requirements, many American teachers were recommending only matriculants should be admitted to their schools.

Implicit in his work at the TSM and his desire to raise the level of admission, was the UCMB. This organization, which controlled licensure to practice medicine in the province, had been a Tory preserve for many years. Drs. Walter Telford, George Herrick, John King, William Bulmer Nicol and William Beaumount had worked under the direction of Widmer to grant that privilege after satisfying the Board-set requirements. No physician outside the Church of England group had ever been appointed to the Board, in spite of Rolph's friendship with Widmer. With Rolph's political ascendancy, he was able to demand and succeed in adding his name, as well as Workman, to the Board. Rolph insisted on this representation because of allegations that candidates from the TSM faced a much stiffer examination than those from Trinity. The *Montreal Medical Chronicle* stated: "Be it ever so brilliant *[the medical student's]* fate may be doomed when it is whispered he did not attend 'our' school and his examinations cannot be begun without first discovering whose classes he followed ..." So membership on the Medical Board was an obvious goal for young Aikins.

There remained two other projects facing the neophyte medico. One of these was to be of aid and assistance to Rolph, whom he respected. The entrance into a partnership arrangement meant that Aikins was, in

effect, carrying Rolph's practice. While his school attachments were
mainly for medical purposes, Aikins also became involved in the ongoing long term campaign which Rolph was conducting for the proper
disposal of the Clergy Reserves.

And the last item to be settled was his own personal life – his marriage to Louisa.

The wedding of Louisa and William on 7th of October 1851 was a
storybook example of romance in the mid-century. Although they had
spent very little time together, the frequent flow of letters had demonstrated that they were made for each other. The deep sense of religion
and dedication to God's work and committment to the future of their
existence in His way provided an irresistible thrust to union. The ceremony was performed by Rev. Enoch Wood, President of the Wesleyan
Conference in the home of Louisa's father, who lived on Carlton Street
and operated a copper and tin smithing shop at 50 Yonge Street, near
King. J. Ross Robertson, in his *Landmarks of Toronto*, recorded that
Hiram Piper had been able to provide his daughters with a good education and Louisa, after studying at the seminary of Rev. Dr. Van Norman at Cobourg had finished her "training in both the solid and
ornamental branches of female education" at the Burlington Academy
in Hamilton. The *Christian Guardian*[5] surmised, at a later date, "it is to
be feared however, that an undue stimulus given to her early mental
powers, sapped the foundation of her physical constitution ... The
piety, which marked her entire life, may have led her to the conviction
... by the spirit of God that she had a depraved nature; and though in
the estimation of others so innocent and so good, she felt that in the
sight of her Maker, she was a great sinner; and with deep contrition
and earnest prayers, she sought until she found pardon and acceptance
with God ...".

Combined with this overwhelming sense of religiosity was an
abiding dedication to her husband. Writing to him at a later date, she
said:

> Dearest most loved husband:
> Twas but yesterday I left my own dear home but already may I not
> say ever is my heart with you. And why not? ... my dear William if
> you but knew with what tender and grateful emotions I think of

you, you who have so watched over and cared for me in sickness
and in health ...

We shall go to your Father's the first day it is convenient – and
they tried kindly enought to make it pleasant today by taking me to
St. Johns. You will be glad to know I am as contented as I could be
anywhere from my blessed husband.

    Devoted and unchangedly.   Your own,

But beneath her professed love for William and her dedication to
God, there was an undercurrent of some undisclosed tension. A private
communication from a surviving family relative reported that "she was
not quite right". Apparently she lived constantly on the second floor of
their home, rarely descending the stairs.

    It is though, a comfort to me I know, in my absence that I am ful-
    filling my husband's wish, by trying to benefit myself and improve
    my health. I am endeavouring to keep myself cheerful and comfort-
    able in order to further that object ; and thus make myself all to my
    William I have the desire to be.

Following the wedding there was a brief honeymoon including a
visit down the Hudson River to New York where they stayed with
Lydia.

There were four children, none of whom married and it was suggested by the surviving relatives that this was because they did not
wish to pass on any disorder they might have inherited. By his second
wife, Lydia, Louisa's sister, there were several children, most of whom
married and had families.

Aikins began lecturing in the fall of 1850 in a room which Geikie
described:

    ... when the number of students had increased to require more
    accommodation than an ordinary private house could furnish, a
    new classroom was fitted up that formed the end of a frame build-
    ing in Rolph's yard. One part of this room had plain pine seats,

ranged one above the other, while the table behind which Dr. Rolph and the other lecturers sat, was the vat in use for anatomical purposes. The rest of the room was provided with boards on trestles, and this constituted a dissecting room where a great deal of good dissection was done for a number of years. Only a thin wooden partition separated this medical college part of the building from the rest of it, in which were comfortably housed Dr. Rolph's horse and cow. So thin was this partition that while the medical students were drinking in their scientific knowledge as they listened to the lecturers, or were working at their dissections, the four-legged occupants of the very adjacent stalls, who cared little and thought less about anatomy, medicine and surgery, could often be distinctly heard heartedly enjoying their more substantial material aliment. [6]

Humble as this building was, teaching was acknowledged by all to be of a very high calibre. Subjects considered at that time to be essential to a good medical education included anatomy, physiology, materia medica and therapeutics, and the necessary knowledge of chemistry, medicine, surgery, midwifery and diseases of the women and children.

At the same the time, the old Sunday school building on Richmond Street West, on Knox Church property was rented and fitted up by Rolph as a second classroom. Some of the lectures were given in the Queen Street lecture room and others on Richmond Street and the students had a short walk and some fresh air going from one to the other. Although clinical lectures with a patient in an amphitheatre had been given for some years in American schools, they were rare in Toronto, and most clinical work was at the bedside and formal lectures in the schools. The old dissecting room in the yard of the Queen Street house was still used for many years. These changes indicated prosperity, nevertheless the school suffered for a short time from the withdrawal of Rolph when he accepted his seat in the Cabinet.

The brochure advertising the course stated that "tickets" were received at par by McGill College, Montreal, and by various medical colleges in the United States. It asserted "... the Toronto School of Medicine is a self-supporting institution; and it draws nothing from the public resources or from the educational resources of the country which should rather be used for common and grammar schools, than to the education of the rich and affluent. The lecturers confidently rely upon the continued patronage and continuance of a liberal and enlightened community". This insistence on non-governmental funding became a credo of the TSM and Rolph and Aikins had no choice but to reiterate it, as there was no possibility of obtaining public funds. It was a continuance of the apprentice type of teaching where a student was attached to a doctor and paid for the privilege.

This perseverance that no public money was received by the TSM was the outcome of a conviction by the staff, and was the position of other community spokesmen. *The Leader* on October 26, 1852 printed:

> There are three Medical Schools in Toronto, why continue to sustain one by public money, when the facts show that the article you want is supplied by two out of three by private enterprise. But some say why not teach law and medicine in the Public University as well as literature ... But to give a profession is another thing. A profession is a doctor's and a lawyer's capital – the source of his income – like the stocks or lands of the capitalist, the ships of the merchant and the goods of the tradesman. This state cannot furnish the capital to all classes.

In addition to the improved lecture facilities, the school calendar in 1851 noted that there was a four bed lying-in Samaritan Hospital. Attached to this was a general dispensary which could be visited by students, if they purchased a ticket.

Aikins had been closely involved with the addition to the school facilities. He and Grace Rolph exchanged letters as to the relative merits of extending the staircase and the second floor a little higher. Aikins wrote: "It seems to me, though, that Mrs. R, is a little out in her estimate of £60 – the alteration would make the first two rooms, three feet longer and give a good landing on the second floor of the passage. These improvements would add to the present and future value and comfort ..." .

Among his other duties, Aikins, who admired von Liebeg's work, was convinced of the necessity of basic science and especially with the teaching of chemistry. Dr. Frances M. Russell had been giving the courses, but Aikins reported to Rolph that he "takes but little interest in the school and only brings reproach upon us, we propose throwing him overboard ..." – a brisk decision for so new a staff member. He suggested Michael Barrett, who was scheduled to go before the Medical Board in July of that year, as a replacement. One of the sources for the course was the *Textbook for Students of Chemistry* by D.B. Reid, M.D., F.R.S.E., past president of the Royal Medical Society in England. Lectures included a description of the elements and combinations using the system of Berzelius, a table of elementary equivalents and a series of experiments to prepare various compounds. It drew heavily on the work of Michael Faraday and Professor Wollaston and included a discussion of electricity, and morphinia, opium, cinchonia and strychnia. There was also a chapter on the recognition of body compounds such as albumin and urea, which Aikins insisted was necessary in making a sound diagnosis. His enthusiasm was based on the information he had garnered through von Liebig's text.

Although he had been slated to lecture in anatomy, with Rolph's absence he took over the lectures in surgery, a major accomplishment considering his qualification only a year before. One of his texts for the course was *The Principles and Practices of Modern Surgery* by Robert Druitt, first published in 1848. He also acknowledged that the opinion and practices of his confreres such as Hunter, Pott, Abernethy, the Bells, Dupytren, Larrey and others had contributed to the work. Aikins admitted to his students that he had first used it while at Jefferson, the previous year and was now giving instructions from the same book.

The opening chapters dealt with "prostration or collapse ... a general depression of the powers and actions of life, which immediately follows any severe injury such as a compound fracture or gunshot wound." These causes were amplified over the next few pages to include "... great and sudden extremes of grief, or joy, or fear, or cold – large doses of poisons such as arsenic or sulphuric acid or tobacco – the sudden impression of miasmata, or of morbid poisons such as the plague; – great loss of blood and mechanical injuries ...". Druitt wrote that the process of recovery from collapse was called reaction. Reaction could be succeeded by fever or prostration with excitment or sometimes death. He reported a case of a man who had his testicles crushed during "some barbarous sports", and the shock to the nervous system was so great "... as to be speedily mortal".

The pulses were described in a great detail with various categories such as quickness (or sharpness), the laboratory feel or thrill and a finding of frequent, hard and full pulses. The last was recommended as the best time for bleeding.

In describing the blood, it was asserted that after healthy blood had coagulated, it was divided into two portions, serum and crassamentum. However, "... when blood is drawn during the fever which accompanies acute inflammation, crassamentum is generally found to be covered with what is called a 'buffing coat', that is a yellowish white layer of fibrin, free from red particles – which layer may vary from one line to one third of the clot in thickness and is frequently so strongly contracted as to make its surface concave, or cupped and its edges fringed ..." The textbook continued that with inflamed blood," ... the attraction of the red globules for each other is greatly increased; so that they form themselves quickly into a sponge work, which quickly contracts, and sinks towards the bottom of the vessel. This causes a squeezing out of liquor sanguinous which separates from the globules to form the bluish white layer which is well known to appear on the surface of inflammed blood, very soon after it is drawn ..." It was some years later that a microscope would reveal the white blood cells in the buffy coat.

The manual was comprehensive including instruction on tetanus, of various types of inflammation and hemorrhage, suppuration and abscesses. There was a section devoted to erysipelas, ulceration or mortification, and scrofula. Malignant growths were characterized as being composed of two parts (with illustrations). The development of malignant disease seemed to depend on "the perversion of nutrition ... the cause of this perversion is not understood and is felt to be a constitutional diathesis, which is very frequently congenital, and inherited, but sometimes appears to arise from various causes and impaired vital energies; of which, mental anxiety and depression are the best established ..."

Aikins quoted from Druitt who distinguished medullary sarcoma from scirrhus by the absence of hardness and lancinating pain, by greater rapidity of growth; by larger size; by the earlier and more decided cachexia and by disposition to fungate rather than to ulcerate.

Under treatment, he wrote, leeches were used to retard its progress as well as cold and ice applications. The use of cautery of the principle arteries supplying the tumour had been recommended by others, but was not worth trying. Extirpation was hardly to be thought of, because the disease was such that it would return, perhaps before the wound had healed. So the description of the tumours did not lend to any specific treatment.

The text considered different types of injuries such as incised, punctured, lacerations and also the effect of poisons on the tissues.

There was an extensive section on venereal diseases with a discussion of their history. This section outlined the argument that a new and different variety of venereal disease had appeared at the end of the 15th century when the French army was beseiging Naples. It concluded that syphilis had existed from very early ages and its increased virulence in the 15th century was attributed to war, famine and intercourse with foreigners. The author denied that it had been imported from America and cited that Peter Martyr, physician to Ferdinand and Isabella, who was actually at Barcelona when Columbus returned from his first voyage had not said a word as to its America origin.

In discussing the origin of syphilis, the eminent British army-surgeon W. Fergusson, was quoted as saying, "... the irregularities of man at all times are punished by the generation of diseases, and the loss of health; and it would be difficult to believe in a superintending providence if this transgression of Divine and human laws should be allowed to pass unpunished ...". There was considerable discussion whether mercury was a specific, as had been recommended by J. Hunter. Experiments conducted by Army-surgeons had concluded that all kinds of primary and secondary symptoms might be reversed without mercury. Army records showed that of 1,940 cases treated without it, 96 had secondary symptoms and out of 2,827 treated with mercury, 51 had secondary symptoms. The results of this statistical study, which followed the Louis technique, was that there was at least seven times as many cases of secondary symptoms, when no mercury had been given.

Although this was one of the principle textbooks for surgical teaching, there was remarkably little description of surgical procedures. The treatment of reducible hernia was to replace it and prevent its return. This was done by taxis and by a truss. "The old fashioned attempts to obtain a radical cure by cutting out the sac ... or by making a large slough of the supra-adjacent skin by means of a red hot iron ... or poking little bladders of gold-beaters skin upon sticks of gelatin into the neck of the sac for the same purpose ... the less that is said about them the better ..."

Taxis was particularly important in strangulated hernia. The bladder was emptied, the patient, while lying flat on his back with his thighs bent towards the belly, was engaged in conversation to prevent him from straining with his respiratory muscles. "... Then the surgeon, if the tumour be large, grasps it with the palms of both hands – gently compresses it in order, if possible, to squeeze a little of the flatus into the abdomen – pushes it in the axis of the neck of the sac and at the same time with his fingers, gently kneads and suades the parts at the neck of the tumour, or perhaps tries to pull them very gently downwards, in order if possible to dislodge them. The operation may be continued for a quarter or half an hour or longer if the tumour was indolent ... If the taxis did not succeed then bleeding, a hot bath, a large dose of opium or morphinia, tobacco enema, a tartar emetic, and purgative enemata were recommended." If these were unsuccessful, an operation could be considered, consisting of opening the sac, dividing the stricture and returning the intestine. For the treatment of inguinal hernia, the procedure performed by Pancoast was recommended when he applied firm pressure with the fingers on the external ring, then introduced a very fine trochar and cannula into the area so that it entered the cavity of the sac. Then the inner surface of the neck of the sac was stretched and scarified with the trochar. The trochar was then withdrawn and an injection of iodine or cantharides was made as close as possible to the external ring, and a well fitting truss was recommended for the next eight to ten days, with the patient remaining in bed.

It was prescribed that piles should be extirpated by a ligature following which nitric acid should be applied to the bleeding mucous membrane.

Stones in the kidney and ureter were reduced inside by a lithotry. Several methods were discussed including, "... a device which grasped the stone and then, by a series of drills and other conveyances contained in the centre of the cannula ..." was drilled and hammered until reduced in size. It was explained that even with the current device suggested by Sir Benjamin Brodie, no treatment was ever entirely satisfactory. "... The martyrology of lithotry pointed out that mortality was probable in at least one in four cases." There was an extensive survey of the results of operations which had been performed in England or France.

When lithotry was not effective, then lithotomy was performed. "... The surgeon passes his left fore-finger, well oiled, into the rectum and explores the surface of the perineum ... with an assistant on each side holding the thighs firmly asunder – another being at hand to give the surgeon his instruments – and a third stationed on the left side holding the staff (a solid steel-like rod, which was inserted into the bladder through the uretha and located the stone) ... the surgeon commences by passing in his knife to the depth of an inch on the left side of the raphe, about an inch before the anus and cuts downwards and outwards to the bottom of the perineum, midway between the anus and the tuberosity of the ischium ...". The stone having been located "... the forceps are cautiously introduced over the finger into the bladder; the finger being gradually withdrawn as the instrument enters ... catches the stone and is brought within their jaws by the gush of urine that escapes ... If, however, the stone is not caught in this ready way, the forceps must be closed and brought in contact with it – the blades are opened over it and made to grasp it – if the stone is seized awkwardly it is relinquished and seized again – then it is extracted by slow cautious undulating movements ...". The surgeon was cautioned not to cut too high or open the urethra too much in front or of wounding the rectum or pudic artery and not to cut completely through the prostate, otherwise, "... the urine will find a ready passage in the loose cellular tissues of the pelvis and the patient will almost surely die ...". The procedure required an iron will on the part of the surgeon and a steel purpose on the part of the patient, as there was no anaesthetic.

Hydrocele was treated by injecting "two to four ounces of some stimulating fluids through the cannula, by means of an elastic bottle fitted with a stopcock. Equal parts of port wine and water zinc lotion are commonly used ... when the fluid has remained from three to five minutes, according to the degree of pain which it causes, it is suffered to flow out, and the cannula is withdrawn. Some degree of inflammation follows and more effusion into the sac – but generally the latter disappears in a fortnight or three weeks. If the cure is not quite perfect, the operation may be repeated after a few weeks ... ."

Orthopaedic conditions such as club foot and ulcers about the nails were illustrated.

A section was devoted to the avoidance of pain, "an object of the highest importance ... Until the end of 1846 we knew of no means of effecting this very desirable object save the previous administration of narcotics and long continued compression of nerves supplying the part to be operated on ... we do not include mesmerism on the list because this so-called science is so initimately connected with quackery, obscenity and imposture ... Whilst, however, this work was being printed, there appeared from Boston in America, the account of a method rendering patients insensible to pain during operations by means of the vapor of ether. This method, which was invented by Drs. Jackson and Morton of Boston was first promulgated in England in January 1847 and has ... been used by almost every surgeon in the Kingdom and in every possible variety of cases, and with very favourable effects." Druitt described an apparatus for the administration of ether. ..." a pickle jar, provided with a good cork, through which passes two glass tubes "... was recommended because it was portable and had a compartment for holding hot water for vapourizing the ether more quickly. "Etherization" was recommended in particular for extirpation of tumours, for amputation at the ankle joint (Syme's operation), and for excision of joints and ligature of arteries.

As an instructor, Aikins was in an excellent position to employ the procedures described by Druitt. But although he and the students knew the latest techniques of medicine, the usual practice was to rely on time-tested remedies. Blistering, one of the favourites, consisted of raising a blister on the skin to cause a counter-irritation to reduce pain. Bleeding continued to be used in the 50's and 60's. It was simply a question of how much should be taken rather than if it should be taken. The drug arsenal was made up of traditional remedies and some of the newer, more "scientific" chemicals. Constipation was a dangerous symptom and required relieving as soon as possible, using a wide variety of laxatives such as aloes, asafoetida, castor oil, rhubarb or croton oil. To these were added some chemical preparations such as epsom salt (magnesium) and senna. Various forms of alcohol, mixed with milk or honey were frequently used as stimulants. Even ardent temperance doctors such as Aikins, did not hesitate to prescribe it. Analgesic medications which were frequently required, particularly during terminal periods, used morphinia, the opium derivative. Dosage was uncertain and frequently resulted in overmedication.

The derivatives of opium had been used with increasing frequency in the first part of the century and by the 1850's were a common prescription. Dover's powder, a mild compound of opium and ipecacuanha was used to relieved gastrointestinal pain, stop diarrhea and also to induce sweating and reduce fevers. It replaced tincture of opium which had been previously used. Morphinia was in common use in 1830's and this increased dramatically in the 1870's when it was possible to administer it by hypodermic injection. This method provided almost instant relief in the doctor's office.

During the early days of Aikins' work at the TSM, the use of morphinia was not only a medical controversy, but it became enmeshed in medical politics. In 1854 a patient who was being treated by a student doctor from Trinity died, allegedly from an overdose. After extensive testimony at the coroner's inquest by the lecture staff of Trinity, including Bovell, the student was declared not responsible. A verdict was delivered that the cause of death was drunkenness, hastened by a drink of cold water. The TSM men, including Aikins, testified that too much morphinia had been used.

In the following year, James Dixon, a student of Rolph's, visited a patient, Job Broom after asking the doctor's permission. It was not uncommon for students to see patients, providing they had clearance from their preceptor. Dixon made a diagnosis of enteritis and prescribed six morphinia powders which he left. The "mulligrubs", as diarrhea was called, continued and the patient was much worse by the following morning. Dixon returned and added another powder. However the patient seemed to lose consciousness "... Broom went off into a kind of stupy," and Dixon hurried back to the office for help. Rolph was absent, so Aikins was recruited. He arrived at the patient's home with a stomach pump as Dixon had confessed that he might have given an overdose of morphinia. The stomach was rapidly emptied, and blistering was attempted by throwing scalding hot water on the body – a treatment given when it was felt that there might be intoxication due to drugs. Broom awoke from his stupor. As his wet clothing was removed portions of the skin peeled away as he had sustained severe burns. Rolph arrived and ordered cold water to be thrown on the patient to relieve his pain.

But the diarrhea continued and passerbys on the street complained of the stench. Broom died four days later.

An autopsy was ordered by the coroner John King. King had no love for Rolph as he had lost his position at the University of Toronto when the medical faculty had been closed, due to Rolph's politicking. Dr. Cornelius Philbrick and William Hallowell, who had been criticized for their care of a Trinity patient the year previously, were appointed to do the autopsy. Their findings, to the suprise of no one at TSM, were that Broom had died from an overdose. Rolph was forced to defend himself. Aikins had stated previously that if a student is sent by a physician then the physician is responsible. The defence was that there had not been an overdose as he had lived for too long a period after any medication had been given. Rolph argued the treatment was well within accepted medical practice. He cited Bovell, who in the investigation of the Trinity case the previous year, had stated that seven grains of morphinia repeated once in three hours was a good practice. However, at the Broom hearing Bovell testified that six grains given once was too much. Rolph's defence, in addition to the fact that the dose of morphinia had not been standardized, was that his student had prescribed it in a normal manner. This argument was bolstered by the fact that neither of the two physicians who carried out the autopsy had bothered to examine the intestines, which seemed unusual given the need for medication.

Dixon was found culpable by the coroner's inquest. However a trial jury freed him. So the accepted amount of morphinia remained unresolved – but the two incidents provided an excellent jousting field for the competing medical schools.

In fact the treatment Broom received was well within normal practice in Upper Canada, or other parts of the medical world. The theory of the cause of disease divided sickness into two categories. The first was caused by overstimulation of the body which upset the natural balance of good health; the second was understimulation. These were termed respectively sthenic and asthenic. Sthenic disorders could be associated with an inflammatory condition and in that case were termed phlogistic. If a patient presented with the symptoms of a sthenic disorder then the treatment regimen was obvious - the system had to be cleared of those influences which were causing the problem by drawing off the excess stimulation from the body. This was usually done by removal of body fluids by cathartics such as camomile, corrosive sublimate or jalap. This reduction of the excitatory factors was called depletive. For a similar goal emetics, which included emetic tartar or ipecacuanha could be used. Broom was obviously suffering from an overstimulation of his body. Therefore; he required "heroic" depletion, a term used when major attempts were made. When the powders did not have the desired effect, a counter-irritant was applied – that is blistering. However one alternate heroic treatment, drawing off blood, was not used.

Heroic depletive treatment was used in the majority of illnesses. The therapy "worked", inasmuch as it was quite possible for the physician to point out that the agitation was reduced following violent enemas, emetics, or blood-letting. In addition, if mercury was used, he could predict that the teeth would become loose and the gums would begin to bleed, which was all part of removing the causative factors of the disease.

When Broom went into a "stupy", it followed that he required blistering.

If it had been felt that his disorder was due to an inflammatory condition, quinine or another anti-phlogistic medications could have been used. Treatment was directed at reducing symptoms in each afflicted individual, as there was no concept of treating a disorder which was common to other patients. Therefore, a philosophy of specific treatment was developed, that is, the treatment was specific for the patient, not for a disease entity. These concepts of disorders had been set out earlier in the century by Benjamin Rush who had dominated teaching in the Philadelphia region for many years. His philosophy of disease was that the capillaries became congested, thus requiring blood letting. In addition, large doses of drugs were vital. "... Nature is like a drunken man reeling to and fro ... Always treat nature in the sick room as you would a noisy dog ... drive her out the door and lock it on her", he lectured in 1809. But he stressed this therapy was specific for the patient.

Competing ideas of the cause of symptoms depended upon which medical school was paramount and in which part of the continent. John

Estin Cook dominated the southern and western United States. His theory was that symptoms arose because of pathology in the liver. Therefore he gave massive doses of camomile which had the specific result of increasing bile flow.

There was occasionally a need for stimulation type therapy rather than depletive. For example, typhoid fever was due to asthenia. In that case quinine, iron compounds and a strenghtening diet was in vogue. By the 1860's whiskey, believed to be a stimulant, became a major medicine. But aside from any general therapeutic regimen, the physician was convinced that any treatment must be for an individual patient and could be successful only if personal factors, geography and social conditions were considered for the diagnosis.

The schools in Toronto were aware of the various philosophies but generally took a middle course. This was also carried out in most New England States which questioned the heroic measures and had some doubts of the doctrine of specificity.

REFERENCES

1. Warren, J. Collins. To Work in the Vineyard of Surgery!. Harvard University Press 1958; p 50.
2. Hunter, Robert. Hydrotherapeutics 1848; pp 78–79.
3. Hodgkins, J.G. The Establishment of Schools and Colleges in Ontario 1792–1910. Vol. XIII, Appendix C 1910; p 2.
4. Hodgkins, J.G. Ibid, 1856–8; p 3.
5. January 28th, 1863; p 19.
6. The Canadian Lancet 1901, vol. XXXIV.

Chapter Three

The Rebel

The wisdom of altering the King's College situation was recognized by even such Tories as John A. Macdonald who introduced a University Bill. It did not pass but the impetus generated by both the Reformers and the Tories eventually led to the Baldwin Act in 1849 which converted King's College into the University of Toronto. In doing so, it removed the control by the Church of England, resulting in the new institution being termed "the Godless university" (by certain sectors of a disestablished society).

The TSM benefited from these changes and continued to vaunt it's claim that there was no charge on the public purse for teaching medicine. Although physicians did not generate a fortune, there was a perception that because of their leading position in society, they should not receive an education at public expense. Similar sentiments applied to lawyers.

On February 26th, 1851 *The Examiner* printed an exposé of the vindictive action of the "Medical University" to further destroy their own credibility. It charged dishonourable "conduct of the Board in lecturing successful candidates on their ignorance before granting them their certificates". Further, it stated that "teachers in the University Medical School, not only examined all other pupils besides their own in secret sessions, without even impartial persons to witness such proceedings ... some of them can make their positions a profitable one ... It is now current among the medical classes, that additional fees are taken from students to prepare them for their examination! The small sum of twenty dollars from sixty students anxious to insure their passing, would make a slight augmentation of salary to the tune of twelve hundred dollars! This fee not only secures information, but is a prediction of the coming examination, and a guarantee against lectures on ignorance before granting certificates".

This article followed another on April 24th, 1850 which was written to further condemn the 'immoral" practices occuring inside the University halls. The writers stated that the University "convocation in this instance, is tantamount to a proclamation that the ascending faction do not scruple to use their power for illegitimate objects, and to prostitute the honour of the University to the unworthy purposes of partizanship."

The publication of these charges, due in part to Aikins advice, prompted him to add further fuel to the controversy by writing "Justice In Medicine":

> The Medical Department of the University has, not withstanding its commanding and unfair influence in the proceedings of the closed door Medical Board, with the disreputable annual plunder of the public purse, found it impossible to gain the confidence of the people. To secure a full attendance of medical pupils and therefore, looking forward to a dreaded event, in the case of its failing to fill the medical classes, has at last resort adopted the following despicable course, as published in a later number of *The Examiner*.
>
> The University in order to tempt students from all rival schools, has actually offered its goods and chattels in the shape of medical learning at the very lowest rate by, first "reduction offers", second by the further benefit of a sort of discount in the shape of a "private examination by them on the Medical Board for licence!" and third by a hint of the said examination and fourth by affording a surmised insurance of success from the five pounds voluntary fee, given by a student and taken by an examiner for a few private grindings preparatory thereto. Upon making enquiries of medical students we understand (for they make no secret of these matters) that in the main our information is correct ... what every medical pupil in Toronto during last winter was quite familiar with ... as regards the passport alias five pounds, voluntary grinding fee. The

insurance fee varies; one examiner offering the passport on all the branches for forty pounds.

Another "harder up" we suppose for ten pounds, a third, the examiner says for five pounds and we certainly have heard of one who passed the students on his branch, the grinding fee being as low as three pounds. Some of these students, however were rejected on other uninsured branches and that more than once until in the end they had to take out the full insurance or what was similar to it ... that the passport fee does secure to the candidate the mental assurance of a favourable final examination is evident from the expressions of some ... thus " if Professor does not vote for me at my examination for licence I will most assuredly expose him, etc., etc". But before leaving the 'insurance fee' we have asked the question, who were the parties said to have been lectured on in their ignorance last winter? And have been answered "young gentlemen who had been advised to secure their passport by students then undergoing the grinding discipline, but they refused the boon offered on such terms and who lectured them?" – "A well known grinder". Verily we thought in our mind that university medicals ought to recover government support to bolster up their depravity and whiten their sepulchres.

Aikins followed with:

Dear Sir;

Resuming our subject, we may notice the opinion held by Mr. James Miller, the present professor of surgery in the University of Edinburgh, and author of a very excellent treatise upon the principles and practice of surgery.

"It should never be forgotten, that the physician, before he can be either accomplished or successful in the profession must be infinitely conversant with the principles if not with the practice of surgery, *and most certainly, no one can ever lay just claim even to the title of surgeon, far less hope for eminence or success, unless he be equally qualified to assume both the appellation and the employment of the physician"*.

Their education on the whole is superior to that of the members of the Royal College of Surgeons and are therefore, much better qualified for every day practice as met with in Canada. Yet we must not be too credulous even here – the title of M.D. per se is very little evidence that its possessor is properly qualified "to stand between the living and the dead" – "to practise a profession where best, chance is dangerous and mistake death".

It is related in the life of the celebrated Dr. Caspar Wistar, that the Faculty of Medicine before whom he had been to be examined for his degree were not all of one theory and each professor examined with an eye to his own system; of this Wistar was aware, and had the address to answer each to his complete satisfaction – of course the degree was conferred on him".

Let a medical student connect himself with a college or university – regularly pay his fees, pass through his three or four years of study, become familiar with the style of his professors' lectures and examinations and he must be a dolt if his degree does not come "of course".

The error lies in the fact of the teacher examining his own pupil – a custom which is theoretically and practically wrong and fraught with the most pernicious consequences to the profession.

Aikins' persistence in the matter of who should examine students stemmed from two sources. Primarily, he endorsed Rolph's position against teachers examining their own students. Part of the argument was that students received a preferential hearing from their own professors, and TSM graduates received short shrift. This was natural because the UCMB, the licencing body, was composed predominantly of King's College faculty and other members of the medical establishment who were part of the family compact group. The students of Rolph, the Reformer, were always regarded with some suspicion of being Republicans .

Another thrust of Aikins' campaign was based on his experiences at Jefferson.

While medical licensure was controlled by the Board in Upper Canada, there was a different situation in the United States. Originally there had been appointed state boards to determine who was suitable for practice. However, in the period after the presidency of Jackson –

the so-called Jacksonian Democracy – these regulatory offices were disbanded. This meant that the production of a diploma from a college was tantamount to a licence to practice. Many American medical reformers, who were taken aback at the low level of teaching in a large number of colleges, objected to this arrangement. In a National Medical Convention in Philadelphia in 1847, composed of representatives of most of the leading schools of the country, a committee strongly urged "uniform and elevated standards or requirements" for colleges. Furthermore, in view of the fact that "each returning spring lets loose upon the community some 1200 or 1300 graduates" who were thereby "licenced to cure or kill", there was a strong need for upgrading in the requirements for graduation, and that "students should not be examined by their own professors." There were other recommendations regarding the length of terms and the content of teaching, however these were not acted on immediately. There was opposition to the recommendation that professors should not examine their students, as it was maintained that frequently the teachers were the best judges of the qualifications of their examinees.

The report of the committee impressed Aikins. It also identified another problem which he detected in that the entrance requirements for students varied considerably. The founder of the Cincinnati College of Medicine lobbied that anyone should be admitted to the course, as long as he passed the examinations subsequently. This included the "steamers, eclectics and other quacks". All these matters motivated the leading educators and philosophers of medicine in the United States with the result that in 1847, the American Medical Association was formed, to provide a forum for discussion and concerted action. The members of the Association never hesitated to speak their minds about the parlous state of medicine. In 1850, Dr. Lemuel Shattuck in a *Report of Sanitary Commission of Massachusetts* wrote that, "anyone male or female, learned or ignorant, an honest man or a knave, can assume the name of physician and 'practice' upon anyone, to cure or to kill, as either may happen, without accountability. It's a free country!"

While some of these sentiments were evident to all the leading physicians of Toronto, Aikins was the only one who spoke forth and tried to make changes. He had limited, labouriously-earned success.

Aikins was intent on building a top-notch teaching staff at the school as quickly as possible. While at Cobourg, he had struck a deep friendship with a classmate, John Howitt, who joined him later as a student at the Rolph School. He, too, followed the path to Jefferson.

In September, he wrote to Aikins that he had stopped over in New York on his way to Philadelphia to meet Rolph Davies, a fellow student. He reported that he didn't like New York "at all, at all". He attended three sermons over the weekend and took a walk around the docks. "As I was walking by foot in the market, it was early in the morning, I felt something touch my leg, I turned round and saw a man in the act of picking up a pocket book. I was aware of what the cove was up to. I walked on and immediately met another man who remarked 'That fellow yonder has found something. It looks like a pocket book filled with notes. Is it yours? It may be, said I, and you may go and claim half for your kindness. Tell the gentleman to drink my health on the remainder'. Surely no man ever put on a more devilish expression than he did on receiving his reply. You are aware of the manner they proceed. The book is filled with bad bills, and they tell you that you are entitled to half of the find'. The bills are of $50.00. They have an odd number, say there are nine, they give you four, the other you are requested to change and they pocket half and half. I could have the shaver taken up for the attempt to swindle, but it would have delayed me."

Howitt continued that he had seen Dunglison and Mitchell who spoke in the very highest terms of Aikins' talents. Mitchell said, "You are never again to call yourself an unworthy pupil. If I were to tell you all they say respecting you, I tell you that even your vanity would be touched". He attended clinics with Dr. Meigs and watched several operations. "The medical gentleman in attendance seemed to do their utmost to impart information to the students. How very different from those in Toronto." Howitt finished his letter by sending his regards to Mrs. Rolph and Dr. Lee and inquired whether Aikins would have married Louisa before he returned. "Now sit down and write. Come, you can see *her* tomorrow night."

He wrote again on the 19th, asking Rolph to certify the number of courses attended at the school, and went on to give details of the school year at Jefferson. They took clinics twice per week. "A Pennsylvania hospital is well conducted. It bears a strong and marked contrast with that of Toronto. It's cleanliness, it wants to attract your attention. The floors, the beds, etc. have an air of comfort. The patients too are treated as they should be. They have all the attention that the sick require. The attendants are punctual to the moment. I was pleased with the apparatus they have for the purpose of allowing the convalescents the benefit of fresh air. They have arm chairs set on wheels which are wheeled about on a level walk under the shade of trees and an atmosphere impregnated with the delicious odour of flowers. It will be long ere in Canada a poor invalid at a public hospital will get such treatment ...".

There were reports that widespread dysentery was prevailing. Opium and ipecac was their treatment and they:

> rammed down that potent narcotic with a vengeance—often as much as twelve grains in 24 hours and sometimes as much as 15. I saw one patient yesterday to whom I thought they had given a little too much. He was perfectly narcoticized, I like the method they treat fractures here, it is so simple. The fracture box and a long splint answers every case of the lower extremity.

After qualifying Howitt returned to Toronto. Part of his move was due to Aikins' urging that he might set up practice in Yorkville, but he went to Puslinch instead and wrote;

> When we were together last you gave some advice with regard to choosing a locality in which to practice. You spoke of Yorkville. Aikins, you know well enough through a long acquaintance with my character and habits, that I am the last person to succeed in a city practice. Beside I should never enjoy happiness in a large town. I want liberty, a large field in which to range about, without this I should be miserable ... I should never make a lecturer–first place it would take too long a course of class study to acquire the necessary information and when acquired you know well enough that I do not possess the gift of imparting it to others ...

Howitt eventually began practicing in Guelph.
Nevertheless Aikins was able to persuade Thomas Sunderland

Parker to join the faculty. Howitt gleefully commented on the appointment on December 22nd, 1851 and wrote:

> I got my mental eye fixed on you, my imagination supplies the rest. There you are, you and Parker. You want him to go to church, he is arguing the point. He is more easily persauded than I was willing to be. He consented—you accompanied him, but professional duties need your attention. He goes to the church and you get into a red doctor's carriage. Your course is an easterly one. Ah! A turn and now you are on the Yonge Street. Tell me the cause of that happy smile that now plays over your features. Yes, yes. I see the young doctor, he is going to see his first patient. Once more I follow you to her bedside, no, not to her bedside for now, thanks to your judicious treatment and mental influence. She is once more in place to receive you. Well upon my word your skill has accomplished wonders.

About the same time Aikins received another letter from his friend.

> I am anxious to learn how you are getting along with the school. If you can contrive to pull through this winter, I entertain little doubt of your success. Nevertheless I do not regret having withdrawn my name from among you. I would not have answered my purpose had I remained.
>
> It's a pity in my opinion that Dr. R. has embarked in politics. In my opinion he will make no more friends by so doing and perhaps not a few enemies. I am aware that you and I do not think precisely alike on this subject, neither are our politic views exactly the same. I hate all extreme parties ... no sudden changes in government is ever attended with much benefit.

Having recruited Parker, Aikins made a try for Dr. Thomas S. Harper, of Richmond Hill, who, after a lengthy consideration, decided that he simply did not want to live or practice in Yorkville. In refusing the offer, he mentioned that Dr. Henry Hover Wright was thinking of moving. He was well-known to Rolph, as he had been instrumental in

warning and aiding the rebel-leader to escape from York, and followed
him to Rochester when the rebellion collapsed. There, he finished his
course and qualifed to practice in 1839. He settled in Dundas and
Markham. According to Harper, Wright had said that he would be
interested in Yorkville if Harper decided not to go. No time was lost in
sending an invitation. Wright answered on the 10th of September that
he was agreeable to a change to a larger place. However he was concerned that he could not be counted on in physiology or materia medica. "... These branches would require a good deal of rubbing up and
fitting to make me luminous in them". Part of his reason for considering relocation was "our population being mostly Dutch, do not call for
much on medical men except in extreme cases, as they quack and use
nostrums. In addition to the prejudices of people against the duplicity
of my professional brethen, for a while to my face they have not seen fit
to be anything but my warmest friends, behind my back by dark insin-
uations they have constantly and steadily aimed at my downfall".

Aside from his concerns over the subjects he would be asked to
teach, Wright was able to reassure Aikins that most likely he would be
able to handle the assignments because Workman had offered to help.
There was one further incentive: "My better half is quite curious for the
move. Already she fancies herself domiciled in some snug little domi-
cile at Yorkville, running around, looking up stray cases of toothache
on which to develop my therapeutic poisons and quite astounding the
natives by my knowledge of the composition of Glaubers' salts". Her
enthusiasm may have been a convincing point because Aikins reported
to Rolph on the 7th of October 1852 that Wright was coming to
Yorkville and would teach the practice of medicine. "This will do our
school, I fancy, a great service and our practices but little injury".

But the best plans laid went astray. On January 5th, 1853 Aikins
reported to Grace Rolph that when Wright visited Yorkville he found
out that Richardson had taken the house where he proposed to open a
practice. This caused more vacillation on Wright's part.

The shortages of teaching staff was an embarassment to the school.
Both Workman and Aikins were carrying two subjects each, but it was
hoped that if Dr. Uzziel Ogden could be recruited, there would be
relief. Ogden had graduated from the TSM and had gone to practice in

Aylmer. Aikins invited him in the early fall of 1852 to come to Toronto and join the teaching staff. Ogden replied that he had "relinquished the idea of settling in Toronto". Aikins sweetened his offer by suggesting that there was a partnership available with Morrison. Ogden was realistic about the proposal. "Now what is this practice worth a year and at what terms should he take a partner; where could I obtain a place of residence, i.e. if we entered into partnership; what share would I be entitled to if I assisted you in school?" He added that he would not be able to come to the city before the beginning of 1853 as he had several months posting of accounts. He also asked whether Morrison was married and if his wife was living.

Aikins' reply was a masterful sales letter. Initially, he intimated that Ogden was being very modest in suggesting that he might not be good enough for the TSM, and continued that Workman had discussed a partnership with Morrison some time previously on the basis of half the proceeds to each. Morrison had consented to a contract for five years. In answer to what the practice was worth a year, he reported that Morrison, "just as Dr. Rolph used to act before he married, that is never send out an account, and only sometimes takes money when it was offered to him; he kept no regular entries for visits and prescriptions as do most physicians, is now trying to post up from memory as much as anything else". In spite of this lax business method, he estimated the income was £400 per year. Then he added:

> nucleus of a practice; the good will and assistance of those connected with our school; the reputation (and I think there is some) of being engaged in Teaching; together with the other advantages necessarily connected with our city as it is and will be ... fees for students can then be raised. At present they do not amount to much. We now number thirty-five pupils, one or two more are expected.

Aikins then offered him Materia Medica and Physiology and the support of Workman, who would lend his written lectures "which you can rehash as you like". It was apparent that physiology was not considered a high priority subject. Aikins also offered any assistance, and added:

> Another thing, (but strictly between ourselves) Dr. Morrison's
> health is poor – if it gets worse he will leave so he stays to meet the
> day. The fee for each pupil is £7.10 (therefore each branch £1.5).

The letter was not posted on the day of writing and he was able to
include before completing that Morrison had taken a turn for the worse
and urgently needed a partner. In spite of the urgency, Ogden did not
come immediately, but continued to mull over the matter and was
almost deciding to move when he heard the news of Richardson moving to York. This put him off again, but eventually he joined the teaching staff in 1855.

In the interim Dr. Samuel John Stratford, a pupil of the great William
Charles Bell and a MRCS, with some experience in eye surgery, joined
the faculty in 1853. He had been a member of the UCMB since 1838 and
later was editor of *The Upper Canada Journal of Medicine, Surgery, &
Physical Science*. Unfortunately he stayed for only two sessions.

One of the significant administrative actions in 1851 was the incorporation of the TSM. This was a direct response to the introduction into
Parliament, by the UCMB, of a new Bill stating that all medical teaching
institutions must be incorporated. *The Examiner* charged that the passage of the Bill was too restrictive and created a monopoly for some
teaching schools, and claimed that the Bill would deny the people the
right of choosing their physician. There was no doubt that the Bill gave
a monopoly to the "lancet and purging physicians" as opposed to the
root doctors.

James Lesslie, the editor of *The Examiner*, an old friend and fellow-
Reformer of Rolph, remonstrated that the TSM would not qualify as it
was an unincorporated institution: "... the Bill will crush all those who
differ with them as to the philosophy of disease, and will destroy if
possible, the Toronto School of Medicine and all similar institutions
which are not incorporated and may outshine the University ...".

Rolph lost no time in creating an escape hatch. He approached Widmer to present a petition to the Legislative Council to incorporate his
school. Widmer agreed and a Bill was taken to the Assembly by Henry
Bolton. There was a strange irony here, as Bolton and Rolph had butted
heads in front of a judge on many legal occasions previously. But a
born-again Bolton, who now got along with Rolph, was happy to repre-

sent and shepherd through the House of Assembly an Act to incorporate the Toronto School of Medicine which passed without significant
opposition. Surprisingly, the Bill was not presented by Robert Baldwin.
According to Dr. J.H. Richardson, the friendship between Baldwin and
Rolph had ceased during the 1837 Rebellion when the two had been
members of the "Flag of Truce" episode, during which Rolph was suspected of having incited the rebels to attack Toronto. "The cordiality
which had existed between Dr. Rolph and the Honourable Baldwin
before the Revolution ceased ...".[1]

It was clear that although the TSM was now incorporated it would be
necessary to have a more formal association with a degree-granting
institution. The freedom with which other "healing" sects operated
meant that the public had no way of deciding which group gave quality care. An M.D., Medical Doctor, behind a name gave more assurance
and set off those with higher training from the less worthy. The certificate which was given by the TSM had limited recognition, and the
major scholastic affiliation was in another province with McGill. Rolph
and Aikins decided that it was expedient to affiliate with the University
of Toronto. Rolph urged Aikins to make a formal application with the
result that instead of "funneling graduates to McGill", they would be
examined at Toronto. "Have you formally put in your application to
the Chancellor? – you can draft one and it should be sent to the Chancellor and the Senate of the University," wrote Rolph.

By November 15th, 1853 Aikins briefed Rolph of his concern for the
future saying, "we have suffered much this session from want of an
affiliation ... the professors at University College are anxious for it also
... this I have from some of the professors themselves". There was pressure not only from the Faculty, but also from the students. Writing
from Quebec on the 14th of November, Rolph said that he had heard
complaints that TSM students were discouraged that there would be no
means, after completing their medical studies, of obtaining a degree.
He was confident that affiliation would be accepted "as soon as the
Senate is organized, which will be shortly".

Two weeks later, a letter from Quebec suggested a bye-law should be
passed by the Senate, affiliating the school under the terms of the University of Toronto Act:

the amount of classical knowledge should be left to the school of medicine itself. If a pupil goes up from the Medical School of Guy's in London, before the Royal College of Surgeons of England for a diploma, no question is put as to his classical requirements, only to his professional attainments. Should the certificate of the school be refused, then a certificate of sufficient attainment on entering the School from any university or college might be substituted ... in taking a M.D. There should be no mixture of classical and professional examination. The duration of studies should be left to the school, and the university be guided by the examination as to the best test if any. Should this be objected to, the minimal should be stated, as "for a period of not less than three years". The certificate duly signed by the teacher of the school should be required. The examination itself might, under the Bye-law, be well made before the lecturer of the school, the President of the Medical Board for the time being, the Chancellor or Vice-Chancellor and such members of the Senate as may attend. This is an important point. Trinity College has examination by and before the medical teachers of the school it affiliates with.

This suggestion, which staked out an area of instruction by M.D. professors, severely limiting the University to a narrow area, would have been unacceptable to the Senate, whose mission was to guard the good name and territory of the school. In addition it continued the practice that teachers examined and passed their own students (in spite of Aikins' ideas) and kept the right in the proprietary schools to determine curriculum duration and content. To reinforce this Rolph advised that, "you may advantageously suggest from yourself a series of articles on the confinement of university instruction and expenditure ... and write to Hincks on the subjects protesting against the medical faculty being fastened on the college and on the public". Along with this specific target he also advised that various newspapers should be recruited in the campaign.

On the 14th of January 1854, Rolph once again pressed Aikins to report his progress with all particulars: "... let me know the progress of affiliation from time to time. Let them have their own way, after having pointed out to them the best that they will suffer from is too great stringency. When it is settled, one can seek modifications". However, more delays were encountered. By the 21st of February, Rolph advised that opposition to the affiliation was that "it assumes a pecuniary gain for all schools ... the whole delay is no doubt to prevent your affiliation and the restoration of the old state of things. I have discovered this and presume upon a prejudice against the school and against me as an enemy ... there are no bounds of wickedness and corruption and perhaps first they might deny the fitness of the School for affiliation".

Aikins made a brilliant suggestion, which influenced medical education for the next twenty years: "let us suppose the worst - viz that we are prevented from affilitation – why not try what was formerly suggested to you, that is, a medical department of Victoria College. We will then be independent – Victoria College at present has 150 students and is backed up by the influence of over 200 ministers scattered over the whole of Canada West. Your school has always had more support from Methodists than from any other denominations".

He immediately began discussion with the Rev. Mr. Sanderson, Secretary of the Victoria Board. Negotiations over several months led to a meeting on October 3rd, 1854 with the College Board. Aikins stated that he was a representative of the TSM and proposed in its name; "that it should be incorporated with or merged in Victoria College and become its medical department". The Board members were the Rev. Dr. E. Wood, President of the Wesleyan Conference; Rev. Dr. S.S. Nelles, President of the College; Rev. Dr. Ryerson, Chief Superintendant of Education; Rev. Dr. Anson Green, Rev. William Case; Rev. I. Musgrave and Sanderson. They discussed the proposition and agreed that "it is highly desirable on many accounts to extend the operations of the Institution by the addition of a Medical Department; be it therefore resolved that the requisite means be forewith adopted and that the Toronto School of Medicine is hereby constituted the Medical Department of Victoria College – and the following gentlemen be the Professors viz The Honourable Dr. Rolph, Dr. Workman, Dr. Aikins, Dr. Wright and Dr. Barrett and that the Medical Faculty of the University may form such Bye-laws for the government of the Medical Department as they deem necessary. Such Bye-laws to be valid when they shall receive the sanction of the Board". Aikins informed the students who had begun the session on the 1st October that they were in the Victoria College, Medical Department and inserted notices in the newspaper, signing himself as Dean. He was a little fast out of the gate for it was as not until October 18th that the agreement was ratified by the Board meeting in Kingston. At that time, Aikins submitted a series of proposals from the TSM which contained details and recommendations for effectively conducting the new department. The submissions were discussed and approved by the Board. Although the change of name was important, as it now permitted a university degree to be given on graduation, in general the public still called it Rolph's School. In truth, Rolph's involvement in the union was minimal and Aikins was the prime mover.

Ironically, the Senate of the University of Toronto, in spite of Rolph's paranoia, had continued its deliberation, and approved a draft statute to recognize the TSM and Trinity as affiliated under the terms of the University of Toronto Act 16, Vic (1853), c.89. The draft was authorized by the Governor General on August 30, but it was not announced until later. By that time the TSM was under the direction of Victoria. It would be another thirty years before a similar union would be considered.

Aikins' concern for a better quality of medical care extended far past the students. His colleagues, not necessarily friends, in the hospital had some obvious shortcomings. In particular, the Trinity professors were suspect. In a letter to Rolph in 1854 he observed:

> Trinity is not failing but is gathering strength everyday ... at the hospital Herrick, who is an attendant physician, gives over all his patients to Hodder and Bovell, the two Trinity men attending – and until we get our anatomical inspector, Beaumont and Telfer will have no questions as to what becomes of their dead friendless patients. But it is quietly arranged that they may go to Trinity ... please remember that Trinity has all the expenses paid by the Bishop and receives all the influence of a sect, the most wealthy and learned, if not the most numerous in Canada – your presence here would turn the scale at once – Napoleon's presence was not the assistance of 10,000, it was a victory ...

There was no means of assessing, by an outsider, the quality of patient care which was given by the doctors at that time although there had been some talk of an anatomical inspector who would judge the level of medical practice. In 1853, there were only eight attending physicians who were authorized by the Board of the hospital. This limited physicians who could use beds. When Rolph returned to Toronto in 1855, a war broke out on the wards.

Aikins noted in his diary on June 30th 1855:

> Beaumount comes in a 1 - 4 afternoon, five minutes later when slying along to visit a lithotomy case – I followed, he saw me and shut the door on my face. I opened it and went in – he was not calm enough to speak – ordered the mother and the nurse not to allow anyone to see him except Dr. Widmer or Dr. Clarke ...

This, of course, was an open challenge to Beaumont and the remainder of the Trinity doctors. The next object of Aikins' surveillance appeared in his diary on July 6th:

> ... Rolph visits the hospital ... Richardson is admitting – when Dr. Rolph walked into the hall, Richardson ordered Burns to shut and lock the door – door was shut but not locked – Dr. Rolph walked in again – to see a case of testicular disease examined by Richardson ...

In challenging Dr. William Rawling Beaumont, M.D., FRCS, Aikins was taking on a major opponent, who not only was a well-qualified surgeon, but also a leading member of the medical and social life of Toronto. He had graduated from St. Bartholomew's Hospital in London and was scheduled to be a military surgeon. However, after emigrating to Canada in 1841, he obtained a license to practice by Governor's General warrant. He was appointed to the professorship of surgery in King's College in 1843 which post was terminated with the abolition of the Faculty of Medicine. He had been a member of the UCMB since 1845. In 1836, he described an instrument for passing sutures in deep-seated parts as in the operation for cleft palate, which was reputed to be the origin of the principle of the Singer Sewing Machine. Several major British surgeons complimented him on the invention which was published in the *Medical Gazette* in 1836 and in *The Lancet* in 1866. He appeared frequently in the latter with articles on traumatic carotid aneurysm, several forms of lithotomy and exostosis of the scapula. (This last appeared in the *Upper Canada Journal*, edited by Stratford, FRCS, Beaumont was vexed that it had been published without his permission with the result Stratford lost his visiting privileges in the hospital.)

He was an inventive surgeon who designed a new type of forceps and also a probe-pointed lithotomy knife. Consequently when Aikins rashly challenged his ability to do lithotomies, a powder train was ignited which led to a major explosion in 1856.

Aikins' zeal to improve the level of practice was causing some admonitions from both his colleagues and the opposition medical school. Rolph wrote on the 20th of June, 1853 from Quebec that, "you perhaps lay too much stress upon the imperfect efforts of our other teachers. It will however be desirable to give such aid as will command respect." This letter was followed on the 29th of August with a sterner warning that "you better ease off as well as you can with the hospital difficulty, the dignity of the house surgeon must of course be reasonably sustained."

While Aikins was criticizing the problems associated with the level of care at the hospital, he was also deeply disturbed by other hospital activities. He was not alone in this matter as others were complaining bitterly about the General, resulting in a rising chorus of dissatisfaction and an article in the *Semi-Weekly Leader* [2]:

> perhaps a dozen persons taking medicine with nothing but a closet stool to resort to, placed at their bedside ... there is not a water closet in the whole building nor within eighty yards of it ... the odour which remains in the building is but too perceptible ... the very walls being corrupt by it ... is almost impossible for a patient to escape this noxious influence as is shown by the constant attacks of erysipelas and other complaints that indiscriminately affect them after residing a short time in hospital ... the greater part of the blankets used would be rejected by any spirited stable boy if offered as a horse rug ... there is no bath house in the building unless one old tin tub can be dignified with that name.

Although the General was the chief hospital of a large area, there was no operating room. Surgical procedures were being carried out in the ward or at the end of a corridor, and even on some occasions at a neighbouring pub. The medical students complained bitterly that they were unable to attend clinical lectures even though they had paid their £2.10 fee for tickets. Their understanding was that they could attend all lectures at the hospital, not just those given by TSM staff. Aikins repeatedly highlighted the practice of Trinity lecturers of not announcing the time of their presentations with the result many TSM students missed the session. In addition, because of the evasiveness of the Trinity teachers, it was necessary, for students to become "spirit rappers" in order to divine the appropriate hour.

In March of 1855, a letter signed by "a Medical Student" laid out a long list of charges saying:

> ... it is impossible in one letter to give even a faint exposition of the corruption which exists and stalks forth in open daylight in this house of sin ...

The author accused Burns, a hospital attendant, "with cruelty and relentless heartlessness and a systematic perpetration of outrages on the patients." In addition one of the nurses, a Mrs. Donnelly, was guilty of cruelty and unacceptable behaviour. It happened that Burns had been charged with assault by a patient some three weeks previously, with the magistrate finding against Burns and fining him, suggesting that he should be dismissed.

The medical student, (there was a warranted suspicion that he was one of Rolph's), stated:

> it has become useless for the physicians to recommend any particular regimen in the case of in-door patients, as no dependence can be placed on the nurses to see the instruction is carried out, as they prefer exercising their own discretion in the matter.

Aikins added a strong indictment of Mrs. Donnelly charging that she had failed to bathe a patient or do the laundry (which was usual) and that the patient was "covered with body lice". There was a plethora of

other charges. The nurse strongly advised a patient under the care of
Aikins that he should transfer his care to Beaumont or Hodder, with
the opinion that he would die if Aikins operated. Another of Aikins'
patients was hurriedly removed from the hospital by Hodder and Phil-
brook, who performed an amputation in a nearby tavern. The Victoria
practitioners were never given sufficient facilities and Wright complained that he could not get proper brandy for his patients and also
that there was a shortage of leeches. Widmer explained, in the *Trustees
Report of an Investigation in Certain Charges Against the Management*,[3] that
the hospital did not have sufficient money to supply leeches and
although the quality of whiskey was not good, a better brandy could
not be purchased.

This storm of events forced the Board of Trustees to hold a public
hearing beginning March 29th with Widmer and James Beatty
appointed as a Board under H.G. Bowes, MPP. J.W. Brent acted as secretary to the Trustees and the Board heard charges and counter-charges
by members of the two medical schools who were now combatting
each other in public. Hodder attributed the want of cleanliness entirely
to the building, and not at all to the servants. He said that it was impossible to keep it clear of vermin, and this condition was no worse than in
other hospitals – although he admitted the General was called "the
lousy hospital."

Then there was a surprising witness. James Dixon, admitting to be a
student at TSM, came forward and affirmed being the author of the letter. He stated:

> the spirit that prompted me to come forward was not a bad one. I
> have nothing against any of the persons connected with the Institu-
> tion personally ...

He said that some of the facts were known to him personally, others
he learned from colleagues. He had attended a meeting of the UCMB to
observe an examination:

> I went into the surgery, and there was quite a number of students
> inside. I cannot be sure, but I think that Dr. Bovell was there. Dr.
> Clarke was there and either he or Dr. Bovell authorized one of the

students to bleed a patient ... the student bled the patient, and when he had done so, the patient fainted away. The student held him up in the arms of a chair, and Dr. Clarke came forward and directed the patient to be laid upon his back on the floor. I then went away and returned in a short time. When I came back to see how the patient was doing, one of the students was applying a bottle of ammonia to the patients' nostrils. I felt the patients' hands. His extremities were cold and the tips of his fingers were blue. I put my hand upon the region of his heart and his action had apparently ceased, and there was a cold, clammy sweat upon his face. There seemed to be a cold spasmodic shuddering running through his whole frame. Just as I was looking at him, Burns came forward with a pail of water in his hand and threw part of it upon the patient and it dashed all over his clothes. He went away and got more water and was in the act of throwing it too, when a nurse came forward and caught his arm and prevented him from throwing it. Burns then took the patient up in his arms by the shoulders and pushed him outside the door. I went away and came back a little while and the patient was still lying outside in the cold, shuddering.

Dixon then told of another incident.

When a poor man, whom I considered to be a patient came in, Burns came forward and lifted his hand and knocked off his hat very violently. Upon another occasion, I was upstairs where there was a considerable number of students, and while there one of the nurses came up and announced that a medical student was at the door wishing to know where the students from Victoria College were. She ushered him in among the students, and in doing so made some taunting remarks to him and put her hands up towards his face in a matter which made the impression upon my mind that she was drunk.

Dixon's testimony was followed by that of another student, John Lennon. He stated that when coming out of surgery he met a coloured man who asked if he could get his tooth drawn. Edward Clarke then gave Lennon the instruments to draw the tooth. Just as Lennon completed the task, Burns came in and took the coloured man by the shoulder and pushed him outside the door. Other evidence was given by Lennon that Clarke refused to draw the teeth of a coloured man who was a good patient to the hospital. However Aikins, who was seeing patients at the time, said that "he would draw the tooth himself and not trouble anyone". Upon retrieving his equipment and examining the tooth, Aikins found the man had an abscess in the gum and treated him.

At the end of the hearing, Mrs. Donnelly was conceded to be a "diamond in the rough" and Hodder admitted that she was not polished, (ten years after Sara Gamp set the example for health workers). It was also admitted that she would "brick-bat the mouths of the students of Rolph's school". It turned out Burns was a pet,[4] of the Trinity gentlemen.

During the hearing Beaumont charged that Aikins and Wright lacked competence. This was backed by Hodder, who had studied and worked in France for a number of years before coming to Toronto to become one of the co-founders of the Upper Canada Medical College. He asserted that a doctor could not be a physician and surgeon unless he had taken instruction abroad.

The Globe, commenting upon the general situation, agreed that the Toronto General Hospital was in the most filthy state. However, the editor was also highly incensed by the "incessant bickering, backbiting and quarreling generally among the medical faculty". He made exceptions of King, O'Brien and Badgley, whom he felt had always acted as gentlemen. He disagreed with Hodder that Aikins and Wright should "content themselves with the lower range of capacity because, poor unhappy men, they were like many others compelled to fight their way unarmed with diplomas and certificates from foreign lands, and all the prestige pertaining thereto, and obliged to rely only on such opportunities as 'this Canada' can afford, aided by industry and perseverance".

The Report of the inquiry did nothing to close the gulf between the two groups. According to *The Church*, April 12th 1855:

It is sufficient for our purpose to state that the charges generally, and especially those which attacked our respected townsmen, Dr. Hodder and the indefagitable Dr. Clark (House Surgeon) had been completely refuted ... there seems to be little doubt that the whole affair was brought up by a party spirit and to use a party purpose.

But the Methodist paper, the *Christian Guardian*, interpreted the affair in a different light:

> We have no hesitation in stating that ample proof was given of the gross mismanagement on the part of two of the principle servants in the hospital, such as should induce the Trustees to dismiss them forthwith and we cannot believe from the evidence given, as well as from his own declaration, that the Resident Surgeon is free from blame for his evident partiality towards the professors and students of Trinity College, while his duty in that institution demanded that all medical attendance of the hospital should be treated with respect. There has obviously been a design and effort to deprive the professors and students of Victoria College, of the advantages which the attendance at the hospital was intended to confer.

George Brown of *The Globe* had his solution. He had opposed the Hinck's Act which had closed the medical school at the University of Toronto. Now he had an excellent opportunity to urge that the province re-establish the school and take medical education out of proprietary schools. His solution to the constant bickering was echoed by the *Medical Chronicle* of Montreal in 1855:

> Be he ever so brilliant, his fate may be doomed when it is whispered that he did not attend "our" school and his examinations cannot be begun without first discovering whose classes he followed.

The Report, which clearly identified a TSM student as the instigator of the charges ensured that the next step was inevitable. On April 14th, Aikins and Wright received letters from the hospital stating that their services were no longer required.

The firing of two of the chief lecturers of the TSM was a severe blow. Although they could continue their assignments at the school, it meant that some bedside teaching was lost. Aikins immediately demanded the reasons for the dismissal. He also contacted John Doel, a member of the Board of Trustees and an old Reformer friend of Rolph. However he "could not glean much". Aikins informed Rolph that what was uncovered was, "at the regular Board meeting, Thursday the 12th of April, there was an effort made by Widmer and Clarkson to push us out – Doel and Beatty in opposition – the matter was postponed til our prescription books could be examined ... on Saturday the 14th, the Board met. Four Trustees were present (Bowes in Quebec). Wright's prescription book was examined – mine I purposely removed from the hospital some days previously in order to ascertain the number of my surgical cases, etc. and at the same time to keep them in the dark as to the success, etc. of my patients. In my book's absence I entered any prescriptions on sheeted paper and gave it to Clark to make up ... well! At this meeting nothing objectional was discovered in Wright's book – I will just digress one moment – Herrick has no book at all and ever since the investigations no more attends his duty than before ... Beaumount also keeps his book at home ... Doel tells me that at this last meeting Beatty voted again with him – Bowes was telegraphed and gave the casting vote – but the ayes and nays were not entered with the rest of the minutes and never were entered until the meeting immediately after Bowes returned, and then Beatty entered his name with the ayes ... Clarkson and Widmer would insist that we were at the bottom of the letter of the medical student and therefore must be turned out".

Aikins also called upon S.S. Nelles, of Victoria College, who responded by writing a letter to the Governor General of the injustice of the action. This fight for justice for himself and Wright was aided by the knowledge that the vote was rigged. There was a formal protest in the Legislature, of which a committee ruled that the decision of the Board had not been unanimous and the Trustees had acted improperly. The discharged doctors were re-instated.

Just as Rolph had shaken the political system during the 20's and 30's, Aikins now picked up the mantle of crusader in the medical forum, and launched a campaign to raise the level of qualifications to practice medicine. From his experiences at Jefferson, he was well aware of the salutary influence of the magnificent French schools on the philosophy of medicine. However, his colleagues and other physicians in Toronto did not share the same intelligence. Dr. William Canniff detailed in his book *The Medical Profession of Upper Canada, 1783 to 1850,*[5] that of practicing physicians thirty-three had graduated from Scottish schools and universities, twenty-seven from English, sixteen from Irish. Only one had graduated from a French school, but seven of the graduates of the U.K. had spent some time in France. Thus, the major corpus of medical knowledge was derived from schools in the United Kingdom. Opposed to that, there were fifty-eight graduates from the United States. Many of these schools were condemned by the reports of the American Medical Association in 1847 as being little more than diploma mills. New York State Medical College at Fairfield, which contributed nine graduates to medical practice in Upper Canada, in 1880 was still, according to the *Philadelphia Record*, churning out medical diplomas.

While the Scottish schools had achieved a high reputation before the French Revolution, they had to yield their standing to the Parisienne faculties in the post-revolutionary period. This in turn was ousted by the Viennese and German schools after the middle of the century.

But in challenging the Trinity professors, Aikins was at a disadvantage. Bovell had studied in all three of the major universities in England, Ireland and Scotland. Bethune, Hodder and Philbrick were graduates of London and Edinburgh. Beaumount and Hodder had studied in France. On the other hand, Aikins' "team" was light. Although Rolph had his MRCS from England, Workman was a graduate of McGill. The same thin academic qualifications applied to Langstaff and Howitt, who although he had been to Jefferson, had taken his major instruction in Toronto. Thomas Parker was also locally bred. Yet Aikins, a graduate of two four month sessions at the TSM and one session at Jefferson, had a philosophy of medical teaching and practice which parallelled that of others with years of experience. Somewhere, somehow a missionary fire had been lighted in his heart, which produced an iron resolve to improve the state of medicine. Part of this determination was tempered by the heat of the ongoing debate in the United States. In 1849 Dr. Worthington Hooker published, *Physician and Patient; Or a Practical View of the Mutual Duties, Relations and Interest of the Medical Profession and the Community.* It was a devastating attack on the state of affairs as they were in the medical world:

> The lower the standard of education is among medical men, the greater will be the number of ignorant pretenders who will gain admission into their ranks, and consequently the greater will be the prevalance of quackery in the profession and of course in the community [6].

One of Hooker's main targets was the "spirit of quackery" which was common in the profession. While there were many good physicians who worked to the best of their ability for the patient's welfare, there were many who disreputably competed for patients for financial gain. In doing so, they promised cures, advertised by testimonials and generally brought nothing but disgrace to the profession of medicine.

Hooker delighted in exposing Benjamin Douglas Perkins who used magnets, called Tractors, to "cure" many diseases. "Not only captains and colonels, and generals, and squires, sounded the praises of the Tractors, but clergymen and senators and doctors and professors ... pain was relieved in a trice by a few strokes of the Tractors; inflammations were drawn out; swellings were dispersed and, in some cases with such rapidity that they were seen to lessen during the application; rheumatism, which had baffled the best medical skill was removed; the paralytic was made to walk ... Perkinism as it was called by acclamation, was hailed as one of the greatest discoveries and it was supposed to form a new era in medicine ...". The author continued, "... less than ten years after the summing up of the five thousand cures, Perkinism was only thought of as a thing that was past and the far-famed Tractors were almost forgotten ... and what became of Benjamin Douglas Perkins ... he returned to his native land with ten thousand pounds of John Bull's money ...". Hooker then proceeded to demolish Thomsonism, homeopathy, natural bone setters and then turned his pen on quack medical doctors. His work stood high in Aikins' thoughts and writings.

While Rolph had been willing to accept almost anyone into his school, Aikins cut a different pattern. He was greatly impressed by the entrance standards maintained at medical schools in Philadelphia and Boston, and began a campaign to raise entrance requirements to medical schools. This was based on the belief that higher requirements would eventually increase the competence of the profession. He saw clearly, as did many of his colleagues, that there was a suspicion and distrust of the graduates of medical schools and felt that this could be lessened if the calibre of students was elevated. One of his earliest efforts was directed at the Medical Board, and in particular, the examination process. He charged that, "university lecturers, in order to tempt students from all rival schools, have actually offered their goods and chattels in the shape of medical learning at the lowest rate, by first 'reduction offers', second by 'the further benefit or a sort of a discount in the shape of a private examination' and third by 'a hint of the set examination' and fourth, 'by affording insurance of success from a $5.00 voluntary fee, given by a student and taken by an examiner for a few private grindings preparatory thereto". The insurance fee was on a sliding scale – "one examiner offering the passport for all branches for £40". Aikins presented his findings to Rolph with the intention that firmer rules would be established for entrance into the TSM. He also published further details of his charges in "Good Doctors and A Safe People".

Both Aikins and Workman vehemently pursued the examination procedures, which they termed a "hole in the wall" affair. Aikins reported a meeting of the Board to Rolph on June 5th 1852 with Drs. Widmer, Herrick, Hodder, Beaumount, Wright, Mitchell, Workman and Aikins. Wright had only recently been appointed to the TSM and had been pushed on to the Board by Rolph according to Aikins:

> The order of the day was Dr. Workman's motion for public examination and for prohibiting any teacher from examining his own pupil – Dr. Widmer wished to defer the notice, although the motion had been given notice ... Widmer wanted to wait until more members were present say towards the end of the week...

Workman protested that members who had attended from the countryside could not wait until the end of the week and, as three months notice had been given, he put the question. Nevertheless Widmer, on his high horse, insisted that the motion should be deferred. This led to a tense confrontation between Workman and Widmer with the former accusing the Chairman of a plan to bring in members from the city adverse to the measure for the purposes of voting it down. He countered Widmer's suggestion by stating that if the motion was deferred he would prefer it to be put off for three months so he could also recruit some members to vote for his motion.

> After some more discussion of a warm nature, the measure was deferred and the secretary directed to notify each member of the faculty, and also of the following notice of Dr. Widmer in favour of conducting their examinations in writing.

Aikins then described that day's examination. Workman quizzed on Materia Medica and asked for the physiological effect of purgatives and their classification. Wright questioned the candidate on the bones of the elbow joint and declared that the response was not good and the candidate was a bad anatomist.

Aikins examined on the Practice of Medicine and asked the candidate to describe pneumonia, the stages, symptoms, general physical and stethoscopical features of each stage and treatment. The candidate answered that the sound of pneumonia was large crepitation. After the question was repeated several times he continued to give the same answer. Aikins then asked what the sound would be if hepatization was resolving. The student answered, large crepitation and vesicular breathing. Aikins then asked the difference in the diagnosis between pleurisy and pleurodynia and the effect of a larger quantity of fluid in the pleura? He quizzed: "If the fluid was of long standing and he would introduce a trochar and draw it off, why would the lung not expand?" No answer was given and the response with regard to hepatization was declared wrong:

> I stopped on my accord as he was bungling so – Beaumont had come over and sat down just behind me. I arose from my chair as the custom is and went to the other side of the table. No sooner had I moved off than Dr. Beaumont slipped himself into the chair and commenced examining, not waiting, as is the case usually, until Dr.

Widmer requested some member to examine next. Dr. Workman and myself here interposed and inquired to the Chairman whether this was proper, as the candidate was a pupil of the University – and we had at the last examination acted on the principle that no teacher should examine his own pupil. Dr. Widmer asked if there was any resolution of the Board recorded in the minutes to this effect; being answered in the negative, he said that we might proceed as usual, that Dr. Beaumont might go on. During the brush Dr. Beaumont held on to the chair 'hem-med and hawed' as to say, if you decided against me, of course I will not examine but otherwise I certainly shall.

Beaumont then asked questions in surgery to describe the symptoms, dangers and treatment of a fracture of the rib. He accepted the answer of strips of sticking plaster half as long as the distance from half-way round to the sternum. He also asked on the treatment of wounded arteries, large and small, a wound of the plantar arch and treatment. Beaumount then ended with questioning about the treatment of fracture of the femur at the junction of the upper with the lower third.

Workman asked about convulsions and their division as well as treatment with the varieties of haemmorhage.

When the candidate retired Dr. Widmer asked the view of each examiner:

> Wright said he was a bad anatomist. Aikins said that he passed a very inferior examination on medicine. Dr. Widmer, very good naturedly, replied to me, that he thought that he passed very well indeed in medicine – the fact is Dr. Widmer cannot hear the half of what his student says. Beaumont said he passed very well in surgery and Workman tolerably well in midwifery. Widmer then said: 'we ought to give him his certificate'.

Aikins ended his letter writing:

> wait til I tell you that the passed candidate told our pupils before he went up, that the University Professors said he was well

enough prepared and he should go through. What think you now
of the man, who, in the face of four members of the Board would,
against their expressed wish, persist in examining his own pupil.
There is something wrong ... The University needs to be taught
modesty yet. why if we examine our own pupils we might pass a
dozen –

The presence of Wright, Aikins and the other TSM members on the
Board was galling to the old guard. This was remarked upon by Aikins
to Rolph on the 7th of July. He mentioned that Herrick, Gwynne and
Nicol, "after making their appearance for a short time, retired, dull,
black and threatening, like so many thunder clouds". Dr. William
Charles Gwynne had taught anatomy and physiology at King's College
and had served on the UCMB over the past ten years: "Gwynne conde-
scended to remain during this and subsequent days in conducting himself like a gentleman".

Aikins examined in anatomy and asked the origin, course, relationships and termination of the thoracic duct. Hodder examined in gout,
rheumatism and peritonitis. Aikins remarked that he was a "superficial
examiner". On the next day, Aikins reported that Herrick "came and
went" often with apoplectic appearance. Aikins was asked by Widmer
to examine in surgery.

Glad of the opportunity, without hesitating, I embraced the offer,
as I wished without the most remote or indirect allusion, to strike a
blow at the practice in the Toronto General Hospital as well indeed
as in the practice of some gentlemen out of it – so I took the candidate on amputations – on the effects of chloroform upon the muscles and how this would modify his operation – Dr. Widmer held
his ear quite close and I made the pupils speak out loud. Examined
him closely on the mode of dressing the stump – then we went on
to wounds and their treatment – everything was quiet, a pin falling
on the floor would have been heard. Gwynne paid the minutest
attention – 'union by the modelling process' which claims, and
worthily – a good deal of attention at Jefferson – was dealt on for
sometime. Then his treatment of burns and of contraction after
burns. His answering was very sound ... Dr. Gwynne came over

and asked me what I meant by the 'modelling process' and how it differs from union by the first intention – and from union by granulation – after I had given him the view of the day upon the subject, he narrated two or three cases of his own when a filling up of the wound took place in the manner described to him. Do not smile too much at my egoism – I was a 'tipo' appointed under recent commission which was very obnoxious to the old members of the Board – any deficiency would be seized as very good capital to use against the government, 'for placing juniors above the heads of their seniors in the profession' this and the conditions of our school, will I hope excuse me for speaking thus.

Aikins continued to press his points with regard to the type of examinations which should be held. However, he was unable to reach Widmer successfully until an accident to Mrs. John Macdonald, the wife of a merchant prince of Toronto and a pillar of the Methodist church. She was thrown out of the Port Dover stage, receiving several contusions, especially of the back. Aikins was called when she reached Toronto and ordered rest generally and leeches locally. However "several of her high church friends insisted upon a consultation much in opposition to her own as well as Mr. Macdonald's wishes". Although Badgeley and Hodder had been recommended by the friends, Aikins insisted on Widmer:

I found him at the hospital examining his outdoor patients; requesting a word in private, he led me into separate rooms where, after hearing my message, he commenced in an indignant tone to lash me for my recent conduct as a partisan of Dr. Workman, etc. etc ... such language had never passed from me in his presence and this was the first time where a meeting subsequent to the difficulty at the Board. He went on to say that he had always taken a lively interest in my professional advancement, etc., etc., but now he considered himself no longer bound to consult or hold any further intercourse with me, etc. etc.

As soon as the first explosion was over I had the opportunity of getting a word in edgeways, I did so telling him that so far as Dr. King was concerned, I was a partisan of Dr. Workman's, and I consider very properly so, that whole occurrence from beginning to end had caused me a great deal of pain especially as I had felt myself compelled to differ from him, to whom I was justly indebted for his parental kindness towards me, that there were many reasons for our conduct of which he was not at all aware ...

Widmer interrupted the conversation at that time and requested that Aikins should await him until the clinic was finished. So he took a seat in Widmer's carriage:

It was now my turn to pour in a broadside and that I commenced to do with my heaviest artillery. Dr. Nicol was so far demolished that Dr. Widmer himself joined in calling down a malediction upon him – I then levelled at His Majesty (King) and Herrick, for their advising pupils to go to the University and they would have an easy examination for their licence – 'I can scarely believe it' but, sir I am prepared to prove it – 'well, sir, it is a disgrace to any University'. I mentioned numerous pupils who had gone to the University for the easier examination – also the open assertions of the University's licentiates and graduates that their pupils had easier examinations – and then asked him if we had not good reason for our objection against a teacher examining his own pupil? 'Yes sir, the principle is quite right, a teacher should not examine his own pupil'. Now this admission he has made to me, over and over again, since, but his conduct was diametrically the reverse at the Board.

They continued to discuss various recent Board appointments. Widmer agreed that Morrison was a proper one as he was a former member. He agreed: "Yes, Dr. Wright was well up in his profession". Widmer also agreed that certain others of Rolph's selection were appropriate:

By this time we had arrived at 53 Queen Street, having previously seen the patient and decided in favour of leeches.

The following day Aikins called upon Widmer again to nail down the agreement that there would be open examinations and that all branches of examination had to be passed before permission could be given to practice.

> Indeed there should be one provincial licencing board, and this for all persons, graduates or non-graduates, British, Yankee or Colonial – for if Nicol can be bribed for a licence, he can be bribed for a degree. Dr. Widmer wished me to write to you about your views about the incorporation of the profession, etc.

Aikins also took his proposal to the Board and succeeded in convincing the members that there should be "open examinations" – made by all members of the Board – and an end to any clandestine type of activity. Rolph commented on the 26th of April 1856, "open examinations are admirable corrections of certain classes of abuses and since their adoption, I have not heard from you at all events of any complaints. I am pleased to hear of your professional success."

The attempts to improve the quality of teaching at the TSM and Trinity caused changes in the curriculum. During the first half of the century the major medical experience of the student was to be under the direction of a preceptor, when he "walked the rounds." It also included being in the office of an established physician, observing the different types of cases, the manner of making a diagnosis and the treatment of the distressed person. While in some cases this could be an exemplary experience for attaining medical knowledge, in other cases it meant being a stable boy and a bill collector. By the 1850's, it was acknowledged that a more valuable experience was gained by observing patients while in hospital. The hospital became part of the school. While Trinity College had no difficulty in teaching its students at the bedside, there were times when attendance by students from the TSM was difficult. Aikins protested the fact that Trinity professors frequently barred TSM students from their rounds, which was a bad situation as Trinity men dominated the attending physicians, while TSM had only two appointees – Aikins and Wright. Furthermore, two other members of the establishment, Herrick and Beaumount, were allowed to admit patients and give lectures as representatives of the University.

This pre-eminence of the High Church group was a constant subject of discussion between Aikins and Wright.

Even after the Hincks Act, which included the appointment of a new Board of Trustees at the Toronto Hospital, Trinity continued to have an overwhelming influence. The presence of a teaching staff which included the acknowledged best medical practitioners in the country, meant Trinity was attracting more students, which led to an even greater level of friction between the two schools. George Brown of *The Globe*, being exasperated with the constant bickering, editorialized that the University should re-establish its medical school, a possibility always in the background during any of the controversies. However attractive as the suggestion was to certain House members, including John A. Macdonald, the staff of each school objected to any change. This was understandable as both depended, in a large part, on fees generated from the students and the re-opening of the University Medical Faculty would mean the collapse of one or both of the proprietary schools. In 1855, the patience of the legislators was thin and there was rumour of a proposal by the Government to repeal the Hincks Act. Trinity faculty rapidly mounted a campaign to oppose this. Ironically, the TSM had similar sentiments and for a short time the warring groups were working together towards a common end. The proprietaries pulse pounded when Attorney General Macdonald stated in one of the House sessions that the Government intended to re-institute the Faculties of Medicine and Law at University College. This drew an immediate response from the *Christian Guardian* which printed a series of letters remonstrating that $40,000.00 spent annually to educate twenty-eight students at the University was a failure on the part of the University and was wasteful of public funds.

With the statement by Macdonald, the Trinity Medical Faculty became alarmed at a real threat. They arranged a personal meeting with the Honourable J. Hillyard Cameron, the Member of Parliament, who, after listening to their concerns, requested a written report. This resulted in, "A Document purporting to be a Plan of an Act to amend the Law relating to the University of Toronto," which recommended that only graduates of a University who held a licence to practice medicine could hold any government appointment, for example to teach in the University. It also stated that University College and Upper Canada College should not be the sole recipients of funds derived from the public domain, but that money should be provided from the same source to affilitated Colleges in Upper Canada. In essence, the Clergy Reserve and endowments should be available to other schools. Also, no new Charters should be granted for affiliation to the University, unless that College possessed the sum of fifty thousand pounds. These clauses were meant to prevent the spread of medical teaching to other institutions, such as the TSM, with increased competition to schools already affiliated.

There was more. The group urged that the UCMB be replaced by a Board of Examiners at the University, which had been drawn from affiliated medical schools, and that the Queen should be requested to grant a Royal Charter similar to that of the University of London. This was a counter-blow to the actions of Rolph in loading the Medical Board with Grits.

At the same time that this document was submitted the teaching physicians, with the exception of Bovell, let it be known that they had been considering taking a position in the re-born University College Medical Faculty, but would not for less than 100 pounds per year! Considering they had taught at Trinity without any pay, this was a shock to Trinity Council, which immediately demanded to know their plans in order to "be prepared for the contingency of resignation".

The Council of Trinity College was upset by the initiative taken by its staff members and issued a memo:

> Any open attempt to prevent the re-establishment of the school of
> medicine in the University College would have been, in the opinion
> of Council, ridiculous; any covert attempt to effect the same would
> have been dishonourable.

This resulted in an apology from the Trinity Medical Faculty who explained that they had been interested in furthering Trinity's progress, rather than going against the wishes of the Council.

Of course, the Faculty was concerned with the number of students, which reflected income for the Professors. On October 18th, 1856 they advertised that lectures would commence and "no Religious Tests Required of Students attending these Lectures. Gentlemen not being members of the Church of England may obtain their degree of M.D. at the University of Toronto on complying with requirements of that institution". This was signed by Dean N. Bethune. The unauthorized advertisement, which challenged the Trinity Council, precipitated an emergency meeting. From this, came a clear declaration of an uncompromising order to the Faculty that:

> ... the attention of the Medical Faculty is again drawn to the Order in Council that no advertisement was to be inserted in newspapers relating to Trinity College expect through the Bursar who is instructed to submit all such advertisements to the Council for their approval and that the present objectionable advertisement be immediately withdrawn.

Hodder, Bovell, Bethune, Halliwell and Russell immediately withdrew the "objectionable" advertisement and repeated their reason that they were attempting to advance the interest of Trinity. In the same letter, the Faculty resigned. In a climate where there were repeated rumours that the Medical Faculty of the University of Toronto was to be re-instituted, the Council felt it was vital to maintain firmly the philosophy of the Church of England. But the Faculty responded that there were simply not enough Anglicans available to maintain an adequate income from fees paid, and complained that anyone could go to Rolph's school, without any ecclesiastical hobbles.

The Faculty acknowledged that their appointments were at the pleasure of the Council. But that same body was adamant that the Document should never have gone outside Trinity without permission. If the Medical Faculty could not understand that principle and still had cause of complaints: "Resolved that the resignations of the Members of the Medical Faculty be accepted".

Bovell was appointed Professor of Physiology, in its relation to Natural Theology, but left for the Barbadoes, to resume his divinity work. The subject was not considered a medical matter, as it was independent of any approach to explaining or caring for the sick. Its role, after determining the mechanics of certain bodily functions, was

to explain how these fitted the Divine plan. The authoritative texts by
R. Todd and W. Bowman, *The Physiological Anatomy and Physiology of
Man*, and Carpenter, *Principles of Human Physiology*, combined moral
with physiological instruction, with greater emphasis on faith than
physics.[7]

The upshot of the affair was that the staff was dispersed and Trinity
left the field of medical teaching. This was a severe loss to the future of
medicine. Bovell was possibly the most knowledgeable physician in
Upper Canada. He was the pioneer in Canada of the use of the microscope and had already been using it in anatomy laboratories to demonstrate cellular pathology, using as his text the work by A.H. Hassell,
The Microscopic Anatomy of the Body in Health and Disease, 1849. He and
Hodder had carried out experiments in the treatment of cholera in 1854
when they administered injections of milk, a daring experiment, which
each physician felt required peer evaluation before commencement.
They went to Widmer who agreed, with a condition:

> Requested us to be very cautious, as to what we did, least in case of
> immediate death, the public mind should become excited ... An
> ordinary glazed earthenware bowl was placed in warm water ... a
> cow which was grazing close at hand, was brought up to the shed,
> keeping the teat close against the side of the vessel to prevent froth-
> ing ... a brass anatomical injecting 4 cc sringe was now filled with
> living milk ... [this was then injected intravenously] ... in a few min-
> utes the pulse was distinctly felt..almost simultaneoulsly the eyes
> responded.

They injected four patients. A student, John McKenzie followed with
two similar procedures. Hodder later reported in *The Practitioner*, in
1873, that he and Bovell had applied to the Corporation of Toronto,
"for a good cow and a few articles indispensible for the comfort and
well being of the patient; these were refused ...". The experiment was
carried out on a rational basis after an article had appeared in the *British American Medical and Physical Journal* which suggested that death
occurred in cholera as a result of loss of fluids, either from vomiting or
bloody flux. In that article, a recommendation was made that fluids
should be injected by catheter into the bladder and Hodder reasoned

that the intravenous injection would be more effective, although that route was not common.

Although the TSM had its ups and downs, Aikins was able to maintain a steady course in attempting to build the best medical school in the province. Possibly he was aided by the fact that Rolph was in Quebec City. Despite a constant flow of letters, the day-to-day handling of the business of the school was in Aikins' hands. The recruiting, hiring, setting of curriculum, collection of fees, the preparation of a financial statement all were within his responsibility. His lectures were informative, but even more importantly, inspirational as he attempted to place the science of medicine in God's plan.

> Gentlemen, the eventful period has at last arrived when we are to commence the important duties of the 10th session of the Toronto School of Medicine (1852). A time which has been looked forward to with much interest and anxiety not only by those conducting the institution, but by all and by friends of all who have now come forward to enrol their names as seekers of medical and associate knowledge within its walls.
>
> I said eventful because from this week you issue upon a career pregnant with the most fearful responsibility.
>
> You now launch upon that great ocean of active life; and though your bark be frail, yet you now hold in one hand a compass and in the other the winds for the voyage.
>
> Think not since you are only medical pupils that you sustain little or no acountability. Alas how common! How fatal an error is this. Nay gentlemen, your conduct during your curriculum study will materially modify and most likely determine your future position if not your ultimate destiny.
>
> Do you desire to be influential, learned, beneficient and loved physicians, then during your student life I would say to each, "Cast thy bread upon the waters for thou shalt find it after many day". How much of woe, how many murdered human beings will in the future hang like millstones around the necks of the once negligent and idle pupils, God only knows. The presence here tonight declares that your conclusions are made that medicine is the profession of your choice. Your aspirance for a position which when

properly filled requires more than any other, unvarying energy, unceasing toil, but which at the same time affords sources of profit and happiness ...

There is a degree of exquisite pleasure in receiving heart-filled gratitude of one whom you rescued from peril, a pleasure which pleases the varying labour of our earlier efforts in the acquirements of the profession. In the apostolic age, Luke was characterized as the beloved physician and how often do our hearts warm when we hear this pleasing epithet applied to men who in miniature resemble the great physician, spend their lives in going about doing good, and pouring the oil of gladness onto saddened souls and in spreading the sunborn rays of hope over the thick black clouds of despair ...

The farther I see into the human nature in the lives of men, the better convinced I am that industry is infinitely more for the world than genius ...

... the most eminent men in our profession have been those elevated by their own industry. At present some of the leading physicians in Paris are from the various depths of poverty and obscurity. Velpeau, who's name has been wafted by fame into every quarter of the world is a striking example. Born 54 years ago, 25 miles from the town of Tours in France, his honest ambitious parents desired their son to follow the trade of blacksmith, the occupation of his father. By some accident his father, although illiterate, possessed all the books of the village ... the son was frequently called upon to treat the sick in the neighbourhood. Some trifling success having been given him a reputation ... he took his degree in 1823 ... the blacksmith's son will stand at the loftiest pinnacle of his profession.

Bouillard, an ornament of the profession in Paris, is reported to have been so poor while studying, that he made use of the fat of the subjects which he was dissecting for his light instead of candles. It is known that Professor Pancoast of Jefferson Medical College, Philadelphia served his time as a tanner until the 21st year of age.

I would urge you therefore to be industrious: our population is rapidly increasing: cities and towns are looming up in all directions: new positions of merit will be opened out, and it remains for you to say whether you will take them, or allow others to press on before you. (Aikins crossed out the following) – at present some of our highest situations in practices are filled by unqualified persons (I speak advisedly and with rage. Most of them form part of the impurities and scum distilled from the Royal College of Surgeons, England and other British institutions, who come to our country with ignorance and impudence and push you Canadians to one side. (End of crossed area). Will you endure this? You who have imbibed the spirit of our land, a spirit of progression, who have drunk from the running brooks the stimulus of necessity of self-dependence and other matters – will you not avail yourselves of your own inherited power and grasp what is within your reach?

Faith, gentlemen, on your powers is as necessary to your success in the world as faith in God to your success in religion.

Take for your motto the answers of Gallileo, who on being informed of the prosecution that awaited him if he persisted in the propagation of a theory conflicting so directly with the long established prejudice of mankind, replied "Never will I barter the freedom of my intellect to one as liable to err as myself".

Before concluding gentlemen allow me to remark that you have other claims upon you besides your studies – those of morality and religion ... Oh, can there be a more worthy vocation of that which summons us to minister, as apostles of science, to the greatest exigencies of life? To cheer the soul under the acute sufferings of maternity, alleviate the decay of nature? To watch over the glimmering dawn and the fading torchlight of existence? To stand beside the mother who sobs that the departure of her first born may be undisturbed and ... what a mastery of sorrow, what requisite mental and corporal are demanded in him who is the observer of scenes like this, whose sympathies are awakened to services such as ours ... whose talents are efficiently enlisted for the triumph and accomplishment of his devout truth.

In spite of this heavy schedule, he had a busy private practice. In 1853 Aikins had attended at least seventy obstetrical cases and remarked "as far as money is concerned, not over five of these, bad pay, that is no pay". In addition he was surgeon to one of the "Odd Fellow's Lodges (though no member thereof). Indeed I cannot tell how I am going to get through the next four months, that is, to the close of the session" he wrote to Mrs. Rolph. His practice size attracted attention and Howitt in a letter on April 2, 1856 said, "I'm told you are rapidly making a fortune".

But, even when absent, Rolph clung tightly to what he had fathered and after the affilitation with Victoria had been announced, with mock courtesy suggested that Dean Aikins should appoint him to a Chair in Surgery. In effect, Rolph was planning his return to Toronto. This move was appropriate. When the Hincks government fell and the Conservatives, under Alan MacNab, took charge, Rolph lost his relish for politics and retreated to the medical arena. Naturally on his return, he prepared once again to don the robe of Dean, but he failed to reckon with the strong feelings of his faculty, which had become proud and jealous of their success, achieved in his absence. Rolph proposed that the school should move to a new site on Little Jarvis Street, Yorkville. Aikins had strong objections because of the distance to the Toronto General, and the reduced time available for teaching. The hospital had moved from King Street to a new location on Gerrard Street, east of Parliament in 1854 which meant a fairly lengthy haul from Yorkville. However the Yorkville property had come cheaply, as it had been donated by Joseph Bloor to the British Wesleyans in 1841. After that, the Central Methodist Church occupied it until 1854 when it was turned over to the medical department and renovated in 1856. When it was opened, at Rolph's insistence, it was described as having a commodious lecture theatre. Aikins' feelings were so incensed by Rolph's obduracy that he resigned from the faculty. The heat of his emotions was fanned by the roughshod manner of Rolph's decision-making. Aikins also objected to the manner in which the Board of Trustees pressured the Faculty to go along with Rolph's decision. It was a rare instance of exasperation in a man who held his Christian tenets so tightly, but his pique peaked and he relented and returned to the Faculty one month after he had formally registered his discontent.

Another crisis surfaced two months later when Rolph wangled from the Victoria Board of Trustees carte blanche to run the Medical School. He hired a Demonstrator in Anatomy, without consulting the staff. It took only two meetings for the Faculty to realize that the school was no longer a corporate body and they had lost their rights as co-proprietors. Rolph took it on himself to decide the course content without full consultation with his Faculty, which precipitated an urgent request for a staff meeting, but he replied that he was unable to attend. Indignant at the usurpation of their roles by someone who had not been working on a daily basis to build the school, the entire staff resigned, one week before the Fall session was to begin in the new schoolhouse. They realized the damage this could cause, but rationalized that it was their only recourse in view of the unreasonableness of the Dean.

The Medical Chronicle lost no time in attaching the blame for this debacle:

> Dr. Rolphs' energies and talents were generally known and acknowledged throughout the province and he was appointed justly, however a more irresponsible Dean, never before held place and in making him such, the serious evil was committed. A power of managing solely and without reference to his colleagues, all matters connected with the School ... was confirmed on him with a simple proviso that he must submit, whatever they determined on, to the Board of Victoria. The Medical Faculty were to do the will of Dr. Rolph, be good boys, and in fact do their work and ask no questions at the end of the session, when they would get what money was coming to them after the funds had been drained by the expenses of management by an irresponsible Dean. Truly he was a one man power established in all its superiority.

In spite of this condemnation, Rolph was able to retain the confidence of the Victoria Board and began recruiting a new staff to give lectures to the 51 students who remained in the course. He delivered most of the lectures in the first two weeks.

REFERENCES

1. Richardson, J.H. Baldwin Room, Reference Library, Toronto.
2. March 22nd, 1853.
3. Rare Book Room 1855, John Robarts Library, University of Toronto.
4. The Globe June 23, 1855.

5. Canniff, W. The Medical Profession in Upper Canada. Toronto 1894.
6. Physician and Patient; Or a Practical View of the Mutual Duties, Relations and Interest of the Medical Profession and the Community; pp 250–253.
7. Hodgins, J.G. Documentary History of Education in Upper Canada 1856, pp 72–76.

Chapter Four

The Builder

The resignation from Victoria was not done lightly. There was a matter of money. The financial statements, drawn up by Aikins for the Session 55-56 showed 55 students in Anatomy for a full year which generated £153. The Institutes of Medicine had 42 students, raising £105. Materia Medicine, Midwifery and Surgery all contributed, so the total income for the school for the year was £703. From this total, Rolph received £168, H.H. Wright £89, Ogden £81, Barrett £81 and Aikins £116 13 shillings 9 pence. There were certain expenses on top of each of these items. For example, Anatomy required cadavers and skeletons cost £30. Postage was another expense and it was necessary to travel to Cobourg on occasion. Advertising was fairly extensive, not only in the Toronto papers, but also Cobourg, Hamilton, Montreal and London, with a total of £40 (The Globe received £9 16 shillings). Rental and taxes amounted to £45, wood and gas £11. Whitewashing of the rooms in October '55 and April '56 cost £2 15 shillings. Given that Morrison's income from his practice was about £400 per year, the school stipends were a needed supplement.

Aikins' letter of resignation to the Rev. E. Wood, Victoria College, on the 6th of October 1856, was very gentle:

> In resigning my connection with Victoria College, permit me to express to you my unreserved thanks for the uniform courtesy and kindness which I have invariably experienced in my intercourse with you in relation to the Medical Department of that institution.

What Aikins concealed was that he and the remainder of the former faculty of Victoria had moved into the old building and continued lecturing to medical students under the name of the Toronto School of Medicine. Rolph spent the remainder of the '56/57 semesters carrying the major load of teaching at Victoria, but gradually recruited a staff. He continued to advertise the medical department as the Toronto School of Medicine, Victoria College Medical Department. This, of course, caused considerable confusion to potential students, and led to a confrontation between the two groups of teachers.

Aikins and his staff boldly brought an action in Chancery prohibiting Victoria College and the Honourable John Rolph from "pretending to be the Toronto School of Medicine and from pretending to be in any way connected with the said school". Rolph, who did not share William's christian forebearance, seethed with outrage at this ungrateful action from someone whom he had coddled for many years. The lawsuit was defended by Victoria College which was represented by Rolph. He reviewed the history of the institution and the fact that he had founded it and had directed it for many years. When he returned from Quebec, he had been appointed Dean and still considered himself Dean of the Toronto School of Medicine which had been incorporated into Victoria College. Aikins, ingenuously, testified that the TSM had never become part of Victoria and blandly stated that the meeting which was held in October 1854 had been attended by seven Victoria Board members. But, quoting from the school constitution, it was laid down clearly in the Articles of the College that a quorum of eight was required before any action could be taken. Aikins guilefully insisted that the statements with regard to the union of the TSM and Victoria were "pretended". Similarly, when the Board met again in Kingston, two weeks later, it once again dealt with "pretended" resolutions. Astonishingly, Aikins was able to make the court accept his statements as truth. It was never brought forward that immediately following those meetings, Aikins, styled as Dean, had inserted advertisements in the newspaper that the Toronto School of Medicine was now the Medical Department of Victoria College. On November 7th 1857, the Court of Chancery delivered its verdict: "This court doth order and decree that the above named defendants, their officers, servants and agents, be particularly enjoined from asserting, claiming, advertising or pretending to the Toronto School of Medicine and from pretending to be in anyway connected with the said Toronto School of Medicine ... the said defendants do immediately after the service upon them of this decree ... pay to the said plantiff or bearer, the costs of this suit to be taxed by the Master of this court".

It was an amazing performance. Minutes of the Board meetings showed clearly that Aikins had identified himself as a representative of the TSM, duly delegated to negotiate with Victoria. The *Christian Guardian* on October 25th, announced the formation of the new department. He denied this in Chancery and stated that he was simply investigating it as one person, and no union had taken place, thus the TSM remained a separate entity. The minutes, written by Sanderson, showed it was clearly established that the TSM did become part of Victoria College, and in accepting the TSM, also named the teaching staff as professors.

Even though it was known at the time that Victoria College was in desperate straits, and needed a cash infusion from student fees, it was unthinkable that the whole of the Board, Reverend gentlemen all, including Dr. Ryerson, would be capable of making such mistakes or conversely, of falsifying the records. Not only did Aikins lie in court, but he also lied in front of his peers and trusted friends. His overbearing passion to teach and to raise the level of medical care outweighed the underbearing religious committment on which he lived his life. What is surprising is that his congregation and preacher did not raise the issue. Others had been disqualified from the church for relatively minor infractions of the Methodist Discipline, such as failing to attend weekly class meetings, or going to the theatre, dancing or card-playing. John Wesley's code based on the text from Colossians "Whatever ye do in word or deed, do all in the name of the Lord Jesus"[1], was a strict code of behaviour and was applied to all church members – but not to Aikins.

Some of the staff from the TSM/Victoria faculty stayed with Aikins however there were gaps in the school and there was uncertainty regarding the role and powers of the Dean. To repair this he turned to his brother, M. Henry Aikins, who was studying medicine in Philadelphia. When Henry spoke with Dunglison, he was surprised that there was some reluctance on the Professor's part to provide much information outside of a few cautious statements. Henry surmised, in a letter on October 31st, 1856 that, "I would not be surprised if Dr. Rolph has been communicating with him, since the difficulties have arisen". Dunglison explained that part of the student fees were devoted to a sinking fund for the purpose of purchasing the building. In addition, demonstrators were appointed by the professor in anatomy and the fees for professors were fixed by statute. Henry also spoke to the Dean of the Homeopathic College, who advised that the Dean had no special powers.

With the new school, there was opportunity for improving the curriculum. Aikins wrote to a friend who was at McGill, J.R. Malcolm, who provided some details on adminstration and timetabling.

Materia Medica – 8 to 9 a.m.
Institutes of Medicine – 9 to 10 a.m.
Midwifery – 10 to 11 a.m.
Surgery – 11 to 12 a.m.
Hospital – 12 to 1 p.m.

The students were then allowed an hour for food, but reported back for;

Anatomy from 2 to 3 p.m.
Practice of Medicine – 3 to 4 p.m.
Medical Jurisprudence – 4 to 5 p.m.

In addition they took Chemistry from 7 to 8 p.m. and Practical Anatomy from 8 to 10 p.m., and were required to take Clinical Medicine twice per week from 12:20 to 1:20. This course was to be taken after some experience with a physician.

Dr. G.W. Brigham of Tillsonburg wrote to Aikins on September 8th saying that he was sending, "two young gentlemen at present under my instruction and I hope they may afford you as much gratification by their industry and rapid progress as they have already given me". He had given a course of instruction in Anatomy. He had also, "ground them up through Churchill and the greater part of Druitt and Fleetwood Churchill, M.D., *On the Theory and Practice of Midwifery*. One of them I am vain enough to believe will be able to cope with the seniors in Midwifery, the other in Chemistry ... both seem fond of the odour of the graveyard, and I assure you will be among the most expert in obtaining dissecting material". Anatomical dissection material was difficult to obtain. M.H. Aikins, writing from Jefferson, had been able to secure a human skeleton at a cost of $15.00, but estimated it would be another $15.00 to assemble it. By Act 7 Vic. c.5, the bodies of those found dead, publicly exposed, or who immediately before their death had been supported by any public instutition, could be delivered to teachers of anatomy or surgery. However, with the cost of dissection cadavers at £20 each, there was still some grave-robbing. Dr. Thomas Deazley of Grahamville was chased by two constables from the Toronto General Hospital when he "borrowed" a corpse. (He was later appointed to the Chair of Surgery at Trinity). It was a common practice for medsmen to defray their tuition charges by supplying a fresh cadaver to the Anatomy department at McGill.

In his attempts to recruit teacher/physicians of Ontario, Aikins was willing to sponsor some students to be added to his staff after graduation. John Lennon, of Rolph's school, went on to Jefferson. On November 9th, 1856, he wrote that he was enjoying the lectures, particularly of Pancoast, Meigs and Gross, and was boarding in the same house as M. Henry. William, who knew Lennon from the Donnelly inquiry, had given him some financial assistance. On December 9th, Lennon wrote, "your kind offer of further assistance to me for which I am deeply grateful and for which you will please accept my thanks. I am nearly out of funds just now and would be exceedingly obliged to you, if as soon as you could make it convenient, you would forward me the money." He described his lectures and how convenient it was to study at Jefferson. "The clinic here is most excellent. It is only now that I can estimate the disadvantage of moving the school to Yorkville and when Mr. Smith told Dr. Mitchell of it (the move), he said it was madness". The year moved along quickly for Lennon and by January 12th, he wrote "I am obliged so much sooner than I expected to again trouble you in consequence of it being one of the requirements of this institute that the graduation fee be handed in along with your thesis. If you would be so kind as to remit me a further loan so as to enable me to accomplish this by the 20th of the present month, I shall be much obliged." He chose for the subject of his thesis, *Concussion of the Brain*, and reported later on February 11th that he had been examined by Pancoast on the brain, nerves of the brain and spinal cord, coeliac axis and vena porta. "Generally he is not a minute examiner. He asked me if you went into the anatomy of the brain in your lecture as minutely as he did." Lennon was successful and gained his M.D. and on returning to Toronto was appointed Demonstrator in the TSM Department of Anatomy.

Aikins had an uphill fight to maintain admission requirements to his school, in view of what was going on at the University of Toronto. The Reverend Dr. Ryerson, in 1860, presented a statement to the Legislative Assembly detailing how the University of Toronto had lowered its matriculation requirements from 1852 onward. Ryerson said that this was a progressive lowering of standards, which included omitting two previously required Greek and three Latin authors. He stated that the Vice Chancellor of the University maintained the necessity of this action because of the insufficiency of grammar schools. Ryerson countered by citing the Grammar School Act of 1853 which forbade the employment of any person as a master of a grammar school who was not a graduate of some university, and thus conversant with the Greek and Latin authors. He also showed that the "system of options which had been available previously had been severely restricted, reducing the student choice."

The Senate of the University of Toronto in 1857 had decided its requirements for the medical degree were to be reduced. The attendance at Lectures on Medical Jurdisprudence and Practical Chemistry was lowered from six to three months. The Medical Department of Victoria College protested declaring that the relaxed requirements which had been, "held sacred in every civilized country ... was such a minimum of requirement that the student cannot be prepared for those scenes of impending death, so peculiar to Midwifery, where a knowledge of prompt action alike are required to avert the fatal issues." Victoria was also concerned about the examiners for medicine. As there was no Faculty of Medicine at the University, it was necessary to call on a member of the Senate, Dr. Barrett, who held his post because of his previous association with the TSM. It had been his advice to lower the qualifications.

These remonstrations were answered by Professor Daniel Wilson of the Senate. He admitted that there had been some changes of the matriculation examination, but justified this on the basis that the University was not solely for the education of the professional classes. Wilson encouraged and hoped that farmer's sons and other candidates of the same level would attend. At the same time, William Hincks was appointed the first professor of Natural History, University College. He achieved this post by defeating Thomas Henry Huxley. Although the latter was a prestigious scholar with recommendations from prominent biologists, including Charles Darwin, William had recommendations "better than all the testimonials in the world", namely his brother Francis, who was the Premier of the Province. This type of patronage was accepted as business as usual as the Legislature made all University appointments. However, with Rolph in the Cabinet, it was quite likely that he raised some objections. It was stated, in many circles, that Rolph was mollified to this appointment and agreed not to question the extensive railroad spectulation by Hincks, given that the Faculty of Medicine had been removed from the University of Toronto.

In fact, the separation from Victoria College was a boon to Aikins. Although he was able to take only three of the faculty with him, his ability to recruit teachers was enhanced. Rolphs' enemies, and there were many, could now consider joining forces with someone who had rebelled against the "Great Rebel." Aikins had no reluctance to take advantage of this windfall, even it meant forgiving and forgetting the events of the past ten years. Hodder, who had disparaged Aikins' education, joined the faculty. The altered perception of the TSM resulted in a flood of talent. Dr. John Bethune, one of the original lecturers in the Upper Canada Medical College, and James Thorburn signed on, as did J. Lizars MRCS, from Edinburgh. He was a welcome addition for Surgical Anatomy and Demonstrator of Anatomy, which continued to be the basis of medical teaching. Form governed function – it was paramount to know the machinery of the body.

In 1861, Aikins secured a prize when he recruited Dr. James A. Richardson for General and Descriptive Anatomy. Richardson's father had been a volunteer in the Provincial Marine in 1812 and served with distinction with a left arm amputation after the attack on Oswego. Following this he was an ardent Methodist and gave up a prosperous and comfortable life to preach with Egerton Ryerson. He became editor of the *Christian Guardian* and was one of the founders of the Upper Canada Academy. His son, James, attended the Academy with James Cox Aikins. In 1841, he was advised by Widmer to study medicine with Rolph in Rochester. Richardson wrote:

> His house was a small one with two rooms upstairs, one my bedroom, the other my dissecting room. I dissected two subjects most minutely during the two years I was there, the subjects being preserved in whiskey with bichloride. Although I had in after years an irreconcilable anatongism with Dr. R., I do him the justice to say that it would have been impossible to find anyone more competent to teach, more indefagitable in teaching, and more considerate and pleasant in his general intercourse with me. My subjects were sent over from Toronto, in barrels of whiskey by the late Dr. H. Wright, who had been a pupil of Dr. R.'s before the Rebellion. [2]

In 1844, when the pardoned Rolph returned to Toronto, Richardson continued his education to matriculate at Kings College and after that to Guy's Hospital in England. He reported that he had got a "cheap trip" on the *Patrick Henry*.

"I was up early morn, had my shower bath on the deck as the sailors were holy stoning and swabbing the decks, became as active as a monkey in the rigging, all of which restored me to robust health and vigour".

Arriving at Guy's, he had a surprising welcome from Dr. Bransby Cooper, a nephew of Sir Astley, who had befriended Rolph in the 1820's when a student at that hospital. Cooper took the letter which Rolph had written in support of Richardson and brusquely exclaimed, "Rolph! He ought to have been hanged long ago".

When Richardson returned to Canada in 1847 he qualified as a physician, however:

> Business was, as it always is, slow in coming ... I bought some carpenter tools and tried to divert my mind in carpentary ... by good chance Dr. Rolph was called to attend a lady named Ritchie, out in the country beyond Mastquatah, the residence of Mr. William Baldwin. It was a case of puerperal convulsion very severe. I succeeded in saving her life and made the acquaintance of Mr. Baldwin.

The result was that Richardson was appointed to the University of Toronto to demonstrate in the museum, providing he gave up all his other practice. However this post vanished when Rolph initiated the movement that terminated the University of Toronto role in medical education.

> I was left to regain practice ... I was a sleepless man, utterly so, for a long time, but I never gave up and ultimately succeeded in establishing a good position ...

He felt thoroughly aggrieved by Rolph and refused to have anything to do with the TSM. However:

> One day crossing the head of Bay Street, I met Dr. Aikins. He accosted me with the remark, "Dr. Richardson, cannot we be friends?" I frankly told him that I was determined never to recognize anyone who had been instrumental in the destruction of the old Medical Faculty. He gave me his personal assurance that he had been deceived by Dr. Rolph and that he regretted what had been done. I accepted Dr. Aikin's explanation and subsequently a very amiable relationship existed between us.

When he took over the demonstration post at King's College he described the surroundings as:

> The anatomical and chemical departments occupied a square clapboard house, which was lighted by skylights, situated west of the Parliament Buildings. My anatomical classes comprised of about twelve students, mostly those who were preparing for examination before the Medical Board, a few only being matriculated students ... the number of students in my class alone amounted to sixty students over three years. At the end of that time a new commodious building had been erected on this site, now occupied by the Biological Building (the old Moss Hall).

In recruiting Richardson, Aikins brought new thoughts into the school. The philosophy of medicine in Toronto which derived from the

teachings of Rush and Jackson had resulted chiefly in the use of depletive type measures. This "Made in America" school of thought, which
supplemented the teachings in British medical schools, was based on
tradition and the personal experience of each physician in dealing with
each individual patient. But, after the French Revolution, a different
philosophy spread through the medical schools of France, particularly
in the capital. This was based on the principle of less interference by the
physician in some diseases because it was argued that these were self-
limiting and ran their course, regardless of what treatment was given.
The Toronto professionals, who had been influenced by direct contact
with the teaching and the writings of the Jefferson medical group, were
aware of the ferment which was questioning the traditional theories
and treatments through the medical journals.

Richardson had gone to Paris for post-graduate work on the advice
of Rolph. The Parisian medical schools insisted on a fresh start and
taught three principles – not to accept authority, when facts were
present; not to guess, when you could know and not to think a man
must take physic because he is sick. In addition, he had direct experience with "the Numerical Method". This approach to disease, which
was taught by Pierre Louis at La Charité in the 20's and 30's, carefully
recorded the response of patients to treatment. Louis observed the
results of therapy and was able to comment on whether a specific treatment led to an overall benefit to the group of patients. This was the
beginning of medical statistics and the first instance of a scientific
approach to the practice of medicine. He studied the effect of venesec-
tion in pneumonitis and showed that the blood letting resulted in little
change in the progression of the disease. A study he conducted later,
distinguished between typhus and typhoid fever.

His effect on medical schools of North America in promoting this scientific method was potentially enormous, as many teachers of American schools went to Paris.. Dunglison passed on some of this
information on the "school of Louis" when Aikins had been his student. However, Dunglison's interpretation of the French work was that
the emphasis on observation of the patient, in association with the
newer methods of examination such as the stethoscope, led to a greater
commitment to the concept that each patient was a specific entity,
requiring specific treatment, not necessarily related to what could or

should happen in another patient with the same symptoms. Richardson was able to add a greater dimension to teaching through his experience in the French school of thought.

The philosophy of medicine in Toronto had been stagnant for many years. Widmer, Rolph and the lecturers in King's College were unswerving proponents of the depletion/stimulation school of diagnosis and treatment. This view had held firm over the first half of the 19th century. Aikins, by inviting other talents on to the teaching staff, generated an opportunity for upgrading the curriculum.

Richardson was not the only welcome addition. James Bovell, who had left Canada with the collapse of Trinity Medical School, returned from Barbadoes and took the lecturership in Institutes of Medicine, (a term used for what was later labelled Physiology) in 1861 and added microscopy the following year. Bovell's studies with Sir William Stokes and Robert Graves of Dublin led to his pre-eminence as a clinician. He was also deeply interested in the new ideas that bacteria caused disease. At a later date, he saw anthrax bacilli, but could not identify them with certainty because he lacked money to buy a high objective lens for his microscope.

This change of heart by "old line doctors" was understandable. They wanted to teach medicine as well as practice it and shared Aikin's inner drive to raise the quality of medical education and health in Upper Canada. There had been no possibility of working with Rolph at Victoria for this group because of his political background – a sentiment which was most likely mutual. Nevertheless, Rolph was also able to add to his teaching staff. Within five years of the break-up, he had recruited Walter Geikie, a graduate of TSM; John N. Reid, of TSM and New York, who was Professor of Physiology; C.B. Berryman and E.A Ogden, who had returned recently from Jefferson.

Although Howitt had written that Aikins was making a great deal of money, he was always generous. Not only did he lend to Lennon, but also to I. Smith who lived in Bothwell. Smith had graduated and set up practice west of London, after borrowing to complete his course. "I am sorry to say that I cannot remit you the money with this letter", he wrote in June of 1856, and explained "it is almost impossible at present to get any money here". His practice had been set up on the basis of, "if success crowns one's effort here, young Canadian physicians can carry all before it and in less than five years". Apparently, part of his expectations were realized so that by September he was able to send Aikins the balance due, which had been held since the previous winter. However, he apologized that he was unable to send the whole of the interest and justified his tardiness by repeating how difficult it was to get money.

When Howitt chaffed Aikins on his income, he had another agenda. The Howitts were distant relatives of Dr. Henry Orton who had practiced around Fergus after migrating to Canada in 1835. He had four sons, who had entered medicine.

Howitt's letter to Aikins asked, "will you be particularly hard on a distant relative of mine? ... I would like to see him get through for his father's sake, for he is not in the position to spend much more upon him". Henry Jr. had left the TSM against his father's wishes and had gone to Trinity from which he had graduated and proceeded to Jefferson College. His training was excellent and Aikins responded to his friend's request with the result that Orton qualified in 1857. His brother, Thomas J. Orton, graduated shortly after that and went as Surgeon-Major to the Crimean War, during which he received a medal for bravery. Subsequently, he again received a medal and clasp for service in India, eventually returning to Canada to practice in Guelph. A third brother, George Turner, took his degree in 1860, practiced in Fergus and was elected to Parliament in 1882 and served in the army at Fish Creek and Batoche. The last sibling, Dr. Richard Orton, practiced at Guelph. This family saga was not unusual, as physicians commonly served their country and profession in many areas.

Aikins had previous correspondence with Henry Orton Sr. In 1853, Orton complained that he was beginning to lose vision and was not as competent or efficient in his surgical procedures. For instance, there were "accidents from threshing machines ... requiring amputation of the fingers and toes, to the thigh or arms; taking up arteries and innumerible muscles". Amputations were performed, usually without anaesthesia, in the home using only the contents of the doctor's bag.

Orton said that help, or an assistant who could use the knife expertly, would be invaluable. "I don't care a jig about his being a thorough anatomist in the ordinary acceptance, that is one who can recite the names of parts; if he only knows the course of the large arteries, their localities and connections and can use freely and well the knife, I can direct him in all the rest". He mentioned that Thomas, had been invaluable as a surgical assistant, even when he knew very little of anatomy. With that experience, Orton Sr. had sent his son Henry to Toronto for a whole winter of dissecting, "not in getting off the names of parts, I could teach him that at home". Orton ended the letter with, "if therefore, you will allow him to dissect without delay and continue in it all the time practicable while in Toronto, he will very greatly obliged". Aikins answered his letter four days later:

> I think you mistake our mode of instruction. We act upon the following as a principle viz; that a student should possess a fair knowledge of anatomy before he commences to dissect, inasmuch as dissection per se does not communicate such knowledge – I have over and over again seen excellent dissectors, who could make beautiful preparations and yet were bad anatomists ...
>
> Bearing upon this point, I may just mention a little circumstance which occurred at the last meeting of the Medical Board. A candidate who was answering pretty well in his anatomy, but of whose practical acquaintance with the part I was doubtful, was presented by myself with the bone he was describing, at the same time desiring him to point out with his finger its important portions and surgical relations. He was completely confounded, turning it over and over, made a half dozen mistakes and finally stated that he had studied it from the book and not from the subject. To another candidate I gave the left scapula to describe, he, even worse that the former, tried to fix into his right shoulder and to articulate the clavicle with the glenoid cavity.

Aikins finished his letter with a surprise for Orton Sr. "Now Dr. Orton, don't be offended with me – you are a candid man and I am candid with you. I would be ashamed of your son Henry, if on the first Monday next April, without dissecting he could not pass a better examination in his anatomy than his brother did with all his dissections. For he, in his examination, stated that the vocal cords were muscles placed transversely on the larynx, that the arches of the palate were formed by the tonsils – this having been denied – he said that they were formed by superior constrictors of the pharynx – then again by a muscle of the uvula. The popliteal nerve was *internal* to the artery and vein, then it was between the etc, etc., I copied these answers from a note that I made at the time which is now lying before me".

He gently chided the older doctor with the statement "Our first course students go into the dissection room and then study, not read, the structures which our seniors are preparing ... if there is one feature of our course upon anatomy more prominent than another, it is its practical applications". Aikins ended his letter with regrets for Orton's ill health and the hope that he would soon be well.

In outlining this approach, Aikins demonstrated his enthusiasm for the teaching techniques that were becoming current in many of the American schools of learning - that is by doing, rather than reading a textbook.

One other correspondent who kept Aikins busy in 1857 was Simon Morrison of Hamilton, who wrote verbose letters touching on politics and life in general. He sent Aikins a proposal for a monograph on Canadian politics and asked him to criticize the document. Part of his motivation in writing the document was his wish to make "a little money by the affair ... Yes, money."

Aikins wrote a stiff criticism of the document and apologized for possibly offending his friend, who replied, "If I cannot ensure the candid criticism of a friend, be assured I am annoyed at nothing except that after the knowledge you have of my temper, you should at all distrust me". Although the letter was written in the late part of 1856, Aikins passed it to Rolph for his comments, which were equally derisive.

By 1855, Aikins had a very busy practice. Since the development of anaesthesia in 1846, more surgery was attempted and was frequently successful. However, without the benefit of anaesthesia, heroic surgery was still practiced. Richardson reported an operation on "old Tom" who was the janitor at the General Hospital before it moved to its new premises in 1857:

> He spent his time on the lawn under the trees with a long clay pipe in his mouth and in foul weather retired to his room or somewhere out of sight and presumably continued to smoke. He eventually developed cancer of the tongue.

Richardson, who frequently passed the time of the day with him, advised that the tongue should be removed as there was a large growth. Tom, who had had his leg amputated at the hip at the Battle of Trafalgar, refused any anaesthesia.

> He said he stood the amputation of his leg with a nail between his teeth, and so he could stand this. And he did, giving a responsive groan at each tightening twist of the instrument until the tongue came off, when Dr. Richardson, placing it on the table, turned to the students and said 'you see of what our sailors are composed'. The next morning Old Tom was under the tree smoking his pipe as usual[3]

Richardson had used an ecraseur, a windlass type of instrument which strangled the tongue until it was severed.

Similar types of operations were carried out in spartan surroundings. Howitt mentioned that he had performed a shoulder disarticulation and amputation of the leg. At the same time, he reported that an "old cove of a Scotchman hanging out his shingle (a clever fellow) too from what I can pick up. He will doubtless do a good practice; his country-men are numerous and you know what they are, they stick together like burrs".

Aikins operated on a 70 year old male, who had hardening of the arteries in the neck, and a tumour that caused marked swelling of his face and involved the maxillary antrum and the floor of the eye. He removed the superior maxilla to see "the whole disease mass" which was carefully scooped out and then filled the cavity with cotton and sutures. Aikins then examined the tumour with a microscope and saw "many of the features of incipient encephaloid disease". He also removed a tumour, the size of a man's fist, from the orbit of an eight year old child. After the mass had been scooped out, microscopic exam-ination showed it too was encephaloid. He had little hope for survival of either of these patients, but did the procedure with the hope he could remove all of the tumor.

Aikins' skill as a surgeon was becoming widely known and he oper-ated on several "scirrhus" carcinomas of the breast with axillary gland dissection. But he also practiced medicine. At that time there was no

distinction between the surgeon and the physician. One of his patients
was Chancellor William Hume Blake of the University, who was
"gouty" and later developed diabetes. Aikins taught with and used the
stethoscope frequently in his clinical practice. His brother, Moses,
reporting from Jefferson, mentioned that the stethoscopist William W.
Gerhard, who had studied with Louis and had differentiated typhoid
from typus fever in 1837, was excellent at detecting pulmonary
changes. Even so, most of Aikins' colleagues were not taken with the
stethoscope. This attitude to the elegance of stethoscopy compared
with the real demands of practice which was reinforced, somewhat by
the appearance of Dr. H. Bowditch's, *The Young Stethoscopist*. This book
was reviewed in the *British American Medical and Physical Journal*:

> We do not think very highly of the above treatise as we do not con-
> sider it capable of communicating any but the most superficial
> knowledge on the subject.

Dr. A.E. Ford, reporting from St. Mary's, saw in a two week period a
case of erysipelas of the head and face, pneumonia, two cases of pleuri-
tis, three of typhoid fever, one fracture of the ribs with extensive contusions, one chronic tonsillitis (which required removal of the right
tonsil); five cases of midwifery and other cases of dyspesia, intermittent
fever, and conjunctivitis. He reported that, "every case has been successful so far. I have broken something over eleven pounds besides
ready pay".

Howitt ended his letter by explaining that "a man ought to retire
after ten years of active life ... curse it, a doctor lives a life of a dog and a
slave ... ".

At the beginning of the 60's, ten years after he joined the TSM, William Aikins could survey his position. His family situation was idyllic,
five children were growing, and the loss of one infant daughter had
been overcome. His younger brother had graduated from Jefferson and
was practicing in the home town of the family while his older brother,
James Cox, was now a member of the Legislature.

William's voice had become known in academic circles with his
insistence on improving the quality of medical school graduates. He
had supported and then had a tempestuous parting from his mentor,

John Rolph, but had been able to salvage the TSM as a separate entity, quite capable of independent action. This had involved recruiting a staff of teachers and arranging for physical accommodation, all of which he had carried out successfully. Indeed he had been over-whelmed by the wealth of teaching talent which became available with the closing of the Trinity School and the subsequent transfer of the top performers to the TSM. To complete the sweet sense of separation, Aikins and Barrett convinced the President of University College to release the anatomical specimens from the original TSM, which had been lodged in the College, to the new TSM. Some of these had been prepared by Rolph, himself. Furthermore, to crown these accomplish-ments, he leased Moss Hall, the home of the Universities Medical School in the 1850's.

In addition Aikins had weathered a major upheaval at the General Hospital, having been dismissed and then re-instated by an action of the Legislature, adding to his political stature. This had supplemented his appointment to the UCMB, which set the standards for the licencing of physicians in Ontario.

He was now financially stable and indeed was rumoured by some to be making a great deal of money. But he obeyed John Wesley's motto: "Gain all you can, save all you can, give all you can".

Most recently in 1859, in association with his older brother, he had made a determined but unsuccessful, well publicized attempt to incor-porate the medical profession of Upper Canada. All of these activities were the hallmarks of a successful practitioner.

More important than his practice and teaching responsibilities, Aikins had to make provision for his deep religious convictions. From Novem-ber 1851 to June 1852, there was an extended revival meeting in Tor-onto by the Methodist Church with Dr. James Caughey, a leader in the Holyness Movement, preaching in the new Richmond Street Church. There was an engulfing surge of piety in the city and so great were the numbers who were converted that it was necessary to build a new church on Elm Street. Aikins, who attended the King Street Chapel was deeply moved by the fervency. Being a Methodist was a consuming vocation. There was compulsory attendance at weekly class meetings and prayer meetings, with morning and evening service on Sundays and a Tuesday worship service. In addition Church members were pressed to attend the Quarterly Love Feast and the monthly Sacraments of the Lord's Supper. Failure to do so, disqualified the adherent from holding official positions in the Church.

The Church had so many attractions to the people of Toronto that there was a constant need for more pews. The Reverend Anson Green[3] wrote that as he was walking by McGill Square (the north west corner of Queen and Church Streets) he was told that the 3¼ acres of land was for sale and that the City of Toronto had refused to purchase it for a site as a proposed City Hall. The price was $25,000.00. Before he finished his walk that day, Green had pledges for $1,500.00 to buy the square. This proposal to purchase was viewed enthusiastically by the Adelaide Street Church and a committee was established including Aikins, who by now was a member of the Berkley Street congregation, as a result of earlier expansion. The committee, which included the merchant, John Macdonald, conducted a city-wide canvass to raise funds from all Methodists and Aikins, himself, donated $1,000.00. So successful was the group and so astute in handling the purchase that the deal was completed in one day, before the City of Toronto reversed its decision.

Aikins remained on the Committee of Management and was the last surviving member on his death. In addition he served as a trustee of the newly-built Metropolitan from 1870. He was one of the planners who decided that the cost of the new church, which was to be a Cathedral of Methodism, was not to exceed $40,000.00 and a prize was offered for the best design. This was awarded to a William George Storm, who wanted his prize money before turning over the plans. The Management Committee cannily insisted that an independent group should determine if the cost was within the $40,000.00 limit. It so happened that Storm's plan was well above that with the result the second prize winner was given the contract.

One year after the Aikins family joined the Berkley Street congregation, they met a Mrs. M.B. Taylor, who was described as having lived a blameless life since her camp meeting conversion in 1825. She became known as a Methodist saint and was held up as a model to women in the congregation. Her state of "Christian perfection" was the result of the blessing of God's grace, and made it impossible for her to transgress any of the abjurations of John Wesley, who interdicted worldly pleasures such as theatre going, dancing and card playing. Wesley based these rules on the text of Colossians; "Whatsoever ye do in word or deed, do all in the name of Lord Jesus". Although Methodists attended sacred concerts, lectures, team meetings and rallies, all other temptations were trivial and were to be avoided.

At her funeral which was attended by most of the Methodist community, including the Aikins family, it was recorded that she had an "almost seraphic appearance and a remarkable gift of prayer. Looking upon her death as a gateway to a brighter and better world, she requested that there should be no mourning for her when she died, but instead, hymms of rejoicing should be sung by those who followed to her burial".[4] Louisa Aikins, like many other Methodist matrons, aspired to such a level of Grace.

Aikins was active in the community, not just in Methodist church circles. Although a male member of the congregation was expected to always present a serious mien, he appreciated some of the pranks that were occurring – but not all.

In 1859 women's right to wear a crinoline was a burning question – to some males. Husbands were expected to "jump through the hoop" when it was a matter of purchasing Easter finery. Tea-time rumour had it that a Bill had been prepared which "required all married women under 50 to have their husband's written permission before they could purchase any article of clothing, whatsoever, let alone a hoop skirt of crinoline. In any case, a married woman and under the age of 50 or who has been married 30 years, when a new article of dress is required (the necessity of whether a new dress shall be determined by the husband) a pattern and a piece of the material shall first be obtained by her from the shopkeeper or person having the selling of the same, which pattern, together with the certificate stating the quantity to be purchased and the price thereof, shall be submitted to the husband, and the husband shall signify his approval of such a pattern by certifying in writing ... where it has been shown to the satisfaction of this honourable House that the ladies of this province have degenerated in their ideas of beauty and priority, have deserted the modest apparel of their ancestors and adopted in view thereof the flowing and elaborate skirts, supported and sustained in their amplitude by a certain number of springs, ladders and hinges and so forth, and certain other apparatus known by the name of crinoline and the expensive trimmings, fashions and the pertinences introduced into this country from a neighouring republic." The Bill went on also to regulate colour and to limit the size of hats.[5] It turned out that the "Bill" was an elaborate April Fools joke, which ridiculed the busyness of the Legislature.

His attainments and general enjoyment of his work and family were severely shocked on 22 January 1863 when his beloved wife died.

The *Christian Guardian* noted her death and in the obituary, after telling of her scholastic achievements explained: "It is to be feared however, that an undue stimulus given to her early mental powers, sapped the foundation of her physical constitution, and superinduced those long years of suffering which terminated her early and lamented death.

"... she was early convinced by the Spirit of God that she had a depraved nature; and though in the estimation of others so innocent and so good, she felt that in the sight of her Maker she was a great sinner; and with deep contrition and earnest prayer she sought until she found pardon and acceptance with God. Some time subsequently she became convinced that a higher state of grace was attainable, that the Bible pointed it out as both the privilege and duty of Christians to 'leave the first principles of the doctrines of Christ and go on to perfection,' and she purposed in her heart that she would not rest until she had realized the attainment of this inestimable blessing ... the more she studied the word of God, and the experience of the pious, the more fully was she convinced that not only her happiness and usefulness, but her safety depended upon her attainment of the blessing of entire sanctification, - and after days and weeks of deep mental distress, after getting such a vivid and humbling view of the depravity of her own nature, and the exceeding sinfulness of sin, as she had never before experienced, she was enabled to apprehend, by faith, the sufficiency of the world's Redeemer to 'save to the uttermost.'

... as her delicate state of health rendered it necessary for her to enjoy the open air, she spent much time with her husband in the chaise during his professional visits, always having with her some good book which she would read to him on the way. Latterly that book was almost invariably the Bible, she remarking to her husband that as she could not read as formerly, she found it increasingly delightful and profitable to go to God's own word.

For the last 10 years she was the subject of almost constant, and at times, most painful suffering.

For six months before her death her sufferings were very severe, so much so, that at times she found it impossible to read or even to compose her mind in prayer, and her nervous affection was such, as to produce at times an uncontrollable mental irritability.

On the 15th of January, she gave birth to a son, and though for some days there appeared fair prospects of her recovery, yet on the 22nd, there was a change for the worse, and it was evident that her end was come. She had no fear of death; its sting was gone, and she knew that for her to die would be gain; and though at times unconscious, yet in her lucid moments her mind was sweetly and peacefully stayed upon her Redeemer. She took an affectionate farewell of her deeply afflicted husband, her five sweet children, her two affectionate sisters to whom she had been mother and sister ... and then, after the eye had refused to see, and the tongue to speak, the smile which lingered upon her lip threw the sunshine of holy joy over the darkness of death."

His grief was compounded when his father died later that year.

Only William's profound religious convictions sustained him following these events, but gradually with the resumption of work he recovered and married her sister, Lydia Ann, in 1865. It was a quiet wedding, possibly foreboding another tragedy, when their first born, Mary Edith, died at one month in March, 1866. Infant death was common and another, Wilhelmina, failed after one year in 1877.

The Piper family became closer to William. Hiram had lost his first wife and daughter in one month in 1856 with diagnosis of meningitis. He purchased a family plot in 1857 and many Aikins were buried there including William's daughter, Mary Eva, in 1861 and of course, Louisa Adelia. Piper married again in 1858 and at the same time appointed W.T. Aikins as an executor of his will, leaving money to the doctor on his death in 1863.

The competition for students continued between the TSM and Victoria, while in the background, there was always McGill waiting to pick up any eastern strays. W.J. Mickle,[6] in a letter to his father in Guelph in the summer of '63, pointed out that "the Toronto School explains everything about it I wish to know, but not so the Montreal. The subjects where examinations are not given and the examination itself only incidentally mentioned". He explained that the course at the McGill College was for four seasons and decided to go to Toronto and reported on October 16th that he was taking lectures from 8 to 12 in the morning and from 3 to 4 in the afternoon and 6 to 7 in the evening. He was at the hospital at 1 p.m. to do dissections which made up approximately six hours lectures daily, plus hospital attendance and anatomy laboratory. He intended to do a primary examination at the end of two years and a secondary after four years. The subjects of the primary were anatomy, philosophy, chemistry and materia medica. Like all students who boarded, he had complaints. "We have had pretty rough living at Mrs. Scott's for the last fortnight. Her girl took ill and had to go to hospital until Thursday and there was not a regular servant in the house. It was not much better before the girl fell sick for she was a lovely creature and a wretched cook. But the board is, I must say, very poor for what we pay ... the only fruit we ever see are apples with slight exception, potatoes the only vegetable". One of his classmates, John Shiltern, wrote to his brother on the treatment of erysipelas. The doctor was having no success whatever, but a neighbour came by and "steamed with alcohol" and in a very short time "she was a lot better", much to the astonishment of the doctor when he "spied the marvellous change". The TSM reported that there were 110 students in the 1862–3 session of whom 13 graduated from the University of Toronto. The following year 18 graduated and six obtained their licence from the UCMB. In 1864–5, eighteen graduated.

This growing number of professionals was behind the formation of the Toronto Medical-Chirugical Society in 1861, to provide a meeting place for doctors and a means of receiving the leading medical and scientific journals. The President was Hodder with H.H. Wright, Aikins and Thorburn among the members. Dr. William Canniff, later Dean of Victoria, was a corresponding secretary.

The TSM annual announcement for the 18th session from the 1st of October 1860 to April 1st said:

> the chemical lecture room and laboratory are provided with every modern improvement and the greatest facilities are offered for the study of both practical and theoretical chemistry, under the able direction of Professor Croft. The dissecting room will be amply

provided with material, well lighted, and under the immediate control of Dr. Lizars, formerly demonstrator of anatomy at the University of Edinburgh.

The Toronto General Hospital is open to students on the payment of eight dollars for six months, or ten dollars for one year. Clinical instruction will be given by Drs. Hodder, Aikins and Richardson. Operations on Saturday at 1 p.m.

The Toronto Lying-In Hospital furnishes obstetrical facilities to those students who have attended one course of midwifery on payment of the fee of five dollars for six months. Two wards have been set aside for special treatment of uterine disease. The fee for courses on general and descriptive anatomy, surgery, materia medica, practice of medicine, midwifery, and Institutes of Medicine, $12.00 each (on each of these branches not less than 100 lectures will be delivered); surgical anatomy $4.00; chemistry and botany $5.00 each; for medical jurisprudence and demonstrations $8.00 each. Fees to be paid strictly in advance.

Subjects will be examined for matriculation, which could be undergone at any time prior to examination. For a scholarship in medicine, or the degree of M.B. latin, mathematics, english, history and geography, chemistry (Chambers *Educational Course*), natural history (Agassiz and Gould's *Comparative Physiology*), and elements of botanical science.

Candidates for matriculation scholarship are required to undergo examination in Greek and Latin languages, mathematics as far as quadratic equations and book one French grammar.

Subjects of examination for scholarships in the first year are anatomy of bones, muscles and ligaments and viscera of abdomen and thorax; general anatomy and physiology of the organs of locomotion, digestion and circulation.

Second year anatomy; physiology, organic chemistry and electricity. Botany, therapeutics and pharmacology.

Third year medicine. Surgery. Midwifery. Medical jurisprudence. Comparative anatomy and practical chemistry.

Requisites for admission to the degree in Bachelor Medicine, one having matriculated in the Faculty of Medicine or in either Faculties of Law or Art, being the full of 21 years, having pursued medical study for a period of four years and having attended lectures in the above mentioned branches, and the practice of some general hospital for 12 months and for at least 6 months clinical lectures on medicine and surgery.

In addition to his role as administrator of the TSM, his private practice and extensive correspondence, Aikins was being called on more frequently for expert evidence in the courts.

This was seen in the case of Jackson versus Hyde. Dr. Hyde of Stratford was sued by a Miss Jackson who maintained that Hyde had improperly advised her and then carried out an above elbow amputation, following a crush injury in a threshing machine. Action was brought that great error had been committed. Aikins testified that "no well informed surgeon would like to place himself in the position of saying whether on the evidence, the operation ought to have been above or below the elbow joint ...". He then proceeded to demonstrate, using the skeleton of a forearm as an exhibit, that due to the findings that were evident in the hand, if the amputation had been carried out more distally, a second operation was inevitable.

During cross examination, he was asked if a mass of skin had been taken off the forearm without fracture, would he have endeavoured to save the limb. "I never saw such a case where some fingers were dragged out by traction and the remaining fingers saved. Inflammation would be almost certain to occur ... I think any surgeon who risked the life of the patient by waiting until gangrene sets in before amputating, ought to be prosecuted. I could not possibly say there was malpractice on the part of Dr. Hyde in this case." This opinion was well ahead of current practices in the contending armies in the war between the States.

The judge summed up that all that was required of a professional man was a fair and reasonable amount of skill and as all the medical witnesses had concluded that the amputation was necessary, the only question was whether it was wrong to cut so high up? The jury was charged to say whether they were satisfied that the amputation had been done in an unskillful manner. After a short consideration, the jury returned a verdict for the plaintiff and $250.00 damage was awarded.

The Canadian Medical Journal and Monthly Record of Medical and Surgi-

cal Science, July 1869, commented "if Dr. Hyde was really guilty, surely this sum is far from an adequate compensation for the loss the girl had sustained in consequence of his criminality. A conviction forces itself upon our mind that the jury were led from sympathy, induced by the presence of the girl, whose arm was sustained to their scrutiny, to commit a great error."

Aikins' skill resulted in being called for many autopsies. On October 31st, 1863 he testified in the trial of Will M. Greenwood in the Sayre Street tragedy. A police constable had been called by an alarmed neighbour who had observed smoke coming from the home of Catherine Walsh. On entering the room, the policeman found a dead female on the bed beneath which there was a fire igniting the mattress. He managed to put out the fire and being unable to ascertain the cause of death, called on Aikins. At the same time the policeman found a dead baby in the cupboard. Aikins testified a "well marked, bloodless, white depression" on the neck of the deceased. He then was able to demonstrate that this had been caused by pulling the nightgown and chemise together around the neck ..." His examination showed that this had been done before death. Similarily he was able to demonstrate that the infant had been suffocated with a cloth over the face. Greenwood was convicted of murder.[7]

Amputations were the commonest surgical procedure. Even though skills had improved during the terrible carnage of the American Civil War, there remained a high death rate until the teachings and techniques of Dr. Joseph Lister (later Lord Lister) were adopted in the 1870's.

Dr. George A. Bingham recalled at a meeting of the Academy of Medicine in Toronto in 1912 that in the pre-Listerian era, an amputation frequently led to stump infection, gangrene and death:

> I can remember when a clinic consisted of a rabble of students following a professor about the foetid smelling ward while he examined unhealed wounds with unwashed hands; then after lowering his olfactory organ to the reeking stump, he would straighten himself up and declare to the class "Gentlemen, this pus is laudable". Yet the patient died just the same. I remember the preparation of a fashionable surgeon for a major operation who insisted in turning

back the cuffs of his Prince Albert coat, which was preferrably an old one, and washing his hands in a very perfunctory way at the tap. The usual treatment for compound fracture was an amputation, otherwise the patient would die, as he often did anyway. I recollect that during one whole winter session the abdominal cavity was open only on three occasions, with two deaths.[8]

It had been taught since Galen's time that "laudable pus" – i.e. a foetid, layer of white tissue - was a sign of natural healing.

Dr. R.B. Nevitt, who graduated from Trinity and later became Dean of the Women's Medical College reported in the *Canadian Journal of Medicine, Surgery*, May 1912, "as yet there was no official recognition of the surgeon as distinct from the physician, Hodder, Aikins and Bethune admitted and attended medical cases, just as Geikie, Henry Wright and Thorburn did surgical work."

The operations consisted principally of amputations or the removal of tumours from accessible parts. Sometimes soap and water were used timidly. Most often the patient with a suppurating wound, inflamed, poisonous and gangrenous, was brought down and put on the table. A vast stinking poultice was removed, with a stench and odour, and the limb was amputated. Instruments and basins were cleaned after the operation in the manner of a camper washing his dinner dishes, then put away for the next operation. The silk and linen thread used for ligatures was cut to convenient lengths as it came from the shop and often passed through the button hole of my coat to be reached for use by the operating surgeon when required to tie a vessel or put in a suture. Scissors and probes were wiped on a towel or bandage and used again without special preparation. I carried in the upper pocket of my vest a probe, a pair of scissors, a pair of dissecting forceps and a scalpel, and would only wash them in water if it was handy. Dr. Bethune had a case which I now recognize as being one of appendiceal abscess, and who was desperately ill. The belly wall was tight and protruberant, the skin slightly oedematous in the region of the superior spine of the ilium. "Pus there, ought to let it out." Without a word I put my hand in my vest pocket and pulled out a scapel and Dr. Bethune cut down upon the abscess and gave vent with explosive violence to a vast quantity of stinking pus, gas and fecal manner. And this patient got well. During an operation, the favourite place for the knife when it was out of use was in the surgeon's mouth to prevent the danger of its edge being dulled by contact with the table.

In 1868 Hodder reported a Listerian procedure:

a female patient, 59 years of age gave a history of tumour develop-ing over a period of 16 years. The removal of the tumour was com-paratively easy and after hemostat control was established, the cut surfaces were wiped over with carbolic acid and oil ... and a strip of lint soaked in a similar solution was laid over the cut edges and kept in place by a few strips of plaster and bandage. A week later it was noted that there has not been any suppuration, even in the course of the ligatures. This patient left hospital in a month with a well healed wound, but with facial paresis.[9]

He was Professor of Obstetrics and Diseases of Women and Children at the TSM. Ovariotomy was performed frequently and he preferred to do the operation at the Burnside Lying-In Hospital, where he removed large tumours in twenty minutes. The anaesthesia was supplemented with brandy.

In some cases chloroform resulted in a death and on January 1863, the *Evening Leader* reported an inquest held at the Toronto General Hospital on the body of Richard Humphreys who had died under ana-esthesia. This was the first recorded chloroform fatality in the T.G.H. Bovell, who was "pouring the chloroform tried to revive the patient with electric shocks to stimulate the phrenic nerve from a galvanic bat-tery but was not successful."

Although surgery seemed to have a higher level of effectiveness than medical treatment, hospital admissions were heavily weighted to non-surgical conditions. In 1871 the General admitted 38 cases of typhoid fever, 36 with rheumatism, 43 of paralysis and hemiplegia and 25 each of phthisis, pneumonia, venereal disease and dipsomania. Three patients were hospitalized for masturbation, two others with tape worms and 28 with constipation. Aside from 54 fractures and dislocations, only 18 tumours and 17 cancers were seen.

Aikins reported a case of scirrhous carcinoma of the breast with axillary dissection.[10] This excellent treatment contrasted with a description given later by Nevitt for a pneumonia;

> when the respirations were 45 and the temperature 104 and 5, the patient was raised up in a sitting posture to ensure the nurse to properly apply the poultice. And if he was still worse, the weaker the patient got, the oftener the poultice was applied. If the patient survived for 5 or 6 days, the next thing to be done was to sponge him with soap and water and then apply a fly blister. After the blister was on for 6 to 8 hours, it was removed. A poultice was again applied. As soon as the part was healed, another blister was applied. On the other hand, if the patient lingered for a long time and did not respond to this treatment, there were a few physicians who would introduce a seton and have it turned round daily, to the great discomfort of the sufferer.[11]

But there were other facilities for patient care and teaching. TSM and Victoria students could purchase a ticket to lectures and attendance at the Toronto Dispensary at 126 York Street where Dr. Uzziel Ogden was in attendance. This was an out-patient clinic which was supported by the Anglican Church. Medicines were free and staff members might make house calls.

The Ophthalmic Hospital on Shuter Street (in 1867 called the Toronto Eye and Ear Dispensary) was supported privately and its chief was Aikins' lecturer, Dr. A.M. Rosebrugh. After graduation he studied in New York and London where he became interested in the examination and treatment of disorders of the eye. Following the invention of the ophthalmoscope by Dr. Herman L. Helmholtz in 1851 Rosebrugh modified the device so that photographs could be made of the fundus of the eye. The infirmary was always crowded and provided excellent teaching for the students.

John Rolph and Victoria operated the Samaritan Infirmary with four beds, which was supported, in part, by student fees.

Obstetrical cases were usually cared for at the Burnside Lying-In

Hospital where 14 beds provided TSM staff, including Drs. Bovell and Hodder, with lecture material. It was supported by government grants, private subscription and student fees. Patients who could pay were charged $2.50 per day.

The Provincial Lunatic Asylum was 2½ miles west from the city hall on Queen Street. Admission of patients was regulated by Act 16 Victoria, Chapter 188 which required a patient to be examined by three licenced practitioners, verified by the Reeve and Mayor collectively, who certified to the insanity. Idiots and persons afflicted with paralysis were inadmissible. A branch of the asylum was established at the old University building. Joseph Workman was the medical superintendant, Benjamin Workman, assistant physician and John E. Kennedy, clinical assistant.

The stories from the hospitals and clinics always made a light fare for tea, but the student's menu was heavier.

Angus McKay, a student of Victoria in 1865, took lectures in surgery. Although there had been much concern about the relevance of the curriculum and the need to send a modern message to the students, there was little new demonstrated from that taught in the early 50's. The treatment for burns was turpentine in the form of ointment, noting that the soft tissues frequently contracted, causing deformity.

The student recorded that gonorrhea was an inflammation which in the male was inside the penis. "You may have inflammation arising from riding on horseback or it may arise from ulcers. The person may have had it innnocent sometimes, it may be had from the privy, if any other person should be in the privy before them. The discharge of gonorrhea is heavier than any healthy pus. It has a green look and an offensive smell ... the disease is introduced by the poison coming in contact with the mucous membrane. There is pain, heat, redness and sometimes swelling. Everytime urine passes along, there is a great deal of pain ... if you are called, you may wash away the poison when you use solutions of nitrate of silver ... injections may be used of water and a weak solution of sugar of lead and a solution of zinc sulphate ... gonorrhea is inflammation, but syphilis is known as sores. It may be called chancres. There are two kinds, soft and hard. The soft chancre is attended with no constitution of disease but the chancre does not give discharge ... you may burn this out with nitric acid". There was no mention of the fact, well known in medical teaching, that these were venereal diseases contracted through sexual activity.

In the lecture he heard from Canniff, his notes show: "... the poison that causes erysipelas is due from poison that is in the air, sometimes the poison is taken from decaying about the house or it may be a pet or it may arise spontaneously. Symptoms are local and constitutional ... the poison irritates the nerves ... constitutional syptoms – you may have inflammation, fever like typhoid fever and generally chills. The whole of the digestive canal is affected. The bowels are constipated at first. The disease spreads by continuity and congruity and may disappear in one part and come to another ... the local inflammation is an act of nature, through the poisons. You must not stop it but must control it. Ferri sulph is used in the form of an ointment. Tincture iodine is used by some, but this is not as good in many cases where you have the dermatitis form ..."

Canniff lectured:

> Erysipelas inflammation is a constitutional disease first. It may be it is a disease of the blood. The corpusals break down and create redness. The whole cellular tissue becomes filled with corpusals. Causes are predisposing and exciting a change in the atomsphere may cause the disease. It is breathed into the system or may be taken into the stomach at times. It is epidemic. It comes on spontaneously and it goes from one to the other. When one has an operation performed, and he has it, it will become inflamed and go from one to the other in a hospital. You must be careful that you do not carry the poison from one to the other. It may be divided into ediopathetic and traumatic. It may come into the face. The eyes will swell.

One of the most contentious areas in medical knowledge was the process of healing. Canniff became fixated with the idea:

> Repair takes place through the agencies of the blood. The fibrine is the principle agent of the blood for repairing or healing. In an inflammatory process, fibrine is increased ... it prevents stagnation

of the blood. It favours the formation of blood vessels. It possesses the power to contract. There are five methods of healing.

There is an immediate union where there is a cut with a sharp instrument. It presses vessel against vessel and nerve against nerve. One or two cases have been shown to account for this.

Second, we have intention union. The fibrine is thrown out and forms a bond and glues together the parts. This is called union by first intention.

Third by granulation. There is no immediate union or there might have been immediate union and there has been too much fibrine. The surface of the part must be in a healthy state. It may be from an ulcer. Where the part cannot come together, there is fibrine thrown out on the sides of a wound. After a while, the fibrine loses its water and forms a scab. This is healing by granulation ... Pus forms by degeneration of fibres.

Fourth is by secondary adhesive. Two granulating surfaces will unite if they can draw the surfaces together, it will heal.

Fifth, is under the scab, the fibres form into pus and the healing proceeds sometimes an abscess forms. The scab dries and healing goes on underneath. There is enough blood flowing to the part to carry on the healing process.

Geikie, who had trained with Aikins lectured on obstetrics:

He talked about the diameter of the outlet and the fact that the head of the child takes the oblique direction. The shortest diameter of the outlet is 4 inches, the long diameter of the outlet is greater.

Organs of generation are described as internal and external. The womb in health should weigh from 1 to 1½ ounces.

Unlike physicians in England who did not perform deliveries, but left it to midwives, Ontario doctors followed the American example. Diseases of women and children were grouped in one lecture series and Angus McKay noted the symptoms of menstruation in 1867. "Pain in the loins when it is very severe is called a disease. It is an ovarian function. When the ovaries are absent, there is no attempt at menstruation. Sometimes when the person is very weak, the menstruation discharge is of a white colour. After one has a child, menstruation is stopped. All the functions go to form a new being hence there cannot be any discharge ... treatment of menstruation. You should let them know that they should keep from the cold, and not to try and stop it ... sometimes it is a year between the fluxes. Menstruation is a physical function, it is not a pathological function at all. When the flow is irregular, it may be a disease. When there is a delay at menstruation, you should not try to hurry it on. Leave it to nature and it will do its work ... sometimes young females going to school and studying very hard find the menstruation becomes very irregular. In some cases when they do not menstruate, the health becomes worse. It comes from bad to worse. There are many cases, when girls that work too hard are very apt to be irregular ... treatment ... If the patient has too much exercise, lessen the exercises, or if they eat too much, try and lessen it. If the bowels are not regular, give them mag sulph in small doses. Some persons cup the loins, but doctors say that a cathartic or let the patient sit in a warm bath. To lessen, give a tonic such as tr. nux. vomic., aloes and myrrh pills are used ... quinine is used sometimes as a tonic, but iron is about the best. When the time comes use the warm water or hip baths. Use an extra dose of aloes at this time. It is used as purgative. You may use ergot in small doses. Iodine of iron is sometimes used. Some inject it into the vagina, but this is not very good. Electricity is used by some."

There was considerable time spent in lectures on signs of pregnancy. The student was cautioned to be careful in expressing an opinion and sometimes menstruation might stop, yet the patient might not be pregnant;

> You may ruin the character of the young lady. You must ascertain from the patient how long since the flow stopped, if the flow was regular and the patient was in good health, you may take it for granted that she is pregnant. To gain time, you may say that a patient is not pregnant and if she is, but you do not very often make this mistake.
>
> Signs of pregnancy, balottement. This is a vaginal examination and it will enable to ascertain the presence of the fetus in the womb. The patient should be in an upright position ... the operator must then introduce his finger and place it under the uterus while the

other hand is employed to keep the uterus and tumour steady. Then suddenly, but slightly jerking upward the point of your finger, you will feel a sensation of something having receded from it. The jerk of the finger on the fetus causes it to float upwards in the amnion.

There was discussion of the signs of death of the fetus and also of threatened abortion:

> If the abortion is coming on in an early gestation, you will find difficulty in detecting the death of the child ... try and stop the abort and save the child. Sometimes you cannot stop the abortion. You must keep the patient at rest and give opium ... if the abortion goes on, you will have pains and in that case, you cannot give ergot. If you cannot stop the bleeding, it is the entire placenta which is involved. You must not use much force, you must try and hook down the placenta. There are some forceps for this purpose, but the fingers are the best hooks for abortion. If there is much hemmorhaging, you must take some contour bags and smear them with lard and plug up the uterus and stop the hemmorhage.

But there was little or no discussion of the actual birthing and the possible attendant problems. By this time physicians, such as Dr. Walter Horacio Burritt in Smith's Falls was engaged in an extensive obstetrical practice. His record showed that between 1835 and 1886, he was at 1,828 obstetrical cases.[12] It was the custom of the physician to remain in attendance from the time he was called, which could amount to several days. Burritt was clearly aware of the "contagiousness of puerperal fever" as it had been described by O.W. Holmes in 1842. With good fortune a mother might not encounter great difficulty in delivering as Burritt reported of his 1,854 cases, 1,677 babies were in the natural position. However it was necessary for Burritt to use a pair of forceps (made by the local smith) in 104 instances. He lost nine babies in that group.

Burritt was a prototype of the "masterful inactivity" school of obstetrics, however he did use ergot for relief of pain in 67 cases.

But inactivity was not in the prescription register for most physicians. Thomas Millman recorded in his diary in 1869, while he attended lectures at Victoria, that Geike stated that cold was one of the best things for apoplectic diseases. It was a stimulant. Geike pointed out "the impurity of the air in churches causes a person to sleep, more than the dryness of the sermon" and added that bad drains in the cities were causes of disease by the slops collecting in the drain and giving rise to gases which were most obnoxious. For example, Prince Albert had died from these causes through typhoid fever.

Canniff lectured that it was essential that the blood should be in a healthy state to carry on a proper repair when there was an injury. When one kidney was not capable of doing its duty, the other would increase its output by that amount. "The blood should flow at a reasonable rate. When inflammation was beginning, there was not a great physiological stimulus, but when the stimulus is greater, the blood flowed more quickly," ergo it was necessary to stimulate.

H.H. Wright's *Physician's Hand-book of Practice* in 1864 gave space to enter patient visits. It also included a classification of diseases in order to facilitate care. Class 1 listed fevers – inflammatory or common; intermittent; remittent; congestive; yellow; typhoid; typhus; plague; irritative; hectic and mercurial. This category was expanded in Class 2, entitled Eruptive Fevers which included variola; discreta (a type of small pox); confluent; maligna (black small pox); varioloid (modified small pox); vaccinia; varicella; rubeola; dropsy; scarlatina; symplex; angiosa and magna. Other categories included constitutional diseases – gout, nervous gout, rheumatism, acute rheumatism, subacute rheumatism, nervous rheumatism, erysipelas, scrofula; and syphilis, secondary and tertiary. The next category dealt with diseases of the blood and included plethora, anemia, acute and chronic scorbutus, purpura, necraemia, hemmorhagic and dropsy. The next categories dealt with diseases of the brain, spinal cord and nerves, diseases of the respiratory organs; of the circulatory organs and of the digestive and absorbent system including diseases of the bowels.

The listings included midwifery and diseases of women and children, with a short paragraph of one of many disorders within each classification. The book had a description of poisons, their symptoms and treatments. One section listed the average frequency of the pulse at different ages. There was also a 30 page summary of remedies for specific conditions and a section on extemporaneous scripts which provided a list of common prescriptions. These, usually single items, were numbered and ended at 689.

The physician was instructed to fill in the patient's name and address and the medication which had been given. The extemporaneous prescriptions included a format for draughts, mixtures, pills, powders, decoctions, liniments or embrocations, plasters and electuaries. Instructions given were to draw under the appropriate day, a vertical line if it was an office visit, a home visit was signified by an oblique line and a night visit by an opposite oblique line. If the visits were paid for cross marks were to be used on these symbols.

Wright's diary shows a majority of patients paid "on the spot". In some cases he entered the amount - 50 or 75 cents. In addition he recorded the lectures that he had given, usually daily, during the academic year. He had a numerical list of his patients and in many cases he simply indicated that number "72" had been seen. He also listed several occasions when he had taught a "private class" or a "clinical lecture". On average he saw 45 patients per week, many on a daily basis.

There was a special section for obstetrics which listed times pregnant and if the same number of children as pregnancies. There was also a coding system for easy, difficult, lingering or instrumental delivery. He also recorded the expected time of confinement. "In but very few cases will the physician find it necessary to devote more than one line to the record of a case", advised the Hand Book. In 60 recorded cases he saw breech presentation in 2 and used forceps in 3 cases. He recorded four still births.

Therapy did not evolve quickly. In 1868 Dr. Walter Lambert of Amherstberg, Ontario wrote in the *Dominion Medical Journal*[13] of a young female who suffered slightly with anemia and scanty menstruation. She had been taking ferruginous preparations with some good effect.

The doctor diagnosed her as chlorosis, a disease contracted exclusively by young women, and prescribed mistura ferri comp and sometimes tinct. ferri and quiniae disulph. This treatment, based on the presumed effectiveness of iron products plus the popularity of quinine continued during the summer and in the fall she developed the symptoms of "progressive and locomotor ataxia". The physician felt she had Duchenne's disease which was apparent when watching her staggering, swaying walk. By that time she was unable to feed herself because of inco-ordination. Her speech was slurred with poor articulation. Sir William Gowers had described the effect of iron and phosphorous on the blood in 1878 and on Lambert's next visit, he gave potass. bromide and "submitted the patient to the action of a magneto-electricity once every 24 hours". He also gave pills of aloes and iron which caused relaxation. She was not improving and when Lambert read the September number of the *New York Medical Journal* of a report by Dr. Dujardin Baametz of the good effect of phosphorous in the disease, he immediately ordered acidi phosphorici diluti.

Her menses recommenced the next day and she began to improve. In two weeks she was able to sit up and had sufficient muscle control to be able to knit. She could walk about the house one month later. When seen by her physician, he stated that he was going to complete her recovery by giving her pyro-phosphate of iron. The patient continued to improve. Such an unexplained recovery made it difficult to appreciate the benefits of "scientific medicine", at that time or in today's medical atmosphere.

Of all the lecturers in the schools, the most prominent and erudite was Bovell. He founded the *Upper Canada Journal of Medical, Surgical and Physical Sciences* in 1851 and the Canadian Institute. In 1862 he published *A Plea for Inebriate Asylums* for the consideration of the Legislators of the Province of Canada. This included an extraordinary range of statistics on drunkeness and its consequences.

He pioneered research work and transfused cow's milk into cholera patients as a trial in 1854. This patterned work that had been done when intravenous saline was used in the 1832 epidemic in Montreal and by Dr. James Samson at Kingston.[14] Bovell may have felt that the milk globules were converted somehow into white blood corpules which would restore, "to the system on the part of its usual circulating pabulum".

Vibrios, the disease vector, had been seen by physicians using a microscope at St. Thomas' Hospital in London, but they were not associated with the cholera. A frustrated Bovell pointed out just before his death that "but I am kept back from want of a high objective lens.

Beck's is $85.00, so I feel quite disspirited ... I am very poor it is true, but my goodness, anything to relieve this cruel boredom ..."

Pierre Borel, court physician to Louis XIV and probably the first physician to make practical use of the micoscope had said "God's majesty becomes more illumed by these tiny Bodies than in gigantic ones, and their perplexing constitution convinces even the most Godless, and leaves them to the notion, the admiration and the veneration of their supreme Maker".

Bovell's *Outlines of Natural Theology*, was the basic text for his lecture course. This book involved "two distinct principles; the proofs of a great first cause or creator, and the exposition of the Divine goodness and wisdom as shown in natural objects and phenomena; and secondly the reconcillation of geological discoveries with the statements of the Mosiac Record".

In addition to his brilliance as a teacher, Bovell brought to the TSM another bonus. William Osler, the son of Rev. Featherstone Lake Osler, was following in his fathers' footsteps. William had spent a lively term at the grammar school in Dundas, from which he had been expelled for a variety of escapades, including locking a flock of sheep in the common room; removing all the furniture from a classroom and eventually shouting disparaging remarks "Come out old McKee",through the keyhole of the door of a local resident. (This episode strongly resembled the occasion when John Rolph at about the same age, locked the Rev. John Strachan, his teacher, in the classroom.) Osler was transferred to a boarding school at Barrie and then to a new school which had opened at Weston. This institution was built and operated by the Rev. William Arthur Johnson, who in addition to his talents as a school master, had a great interest in microscopy. Osler became entranced with examining specimens from rivers and ponds. Johnson, an ardent naturalist, fired the young student's imagination and provided a six hundred volume library including works by Sir Charles Lyell, whose books had influenced and inspired Charles Darwin, and *The Microscope and Its Revelations* by Dr. William B. Carpenter of the University of London. The latter was the current best seller with its detailed description of the mechanics of a microscope and a number of magnificent drawings of objects in the plant, animal or microscopic world. Bovell, who was the school doctor, also added his knowledge of microscopy. This interest was expanded by the influence of Dr. H. Holford Walker of Dundas, a family physician, who was adept at the microscope and provided more opportunities for the young student. The world viewed through a low power objective lens engulfed all of the neophytes' spare hours.

On matriculating from the Weston school, Osler entered Trinity and, although there was strong pressure from the family to proceed further in Divinity, after his first week he wrote to Johnson "this (naturalist) is the work for me. I am going no further in the studies for Divinity".[15] This caused a storm in the Osler home and the Rev. Featherstone wrote a strong letter of disapproval, however William's mind was set and he enrolled in the school in which Bovell was a Professor, the TSM.

But Osler did not relish his studies, aside from the Bovell lectures. Writing at a later date in the *British Medical Journal*, [16] he recalled that when he was a freshman in 1868, he preferred to spend every Saturday morning at Bovell's office working on the microscope, in the company of a fellow student, James E. Graham. "It was a great privilege after the dry program of the week, to be brought in contact with a genuine enthusiast who loved to work at as well as to think about the problems of disease". His dislike of formal lectures was understandable because, in most cases, it was a matter of recording each of the professors' words and repeating them to pass an exam. There was little or no opportunity for the student to teach himself, a philosophy which Osler championed when he became an instructor.

The time spent with the microscope was rewarded by a seminal event. In February of 1870, when dissecting a subject with a fellow student, Richard Zimmerman, he discovered "numerous trichinae throughout the whole muscular system, all of which were densely encysted, many having become calcified". This was the dawning of the science of medicine, the connection between vector and victim for the exultant student. Osler published the findings of this autopsy.[17]

He did not complete the course at TSM, but transferred to McGill in 1870, "because the hospital facilities in Montreal, the availabilty of clinical experience, were better". Those were tense times in Toronto, between the continuing strife of the medical schools and the poor support by the city and Province of the Toronto General, which closed in 1868 and 1869. When it re-opened, there were only 25 beds available for students of medicine. Osler's choice was vindicated as it was not

W.T. Aikins – The Dean

Dr. Aikins, about 1875.

A younger Aikins, about 1870.

Victoria College, about 1840 in Cobourg, Ontario, which was originally the Upper Canada Academy.

This building was the first Medical School of Upper Canada. It was part of King's College and was used for anatomical dissection.

Rolph's house and the first Toronto School of Medicine on Lot, later Queen Street, 1930's picture.

The Toronto General Hospital at Gerrard Street East in Toronto. The letter informs Aikins that he has been removed from the staff of the hospital.

This red brick building on the North side of Richmond Street, was used by Aikins as a dissecting room while he continued to search for a more permanent building.

The Toronto School of Medicine, Sumach and Gerrard Streets. This is after the addition had been added to the west of the building.

The building of the College of Physicians and Surgeons at Bay and Richmond Street.

The new Medical School, opened 1903.

Sir William Mulock, was a driving force in
founding the Medical Faculty.

The contentious Biology Building which caused a committee of
enquiry.

Ape Caricature of T.H. Huxley
date January 28, 1871.

Professor William Hincks, who was selected over T.H. Huxley as Professor of Natural History.

Prof. Henry Alleyn Nicholson.

In 1855 the Upper Canada Medical Board examined Aaron Walter Gamble. The candidate is on the left and is being examined by Drs. Henrick, Bovell, Workman, King and Widmer.

Professor Robert Ramsay Wright, brought science education to the University.

Dr. Christopher Widmer, the doyen of medical practice in the first half of the nineteenth century.

Dr. James Bovell, the Dean of Trinity and a major figure in medical education.

Dr. John Rolph styled the Father of Medicine in Upper Canada.

William Osler about the time of his graduation.

Dr. William Osler, about 1890 while at Johns Hopkins. Sitting from right to left are W.W. Francis, W.S. Thayer, and H.A. LaFleur.

Dr. W.B. Nevitt, Dean Women's Medical College from 1888 to 1895.

Dr. A.A. MacDonald.

Dr. F.H. Richardson, had known Rolph and Aikins and had been a fixture in the teaching of medicine for more than fifty years.

Dr. J.E. Graham. He married into the Aikins family and attended William in his dying days.

Dr. Uzziel Ogden, who succeeded Aikins as Dean

Dr. J. Thorburn.

Dr. Daniel Clarke.

Dr. Adam Wright.

Dr. E.M. Hodder, surgeon and sailor.
He charted Lake Ontario.

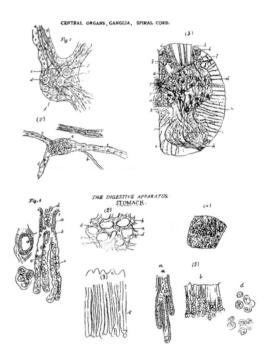

Specimen from student's science book, 1878.

The first University gymnasium.

Illustrations from The Fall of Man, 1871.

Aikin's splint for humeral fractures.

The upper room of the building, which was called the Toronto School of Medicine, held the dissecting area. At the table are (1) Dr. John King (2) Dr. George DeGrassi (3) Tom Hays and assistant (4) Old Ned the janitor (5) Student, Dr. W.W. Francis who later practiced in Manitoulin. From Robertson-MacKenzie Collection. Ont Arch.

An Operation Circa 1895
Back row W.A. Shannon,
D.A. Dobie, E. Clause,
W.O. Scott
Front row W.O. Stewart,
Geo Acheson

The operating room at the Toronto General Hospital about 1898. Steam sterilizers on the left and absence of Lister's apparatus. The lighting is one focussed set of bulbs. The furniture and floor is wood.

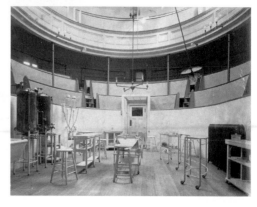

Toronto School of Medicine 3rd year 1884-85. Rear row: T.J. McDonald. J. McCallum, B.A. A.W. Richardson. C.E. Lawrence. J.C. Carlyle. A.B. Riddell H. McGillivray. J. Sanson. A.J. Hunter. A.W. Bigelow. W.C. Heggie. C.G. Noecker. J. Simenton. D.R. Johnston. D.M. Williams. S. West E. Bromley, B.A.. J.R. Dales. J. Marty. J.W. Peaker. H.A. Wright. W.J. Logie, B.A. C.J. Hastings. J.R. Cruikshank, B.A. W.M. English. N.C. McKinnon. W.T. Parry. E.E. King. P.P. Park. H.J. Hamilton W.J. Greig, B.A. J.W. Mustard, B.A. W.H. Wright. L.L. Hooper. O. Weld, B.A. J.M. Foster. R.M. Bateman. J.E. Pickard. W.B. Hopkins. C.A. Hodgetts. L.G. Smith. Front row: J.A. Rutherford. G.A. Peters. R.J. Wood.

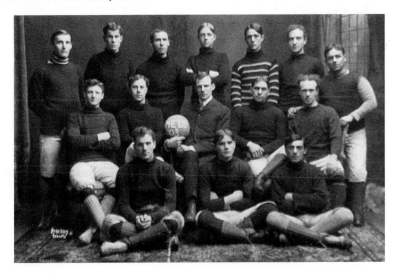

Toronto Medicals Intercollegiate Champions 1903 Rear row: F.W. Morgan (half-back). J. Galbraith (spare). F. Rogers (half-back). C. Johnson (foward). J. Robert (goal). A.W. McPherson (center half-back). Second row: E.E. Bryans (right-wing). B. McCormick (back). W.E. Bryans (manager). E. Richardson (back). C.W. Sleemon (left-wing). C. Schliter (spare). Front row: R. Allison (right-wing). W.G. Fowlar (centre forward). W. Lepatnikoff (left-wing).

The graduating class Toronto School of Medicine 1870-71. Front row G.W. Jackes, William Forrest, C.Y. Moore, A. Taylor. Rear Row S.R. Richardson, J. Donaldson, G.H. Cowen, R.H. De la Matter.

Officers of the Toronto University of Medical Society 1892-93. Left to right: W.B. McKechnie. W.T. McArthur (Curator). C.E. Smythe (Second Vice-President). J.J. Williams. F.N.G. Starr (Treasurer). A. Gibson (Asst. Treasurer). W.B. Thistle (President). A.K. McLean. F. Blanchard. E.D. Graham. F. Martin (First Vice-President). G.D. Porter. F.J. Ball (Corresponding Secretary). K.C. McIlwraith.

Graduating class, Medicine, University of Toronto 1873-74. Rear: I.H. Cameron, A.J. Campbell, A. Farwell, N.H. Beemar, A. Luke, A.J. Whitehead. Front: J.D. Ball, G. Smith, O.C. Brown, R. Whiteman, George Shaw, C.E. Taylor.

unusual for TSM students to transfer to the Montreal school. McGill's predominance in Canadian teaching at the end of the nineteenth century was undoubtedly due, in part, to Osler's presence.

Later Osler said "to Dr. Bovell the fields of Science, Philosophy and Theology were especially attractive and were cultured equally with the field of medicine in which it was a chief duty to work. With equal readiness, he would discuss the Origin of Species, the theories of Kant, Hamilton and Comte, or the doctrine of Real Presence; and what he said was well worthy of attention, for his powers of criticism and analysis were good. But his versatility was an element of his weakness, as he himself knew". [18]

Although Bovell's overriding loyalty was to the Anglican Church, some of his views offended Bishop Strachan who found that he was "too Puseyite for him to condone". The Bishop requested his presence on November 29th 1860 and stated "... in the meantime stay your proceedings and do nothing. As bad as things appear to be, I do not consider them beyond remedy. Come therefore in the spirit of meekness and forgiveness and in that spirit let the discussion between us proceed ..." This letter was caused by circumstances when the Bishop of Huron, who was feuding with Bishop Strachan, expressed "extreme evangelical views which had little in common with the view of the promoters and supporters of Trinity". The Bishop of Toronto felt that Bovell's "romanish" pastoral views were unsuitable. Bovell defended himself but unfortunatly a letter which he had circulated to a few friends appeared in *The Globe* on November 15th, 1860. Bovell tried to suppress the letter by speaking to the editor, but the deed was done and the Provost of Trinity summoned a meeting of the Corporation which "disallowed and repudiated" the pastoral statements of the Bishop of Huron. Bovell then resigned the chair of Natural Theology. Even though he did not proceed any further and although Strachan avowed that the Bishop of Huron was "a low Churchman and better fitted for political agitator than a Bishop", Bovell's resignation was accepted. Thus Upper Canada lost of its prime medical star.

The death of Sara Jane Wright from Richmond Hill on March 21st 1868, was a challenge to Aikins' compassion or conviction. She had worked as a domestic for the family of Mr. Amos Wright, MPP for East York. On visiting the city she saw a Dr. Moses Williams, a recent graduate of Victoria. *The Daily Leader* reported that she wanted an abortion and Williams acceded to her wishes. When she failed to progress favourably, he wrote to the girl's friends informing them of her dangerous state. The friends rushed to the city, with Langstaff, the family's physician.

Sara had known Langstaff since her childhood and she confessed to him that Williams had "used an instrument that produced pain". She was so sick it was not possible to move her to her parent's home in Richmond Hill, so he requested Aikins to take over her care. Aikins refused because "Williams was an abortonist", but relented. Sara died and Langstaff was worried that he might be sued by her father.

At an inquest performed by Dr. Buchanan it was revealed that she had been in poor health over the past twelve months. Williams' father, his wife and their washer-woman, all testified the girl had been sick when she came to the doctor's house. Williams reported that he had "found that she was suffering from intense pain across the abdomen; she told me she thought it was inflammation of the bowel; I asked her why she thought so and she said she had several attacks before and knew just how it commenced ... she kept getting worse until Saturday when she became serious; meanwhile I had been treating her for the inflammed bowels; on Saturday I used the syringe and injected luke-warm water into the bowels and vagina in order to allay the inflammation. Although she seemed better the following day, she worsened ... I sent for Dr. Buchanan to come in consultation ... it was believed she had peritonitis ... Dr. Langstaff chose Dr. Aikins to attend in his place as he could not himself; Dr. Aikins came and he took full charge of the case without consulting me at all; I had nothing to do with the deceased from the time Dr. Aikins took her in charge until she died."

Aikins was a vehement foe of abortionists and despised any physician who carried out the procedure. However he was aware of the fact that there were abortionists in Toronto and the surrounding region, although their presence was usually ignored unless a death occurred. A Mrs. Martha Bassingate had consulted Langstaff after she had received medication from Williams, following which she aborted. She died four weeks later. Eventually a warrant was sworn out for Williams' arrest, however he vanished.

The allopaths were given a juicy tidbit in their quarreling with the homeopaths and at the same opportunity Aikins was able to express his abhorrence of interference in birthing, when Mary Boyd, a former servant of the homeopath Dr. Campbell died. He was accused of "highly improper" treatment of the patient.

"No one knows whom to blame; the medical men who put their heads together to endeavor to injure a successful rival, or the members of the jury, who, in the profundity of wisdom and knowledge had the impertinence to pass censure on Dr. Campbell's treatment" opined *The Leader* and this opinion was bolstered by a letter from Dr. J. Adams, homeopath, who stated that he had full knowledge of the remedial measures that were used and that Campbell's treatment of the patient was perfectly judicious. He applied galvanism in this case which Adams recommended as it was used by far higher medical authorities than those who presumed to censure its use.

Campbell fought the accusation and his cause was picked up by *The Globe*. On June 5th 1868 it printed:

> Dr. Campbell, whose conduct was impugned by an ignorant jury, acting under the prompting of a ring of doctors of a rival school, defended himself with great competence and ability. So effective in fact was his defence that the journal which admitted the attacks upon him, was afraid to publish his closing and most crushing reply.

Following that Campbell published a document which contained all of the evidence, editorials, letters pro and con and was sent it to all the medical men and the newspapers in the province.

The Globe stated that the charge against the good doctor was trumped up by medical rivals and would never have been heard if had he been a practitioner of a orthodox school." This demonstrates the extent of in-fighting that exists between the medical men and the medical schools."

However Aikins' job on the abortion committee was not an easy one. The 1889 *Canada Lancet* asked, "What physician, in practice for any length of time, has not had many applications, often accompanied by a considerable bribe, to relieve the victim of the seducer from the social disgrace attached to her sin, or the selfish and degraded married female from the care and trouble naturally devolving on her?"[19] For every problem there was a solution, according to the street lore and these answers abounded in the popular press:

> Tansy and pennyroyal pills.
> Never fails. Any stage. Thousands of happy ladies. Safe, sure and absolutely harmless. These pills are positively superior to all others. Many thousands of ladies in this country and Europe have secretly endorsed these pills. Beware of dangerous substitutes and imitations. Price $2.00 by mail, or send stamp for particulars. Sold only by ...

Many other recipes were available to cause an abortion such as Radway's pills for female irregularities or Sir James Clarke's Female Pills or "Old Dr. Gordons' Pearls of Health – never fails in curing all suppressions and irregularities used monthly". Clarke was Physician-to-the-Queen.

Abortions continued to plague Aikins and other members of the profession. On June 19th 1868, as a result of a communication from the United States which labled abortion as "the national sin of the United States." following a passionate plea by Workman to the Medical Council, McGill, Aikins and Turquand were appointed a committee to draw up a resolution which would be conveyed to various clergymen of the province, asking their act of cooperation to endeavour to prevent the continuation of the "national sin". Workman claimed that there was an ever increasing rate of criminal abortion. In addition he thundered that he was aware that members of what was called the "legitimate profession" were aiding and abetting.

Although the Committee struggled to suggest a reasonable approach to the problem, by the 1890's more abortions were being performed, by physicians and others – and women dying of septicemia or other complications. Part of the reason for increase was that most of the women who were demanding abortions, were married. Although the large Victorian family remained the norm, the nascent liberalization of the female status; the opportunities for higher education and the popularization of abortifacients combined to change the face of the family.

REFERENCES

1. St. John, Judith. Firm Foundations 1988.
2. Richardson, Dr. James A.. Baldwin Room, Reference Library, Toronto.
3. Green, A. The Life and Times of The Rev. Anson Green, 1887.
4. Pearson, W.H.. Recollections and Records of Toronto of Old. William Briggs 1914.
5. Ontario Archives, Miscellaneous Collection, 2113.
6. Dr. James C. Goodwin Collection, Ontario Archives, MU7543.
7. Evening Leader October 31, 1863.
8. Clarke, C.K. A History of the Toronto General Hospital 1913; p 84.
9. Dominion Medical Journal 1 1869.
10. Can Jour of Surgery April 1862.
11. Clarke. Ibid; p 83.
12. Watson, M.C.. An account of obstetrical practice in Upper Canada. CMAJ 1939; pp 181–188.
13. Dominion Medical Journal; p 177.
14. Henry, Walter. Trifles from my Port-Folio 1839.
15. Cushing, H. The Life of Sir William Osler. p 120.
16. Proceedings of the Royal Society of Medicine, Volume 7, 1914; p 247.
17. Gwyn, Norman. Early Life of Sir William Osler in Appreciation and Reminiscences of Sir William Osler, Bart. Bulletin IX; p149.
18. British Medical Journal July 29th, 1899; p 317.
19. Canada Lancet 1889; p 217.

Chapter Five

The Organizer

Aikins' star was in the ascendant in 1853. Not only was his medical practice flourishing, but his first born was a boy. William Heber grew up in his father's footsteps and qualified as a physician. When attending the TSM in the 1870s he received no special privileges although life for a student in those days was slightly better than it had been when his father qualified. And unlike his father, William did not marry and most likely spent most of his time at his studies or sports.

There was little opportunity for games or other recreation in Toronto. Although a cricket club had been formed at Trinity College in 1852, it remained the only sport until the mid-sixties when English rugger was played. Soccer was not common, as it was a ruffian's game played by gentlemen, while rugger was a gentleman's game – played by ruffians. The Trinity cricket team was not allowed to play the University of Toronto as they did not wish to offend Bishop Strachan, who was sure to be against mixed cricketering as adamantly as with mixed marriages. However the Toronto Cricket Club was available for a match. The zest for the game was tempered as a proper pitch was not available until the 80's. Rugger was even more difficult as the field was uneven and the goal posts were simply sticks stuck into the ground. But by 1888 conditions had improved and it was possible for Trinity to play the University of Toronto or other teams without causing political problems. Harvard and McGill had football matches beginning in 1874, and the match-making soon spread to other schools.

Boxing, fencing, weightlifting and tumbling were performed in an unheated barn, frequently viewed by rats or perching hens. And in the winter there was always curling, which had begun in 1853 when teams from Scarborough and Toronto held a match on the frozen water of Toronto Bay near Rees's Wharf, owned by Dr. William Rees, who had donated the land for the Provincial Lunatic Asylum on Queen Street West. His public spiritedness resulted in other amenities in the city, including public baths for immigrants, support for female and orphan societies and a detoxification centre for adults.

In 1862 a skating rink on the Esplanade was available. *The Globe* described this scene as

> Nearby, down the embankment boys and men rode upon sleds and up above were spectators cozily wrapped up in furs, some in their handsome sleighs, all of which tended to exalt gaiety of the occasion.

However, the truly Canadian game of lacrosse fared a little better. In 1873 grounds were opened at Jarvis and Wellesley Street and there was a 2,000 seat grandstand located on the west side. Several years later, the Alexander Street Baptist Church was located on this site and later the Emmanuel Baptist.

A few years later it was possible to play golf on a newly constructed course on the Kingston Road, but it was against the law to have a round on Sundays.

Some of these recreation facilities were used by William's other children.

A daughter, Lydia Eleanor was born in 1855 and two years later, Henry Wilberforce arrived. Like his older brother, he followed his father into medicine after preliminary education at Upper Canada College, graduating in 1881. At the same time he received a M.D.C.M. from Victoria University. Subsequently he travelled extensively to New York, London and Vienna, gaining more degrees. However H.W. Aikins had only a small medical practice with an appointment at St. Michael's Hospital. When recording his military service for a biographical form to be kept at the Academy of Medicine in Toronto, he stated "I belong to Company I, Queen's Own Rifles. At the Bluffs I fired at and hit the centre of the target (200 yard range). I never tried again, feeling that I can't better perfection". He also recorded that his marriage date was unknown, the place was unknown and his wife's name "likewise unknown". He died in 1942.

A third son, Frederick Theophilous was born in 1858 and lived to be 70. He predeceased the last born of the children of Louisa Adelia, who died in 1941 at the age of 78. His younger sister, Mary Eva lived only four months. None of Louisa's children married.

••••••

In parallel with his attempts to raise the level of medical care, Aikins, after improving the examination system for licencing and raising the matriculation level for entrance to the profession, next gave his attention to the status of the profession. He had the example of the American Medical Association and immediately started a campaign to reform medical education. To the contrary, physicians in Ontario had no formal organization where they could present and discuss their ideas for upgrading the profession. Such a forum was necessary not only to gratify the ambitions of some the leading educators, but also to justify the profession's standing in the public mind.

The Medical Act of 1827 (Geo. IV, c63) described who could practice but did not specify details of their education. It also detailed penalties for practicing without a licence, but it failed in several areas, including a written recognition of the profession. Consequently there were numerous attempts to amend. In 1839 a petition to the Legislature asked "that the medical profession be placed on a more honourable and favourable footing." "Favourable" meant that a doctor could sue to collect unpaid bills. Parliament responded with an Act establishing the College of Physicians and Surgeons of Upper Canada, which was disallowed by the Imperial Parliament in 1840. In 1846 a petition was sent to Parliament asking "... for the examination of candidates, granting licences, the expulsion or the suspension of unworthy members, and other purposes, there should be established a General Provincial Medical Board or Council, possessing the confidence of their brethren in the profession".

It was argued that a Provincial Medical Society would unite in one common centre the views and wishes of the whole profession and confer upon medical practitioners, "the independence, respectability, and advantages which the incorporation of the Law Society has obtained for its members, and thus ultimately raise the medical profession to that position in public regard to which it is, by its utility and importance, so justly entitled".[1] However this petition was seen by some as a means to enforce a schedule of fees and an exclusion of "non-regular" practitioners from practice. In spite of a strong doctor lobby, there was an equally effective voice from the homeopaths and eclectics (and their patients!) against passage of such a measure.

In 1851, there was a further attempt and the *Upper Canada Journal of Medical Surgical and Physical Science* published the draft of a Bill proposed by a meeting of the leading practitioners of York County, including Aikins. This urged the establishment of a College with a medical examining Board. This Board was to set preliminary qualifications, duration of study and a curriculum to be followed by medical candidates. It also proposed that, depending upon the Board's deliberations, attendance at certain universities would exempt the candidate from sitting the examination.

Once again, the proposal met heavy weather in the House, chiefly because it seemed to say that graduates or licentiates of British schools would be required to take a further examination before being permitted to practice in Canada West. This led to the withdrawal of that particular phrase of the Bill, but the public in general was not convinced that one school of medical thought should be given the exclusive licence to practice.

> We are told that the country desires free trade in physic, and that people will employ whom they choose as their medical attendants. Then we say, that these men, if guilty of malpractice should be subject to criminal prosecution, and punished for felony or misdemeanor, according to the extent of the mischief done by them ...

maintained the *Upper Canada Journal* as it advocated raising the status of the profession from "capable of being exercised by the veriest clodhopper or the most ignorant artisan". [2]

Part of the press continued to promote these views. On April 1st 1854 the *Medical Chronicle* editorial on "Incorporation of the Profession in C.W." asked why the profession was not entitled to "the same privileges in Upper as is in Lower Canada, and why without these, its condition must border on anarchy". It expanded the idea that the public "must, like children", be prevented from injuring themselves by using "those whose knowledge is intutive, and who perhaps, are disabled from following their proper callings, and finding in medicine a better business than horse-shoeing or sow-gelding". This escalation of rhetoric was matched by the eclectic groups, which called on "all friends of medical reform" to speak out and exert any power they had to insist that they should continue in their normal practice pattern. The situation was made more urgent in 1859 when the Provincial Legislature passed a Bill which was the equal of the Medical Act of 1827 under which physicians were practicing, only the new Act recognized the existence of homeopathic physicians and allowed them to appoint their own Board of Examiners. This galled the allopaths as their Board was appointed by the Lieutenant Governor.

Yet another attempt to pass the Bill was a repeat story of previous tries to regulate the qualifications of practitioners in medicine and surgery. When presented in the Legislative Council by the Honourable Mr. Cayley, he explained the make-up of the proposed College and stressed that it was a combination of members elected from all over Upper Canada. J.C. Aikins added that a fourth clause had been inserted so that it would not include homeopaths, thus permitting them to continue with their own development. He pointed out that the Bill had been approved by all of the medical men, with the exception of three or four from Toronto, and by nearly all those of Montreal. But there was strong resistance, such as had countered all efforts to incorporate the profession previously. "The people of Upper Canada were perfectly satisfied with the present laws upon the subject" said one member. "... is calculated to throw the whole power of the profession into the hands of a few gentlemen in Toronto". Even the Honourable Attorney General West said "... believe that among the medical men of Upper Canada, the feeling was against this Bill. It had been got up to favour the interests or soothe the quarrels of a few gentlemen of Toronto; and it would also materially affect the interests of the homeopathists." J.C. Aikins tried valiantly to preserve the Bill, but it was voted to a Select Committee and disappeared. [3]

To add more urgency toward a more formal acceptance of medical physicians, the eclectic group was recognized in 1861 in a similar Act.

Now the non-regulars had government backing for their claims to legitimacy, much to the embarrassment of the allopaths. But the two new Acts changed the qualifications from simply an apprenticeship to an academic discipline and specified four years of medical studies, with two years at medical school. This caused problems as there were no homepathic or eclectic schools in Canada.

Not only was the American example in front of Aikins, plus the success which had been gained by the two competing sects, there were also the events in England, where a movement had begun in 1837 to establish a Medical Reform Committee which attempted to set up a State examining board to replace other examining mechanisms. This led to the passage of the Medical Act of 1858 which set standards of education in the United Kingdom. Aikins, and his brother, next endeavoured to form an association of physicians and surgeons in Upper Canada and to incorporate them as a College of Physicians and Surgeons. William spent a great deal of time researching the issue and giving to James the essence of a Bill, which was "the first Bill for the incorporation of the Profession ever brought before the Legislature" according to *The Globe* of May 4th, 1866. However in spite of extensive lobbying that had been done in its preparation, the Bill was not enacted as it was felt that it gave the TSM almost a monopoly over who should be given licence to practice, because at that time the TSM had a majority of members of the UCMB. Rolph, in his redoubt at Victoria, did not lose the opportunity of highlighting this in a broadside he distributed.

Rolph became more involved in the matter when an allegation was made via a circulated letter which read that Victoria students could easily gain a graduation through a clandestine examination by the Dean. It was an old charge, made frequently by each camp against the other. Rolph objected vigorously and stated that examinations were as open as in any college in the world and that students completed "an ample curriculum" before graduating. Further to a stringent examination, Rolph claimed that at the very least all students spent four years in studying medical subjects, and some more than five. This was well in excess of what was prescribed by the Medical Board examinations and included a year's hospital practice. Rolph saw the proposed Bill as being the actions of a group of ex-professors from Victoria College who, since their desertion in 1856, "have never ceased to carry on against it, a vindictive, avowed hostility". He stated that the anonymous letter had been drawn up and circulated by Drs. Barrett, Aikins and Wright and contained mis-statements with regard to Victoria College examination procedures and also damaged the reputation of Queen's College, Kingston.

This attempt to legislate the disparate medical profession in Upper Canada was the natural outcome of Aikins' long term advice to Rolph beginning in 1852 when he had written "indeed there should be but one provincial licencing board, and this, for all persons, graduates or non graduates – British, Yankee or Colonial". The unusual reaction by Rolph against the attempt "to unite the profession" reflected the bitterness that had developed with the break-up.

Persistence, doggedness and a determination to upgrade the system finally paid off. In 1865 Dr. Thomas Parker, an old friend of Aikins who had joined the teaching staff of the TSM, introduced and shepherded the Ontario Medical Act through the Legislature. For the first time, the Government enacted control of the study and practice of medicine to the profession. Previously the major emphasis had been on who should practice, now the weight shifted to the quality of medical education. But, in acceding to the repeated demands, a full passage of power to the profession was not clearly delineated. In effect the Act was a compromise between what the professionals wanted and what the Universities wanted. A General Council of Medical Education and Registration (GCMER) for Upper Canada was established with representatives to be elected from each of twelve territorial districts in the Province from the pool of registered doctors. The remainder of the Council was made up of delegates of each of the degree granting institutions.

A Registrar, to be selected from the Council, was charged to maintain, and publish yearly, a record of those physicians who were licenced to practice, and to publish this list each year. It was incumbent on each member of the Council to notify the Registrar of any changes in their constituency. Registration was to be granted if a certificate of qualification was awarded by one of the educational bodies. The examination which had been held previously by the UCMB was no longer the entrance to practice.

In effect the Council assumed a rubber stamp function, based on the medical school certificate, and no longer held examinations to judge a candidate's fitness to practice. But in return for this loss of control by the old Board, the new Council was responsible for setting the standards of the preliminary education of medical students and to establish the curriculum of study. It was incumbent on medical schools to submit their curriculae to the Council and also be prepared for inspection by Council members. If the Council did not agree with the course content, it could refuse registration to the graduates of that particular school. Part of the impetus of the Council was to ensure that a student could pursue his choice of philosophy of medicine and could not be forced into any other school of thought.

Unauthorized practitioners were forbidden to use the courts to recover fees for their services and were liable to a $100.00 fine, payable to the Treasurer of the Council, if they carried on a practice.

The first meeting of the General Council was held the next spring on May 4th. Dr. Clarke of Guelph had been appointed Chairman by the Act and Aikins was elected Treasurer, without salary. The clause specifying that delegates from medical schools should be on the Council, led to considerable dispute over the formation of a Committee on Education. The Province had ruled that there should be one independent examining committee which set entrance levels and curriculum for the whole of the province and specified every student should be qualified by the Committee for his licence. The wording was not clear as to whether various members should be excluded from any activities, and one of the first questions that arose was whether representatives of medical schools should serve on this Committee. Aikins responded vigorously and contended that it was reasonable for school representation. He asserted that "the Toronto School of Medicine had been to a great deal of expense in the promotion of the Bill and he, himself, had lobbied hard in its favour and therefore it did seem out of place for any member of the Council to make allusions to the representations of the colleges as not being capable of independent actions ...".

He continued that various Bills had failed in the House, even though on one occasion he had brought a transcript of the English Medical Act in order to bolster passage of the Bill.

"The school which he represented was to a good deal responsible for the very Act under which they were assembled in Council. And when they came here, it was hard to hear those improper and wholy unwarranted aspersions passed upon the medical institutions of the country and upon their representatives. He was astonished and grieved to observe that when gentlemen made the most unkind remarks of this nature, they were actually cheered by other members".

Clarke rose in defence and replied that he had spoken for the Council and that there was no use in "blinking the fact that there was an impression widespread in the country that the Toronto School of Medicine, had, by its course of action, forfeited the public confidence. Public opinion unmistakably condemned it. If he appealed for a confirmation of his words from the other representatives present, in 19 out of 20 cases it would be found that the people had lost confidence in the Canadian schools of medicine. He did not share the public opinion on this point, but he did not hesitate to state that if he had had the framing of the Medical Act under which they were in session, it would have not given a single one of the colleges a representative in the Council ... men who made money by cramming the profession with recruits ought not to come there to take part in framing a curriculum and fixing the terms under which the licences would be granted. He too had introduced a Bill in Parliament for incorporation of the profession and so framed as to exclude all professors and colleges from seats on the Examining Board. The Bill was lost on account of the opposition which that class called forth. What was required was an Examing Committee entirely independent of the schools". [4]

Aikins responded that he had not spoken in order to be part of the Committee on Education. As a matter of fact, he was glad he was not on the committee, but he had taken the occasion to vindicate the TSM. He quoted from its annual report to the effect that in the past, as in the future, "he was ever ready to assist any effort made toward establishing a uniform standard of qualifications for graduating for all the seven medical institutions of Upper and Lower Canada". His arguments held and medical school members were accepted.

War sounds were heard from the Council chamber the following day. The Board refused Dr. Duncan Campbell, a homeopath, permission to seat himself as a representative of the Homeopathic Medical Board. Aikins, combined with Dr. Horatio Yates of Queen's College, Berryman from Victoria and Richardson from Toronto said that he should not be allowed admission. Dr. William McGill allowed that if Dr. Campbell was left off the Board, he would be "just where he ought to be, and they all very desire to see him – outside of the Council". Aikins made a resolution, which was passed, which deprived Campbell of any legal right to sit on the Board and at the same time that he should be excluded from taking any part in its proceedings.

This was a thorny legal point as the fourth clause of the Act allowed every college or body of Upper Canada, authorized by law to grant medical or surgical degrees, to send a representative to the Medical Council. However Clause 36 provided that nothing in the Act should be held in any way to affect the rights previously conceded to homeopaths and eclectics. From this, it was argued that the intention was to exclude those bodies from the operation of the Act.

The Globe wrote "there is something very laughable in the feelings of horror with which the members of the Council really seem to regard a homeopathist. The presence of a medical heretic, who did not practice allopathy, seemed to be looked upon as something akin the plague ..."

The Council attempted to strike a standard for matriculation. There were arguments and "the subsection exacting a certain knowledge of Greek, was especially, a bone of contention. Some members desiring to have it struck out and others that it should not come into operation for one or more years". In fact only a chapter of Saint John was required for Greek translation and several members of the Council felt that any smart young lad with reasonable education and instruction could manage this within three days. "What benefit would it be to a student to merely be able to read one chapter in Greek?" was the question. Aikins added to the debate by pointing out that there were three gentlemen in Council who had graduated from McGill College and in view of the fact that McGill was known to have a high standard of education, it was interesting to observe that their matriculation did not require an examination in Greek. While he was in favour of elevating the standard of education required before entering the profession, and was sure that he was prepared to go as far as any gentleman in that direction, "as with the administration of medicine, it was not always judicious to give a large dose at the start. It would be well to allow the clause to stand so that students would know what was coming, but to delay the period of its taking effect". Some educators continued to revere the gifts Greek brought.

Meanwhile Campbell had re-appeared fortified with a legal opinion that the Homeopathic Medical Board was entitled to send a representative to the Council and presented his credentials "and battled for what he deemed his rights with an energy worthy of an important cause". His cause was further bolstered by a Letter to the Editor of the *The Globe* on May 16th which explained how well homeopaths were regarded in New York State and contained an excerpt from the proceedings of the New York Board of Health which was highly laudatory.

At the end of the meeting the members were transported by special car, provided by the manager of the street railway to 999 Queen Street, the Lunatic Asylum. Workman was anxious that the medical profession as a whole should view first hand some of the problems associated with the insane.

The Council got down to business and on July 31st, 1866 published in the newspapers that recognition of matriculation was given to all candidates who had matriculated before May 1st 1866. It then specified that any candidate in attendance at lectures after May 1866 was required to pass a matriculation by September 1868. The content of the matriculation examination was; reading aloud a passage from some English author; writing from dictation; English grammar; writing a short English composition; arithmetic, including fractions and decimals; questions in general geography ; general history; elements of natural philosophy; Euclid the first two books; algebra to simple equations inclusive; translations of a passage from the first book of Caesar's *Commentaries, De Bello Gallico* and a passage from Gregory's *Conspectus*. In English history students were to be examined from Hamilton's *Outlines of English History* to the present time and in ancient history from Schmitz's *Manual of Ancient History* extending down to the death of Nero in Rome and to the death of Alexander in Grecian history. It was noted that all of these subjects would be judged on the quality of knowledge, spelling and handwriting was taken into account. Candidates were also warned that after the first of May 1867, they would be required to pass an examination in Greek.

While the Act gave the Council control over the content of medical education, it still lacked the power and presence of a central organization capable of administering a universal qualifying examination. Parker explained in *The Leader* of July 10th, 1866 "there are particulars in which the Act of the last Session was defective". This statement, plus other objections from various quarters led to a second Act in 1869.

Aikins was elated that steps had been taken ultimately to increase the course length to four years and that there was to be a standard of entrance qualifications. However there remained other areas for improvement. The Act did not state that the four years should have a graded curriculum, leading eventually to a stage where a well-educated physician could be turned out. In addition it replaced the Boards which had been set up for the homeopaths and the eclectics. Those candidates appeared before the Council and were examined by the Board as a whole, and only in their special areas of Materia Medica or Therapeutics and theory or practice of physic or surgery or midwifery (except in operative parts) were homeopaths or eclectics examiners allowed to participate. This caused discontent amongst those groups who petitioned without success to have the Act amended. Other groups were dissatisfied. McGill Medical School objected to the possibility that their graduates would require further examination. Medical schools in Canada West knew that they had lost some power. Orthodox physicians objected to the inclusion of homeopaths and eclectics on the Board as this raised the status of those groups and Richardson moved to have their special status cancelled, but lost the resolution. Workman, of Victoria, addressing the meeting of the Canadian Medical Association in 1869 felt that the Act made the profession "as low as the most modest and humble among us could for the sake of spiritual modification, desire to go."

In spite of these objections and the initial difficulties in implementing the Act, there was a gradual realization by the profession that there were many good features. For example, the number of licenced irregular practitioners dropped off sharply after 1869. Campbell, who had been President of the Homeopathic Board and was a spokesman for the two groups, complained that since the GCMER and CPSO had been emplaced, not one homeopathic or eclectic candidate had appeared for examination and cited the *Canadian Medical Journal* of November,1869 which published a table showing a sharp drop-off in the number of successful candidates.

The Medical Act of 1869 was a definitive footstep on the path to the goal of a sound professional organization. It laid out clearly legislation of what was necessary to be termed a doctor, the rules of achieving that status and how a medical person could maintain his fitness to practice from the standpoint of the public, the Legislators and his peers. This landmark legislation remained vitually unchanged until the beginning of the 20th century. It was introduced by Parker but the initial thrust had come from Dr. William Marsden of the Quebec Medical Society who attended the 1867 convention of the American Medical Association and noted the rising tide amongst educators to establish one licencing board for all physicians throughout the United States. Subsequent to that the Quebec Medical Association came out strongly for a uniform system of licensure, without consideration of the type of training the candidate had experienced. The *Canada Medical Journal*,[5] explained that "the law under which the profession in Canada is governed is very ineffective and there is no terror to wrong-doers. It is indefinitive and inoperative; a conviction under the laws as it stands for practicing medicine, surgery or midwifery without a licence, is next to impossible; as a result we have throughout our country, and more especially in large cities, all sorts of quacks; Thomsonians, steam doctors, bone setters, eclectic, homeopaths, tumbleties, electricians, vacuo vaccums and phrenologists and every shade and degree of wondermonger all clamoring for public favour and public support. This is not a new story. In 1851 the *Upper Canada Medical Surgical and Physical Science* had laid out the same thoughts in suggesting the formation of a society to govern medical practice."

October 9th, 1867 was a day of gratification for the medical profession. Approximately 150 doctors from the newly created Dominion gathered in Quebec City in response to an invitation put out by the Quebec Medical Society to form a Canadian Medical Association. During the previous summer the Quebec group had passed a series of resolutions referring to the necessity of having a uniform system of granting licences and that degrees from Universities should only have an honorary value and that licences to practice should emanate from a central board. William Aikins and his brother, Moses, were among the delegates from Ontario.

Dr. Sewell, of the Quebec Medical Association, opened the proceedings by expressing his satisfaction that the meeting had a national as well as a scientific importance. He could point to the high status which Medicine held in Great Britain and Ireland as a result of a national medical association. He was able to show how such an organization had contributed to the scientific reputation. He referred to the "improved system of education, both general and professional, which is now insisted upon throughout the world, to the sifting ordeal through which young men have to pass before they are entrusted with the lives of their fellow creatures; to the many points connected with hygiene, so intimately interwoven with the welfare of mankind ...". [6]

The first order of business was to examine and verify the credentials of the delegates and a committee was proposed to carry out the task. However a Sherbrooke representative felt that this was unnecessary and that "all were medical men duly licenced – not homeopaths, etc.". The matter was resolved by asking each participant to register, ensuring that each was a legally qualified medical practitioner. Following that various members were elected from the group and Aikins nominated and strongly supported that Hodder should be the Ontario Vice President, beating out Beaumount. Canniff of Belleville was elected Secretary for Ontario. The evening was spent in social activities which may have set a pattern for the following one hundred and twenty-eight years of science, supper and sobriety.

This was duly marked on October 10th when *The Journal* reported "nine o'clock this morning was the hour named for the Association to re-assemble, but the dissipation of the previous night made many rise somewhat later, it was quite ten o'clock when Dr. C.B. Tupper, took the chair and called the meeting to order."

A committee was struck, including Dr. John H. Sangster of Port Perry and Aikins, to consider the question of preliminary education. Aikins also seconded a motion to establish a uniform system of granting licences to practice medicine, surgery and midwifery in the Dominion, and another motion that a committee be struck to consider the best means of securing the proper registration of licenced practitioners throughout the Dominion.

At this inaugural meeting a resolution was passed adopting a code of ethics parallel to that of the American Medical Association which included accepting a general fee schedule and an interdiction from advertising. A number of physicians from Ontario, including the future President of the Ontario Medical Association, were at the meeting and brought back to Toronto several recommendations with regard to education. These included that there should be a four year course of study, three courses of lectures of nine months duration each at a medical college or school approved by the Association.

However despite the high intentions of the group in the GCMER, there remained the solid presence of those of another persuasion – the homeopaths and eclectics. Any attempt to achieve the goal of a national standard had to face the fact that these groups must be recognized. This was a bitter pill for many of the allopaths, but it was realized pragmatically that the bullet, used so frequently in capital operations, must be bitten by the allopaths. Dr. Horatio Yates of Kingston moved at the meeting in May 1867 that all homeopaths and eclectics should be recognized, but in order to obtain a licence to practice, should conform in all respects to the conditions for allopaths, except in the examination in the practice of physic. This exception was the door-opening key to passage through the House. It accepted that there were alternate methods of medical therapy and ended the years of philosophical controversy. The General Council of Medical Education in 1868 agreed on that basis that the homeopath and eclectic boards would be abolished.

The new Ontario Medical Bill was carried through the Legislature by McGill, successor of Parker who had died from injuries received from falling into a culvert on the Grand Trunk Railway near Guelph. He sustained a fracture of the left femur and it was felt he would recover, but internal injuries resulted in death.

The Act replaced the GCMER by a College of Physicians and Surgeons of Ontario (CPSO). It was explained in *The Globe* on November 27th, 1868 that although the presence of homeopaths and eclectics in the College had not been considered previously, the medical profession now agreed to their entrance. After an examination on all areas which had been ratified by all groups, McGill's placatory presentation convinced the Legislature to pass the new Medical Act which incorporated both homeopathic and eclectic representation on the Council of the College. This added five homeopaths and five eclectic representatives to the organization which was charged with setting the requirements for preliminary education, appointing examiners and determining the duration of the study of the curriculum in Ontario medical colleges. It included a clause which allowed practitioners who had been in Ontario or had practiced for the last six years to be "grandfathered". Most importantly, CPSO was to administer licencing examinations. This initiative by the profession was not embraced full-heartedly by the medical schools which realized that their degrees no longer were a licence to practice, but Aikins was undisturbed as he held office in the College.

There were few allopaths in Upper Canada who felt that there was any place in a medical scheme of things for homeopaths or eclectics. For a reasonable person this prejudice was difficult to understand. Homeopaths had as much of a therapeutical basis for the practice of medicine as did the allopaths. Hahnemann had established a framework which made as much sense as that of the allopaths, with the exception of surgical procedures. The fact that homeopaths used such minute doses of medicine meant that they rarely poisoned their patients as did regular practitioners.

Aikins had never given a second thought to the possibility that some homeopaths might have some merit. He began and remained until the end adamant in opposition, however, there was a strong streak of pragmatism in his prejudice. He knew, largely through consultation with his brother in the Legislature, that unless the homeopaths and eclectics were given place under the Ontario Medical Act, the Bill would never pass. So he agreed to their inclusion, much to the disgust of his fellow practitioners and the *Canada Medical Journal*, which spurred on by Dr. Thomas Agnew of Toronto, strongly condemned members of the Council who had degraded themselves by consenting to become associated with the irregulars. "We recognize this as an indication of a healthy and dignified feeling among our brethen of Ontario, and as a condemnation of the unprofessional conduct of such men as McGill, Clarke, Aikins and their humble followers".[7]

The *Journal* threatened the newly elected members of the College that if "they, or anyone else, manifested a disposition to fraternize with quackery – with men who, while professing to be the followers of Hahnemann, adhere not to his teaching; with Thomsonians who falsely declare they only give vegetable drugs, with any sect to say 'we are not as other men' we promise them the benefit of a notice and a credit of recreancy".

Although Aikins reluctantly agreed to go along with the inclusion of the two sects, there was considerable foot dragging over the years. Dr. Duncan Campbell, the homeopathic representative on the Council, was the target of constant attacks. For example the Education Committee,

which Aikins chaired, heard Campbell move that homeopathic examiners should be used for the subjects of diagnosis and pathology. This
suggested special consideration for the homeopaths and caused outrage by Doctors Agnew, Oldright and others. They did not understand
why homeopathic students should not pass the normal examination.
Campbell, who was a skilled debater, constantly held the threat that if
he did not get his way, he would withdraw from the Council, thus
throwing the whole matter back onto the floor of the Legislature. The
impasse was temporarily shelved with an overwhelming vote against
Campbell's motions. An interesting point was made by Berryman that
he doubted that the Diploma of the CPSO would be recognized in
Great Britain as long as homeopaths were included on the Council or
Examining Board. The English College refused to have anything to do
with homeopaths and expelled any physician who consulted with
them.

The enmity was shared by Campbell. In 1873 he charged that Aikins
had reported to the Legislature that he had paid an account for papers
for the last Council election, when he had failed to do so "... and that
Dr. Aikins by such statements wilfully and fraudulently misled the
parliamentary committee with a possible loss of $6,000.00 etc, etc." He
demanded that Aikins should resign. The charges were investigated by
a committee of the Council which reported that "they are proved to be
entirely without foundation ... that such rash and reckless charges
without mature evidence deserves a censure of this Council". So vehement was Campbell's representation of his group that although he was
Vice-President in 1873, contrary to the normal progression, he was not
elected President for the following.

The discussion regarding medical education and the granting of
licences continued to occupy the CMA for many years. It was debated
hotly at the Annual Meeting in September 1869 when, in particular, the
members from Ontario, felt that the Medical Act in Britain had been
"rotten, useless and worthless". In parallel to these comments, another
committee was charged with preparing a Bill to be submitted to the
Federal Parliament to provide a uniform system of medical education
and examination. Aikins strongly supported this move.

A draft was presented to the Annual Meeting in 1870 which proposed a Council with representation from the Universities, many of

which had no affilitated medical school, and with representation from the profession at large. It was proposed that a Council would appoint three Boards of Examiners. The Council would also determine the "curriculum of professional studies to be pursued by medical students". There was argument for and against the inclusion of homeopathic and eclectic members, and concern that there should be "a central Board, whose examination would like Caesar's wife, be above suspicion". The proposal failed to receive approval.

By 1872 the dissension continued and in particular Ontario, even though there had been some modifications, was not in favour as it was felt that the Ontario Medical Act was sufficient. The matter was laid to rest finally in October of 1874 when the CMA President, Dr. William Marsden, observed that discussion of the Bill had "been suspended like Mohammed's coffin, between heaven and earth, for two years past and will possibly come up for action at this meeting. Doubts had been expressed by lawyers, as well as legislators (and by no less of an authority than Dr. Tupper) of the power of the Parliament of the Dominion to pass any medical act for the whole Dominion, unless and until previous concerted action has been taken by local legislators ... let us carefully avoid all medical legislative action for the present, for to my mind, no greater blunder could be committed in this democratic age, than seeking medical legislation, as the sympathies of the legislators generally, and especially the unscientific who compose the majority, are in favour of quackery and free-trade in medicine."

In addition to his heavy duties as the Dean of TSM and his major commitments to the Methodist Church, Aikins felt that there was more to be done. In 1867 he allowed his name to stand for election to Parliament. He had always had clear sympathies with the Clear Grits and his association with Rolph had strengthened many of these feelings. Even after their break-up, Aikins continued to have a commitment to reform and better government. In this he allied himself with George Brown of *The Globe* who became the leader of the Reformers in the 60s and signed a petition urging Langstaff to stand for office under the Reform banner. Whether the enmity between Brown and Rolph was a factor in Aikins entering the Brownite camp is not certain, however, taking a cue from the laudatory statements in *The Globe*, he ran against James Beaty, who was owner of *The Leader* in the federal riding in east Toronto.

The entry into politics was not a fait accompli. At the nomination meeting of the Reformers of East Toronto on August 21st 1867, he had an opponent, a Mr. Stock. Aikins' nominator claimed that he had commenced practice as a physician early in his life, was now one of the oldest medical practitioners and was lauded for his abilities as a lecturer in the TSM, was a devoted attendant of the hospital and had taken a prominent and active part in all philanthropic and public enterprises. In addition, he was a good speaker, even though, as on the night of his nomination, he had a temporary illness. *The Daily Globe* wrote "Dr. Aikins has always been a Reformer, as well as all of his family, and his clear and manly utterances on the present position of affairs excited the greatest enthusiasm among Reformers who heard him last night. He was cheered to the echo".

In accepting the nomination, Aikins stated that he was and always had been a Reformer. He came of good Reform stock. (He did not mention his severed relationship with the great reformer, John Rolph.)

One of his main platform planks was that he was opposed to a Coalition Government. The election, in which he was running, took place shortly after Confederation and he proposed that "this is a very serious enterprise we are entering upon, of founding a new nation and ... we must have no parties ... perhaps if there may be a national war, we should select men who will support the government". He felt strongly that the problems associated with the founding should not be subject to party politics. He added that he was unable to believe that the government which had been in place since the 1st of July, was sincere. To bolster this opinion he pointed out that when federal government members came to Upper Canada they preached "a gospel of conciliation ... They told us we should put away all thoughts of the past, and that those who hitherto had been opposed, should unite and go forward, arm and arm, for the good of the country ... when they went to the province of Quebec, they had another story altogether. Here, Reformers and Conservatives must be united. There, there could be no union with Reformers". At that time the Liberal party in Lower Canada, which was comprised of the best-educated men in the country, had 30 members in Parliament.

He continued to berate the federal parties that "at the onset of our best new career of existence, we were called upon to resist the grasping at power by those who are not entitled to it". He bemoaned the fact that "we witness season after season, the painful spectacle on our esplanade of train-load after train-load of strong healthy immigrants passing by us to the far west in the United States". He blamed this on the government for not opening new townships for settlement.

An elector interjected from the floor "They want to keep the public lands to make presents to their friends".

Aikins agreed with a mighty "*yes*". He was becoming skilled at working a crowd and had no hesitation in stating he was from East Toronto, lived, worked and intended to say there (Great cheers). He then accused the Government of mis-spending money over the last few years rather than arranging for a better system of settlement of wild lands. Only this would enable Canada to compete with the United States where great tracts of land were available for homesteading.

Another plank in his platform was that there should be an extension of the Common School education, particularly in the areas of mechanical instruction. "Let our boys, in addition to what they are now taught, learn also elementary mechanics and elementary chemistry ... the education of all of our youth should be made to extend into those departments, as well in the branches commonly taught".

The Conservatives nominated the rival candidate, James Gooderham Worts, a distiller and grain merchant. *The Daily Globe*, Friday August 23rd, printed; "... whose whole soul has been, during his entire life, devoted to business, and left no time for other pursuits. He does not speak well in public, and his mind neither works smoothly nor grasps at ease anything beyond the details of trade ... he has no taste for public life and has only been brought out by the Tories because they despise Mr. Beaty". Beaty, who wanted the nomination, claimed that he kept the Conservative Party together and without his aid, it would have been broken and destroyed. He had switched allegiance from Reform to Conservative around 1854 when he was publisher of *The Leader*. That paper was, and continued to be, a harsh cirtic of Aikins.

Prior to election day Aikins spoke at the All Candidates Meeting. He repeated the view that he was "in favour of extending the railroads ... in favour of granting lands to pay for the formation of those railways, without increasing our national debt ... in favour of helping the immigrant, when he came here, until he became familiar with the mode of clearing our forests ... in favour of widening and deepening the St. Lawrence canals, so the ocean vessels, without breaking the bulk in Lower Canada, might come up to our own moorings." He was anxious that banking institutions should not be a monopoly and opposed entrusting any Government with power over the banks of the country.

Aikins took a strong stand against a coalition government which the Tories were advocating. This opposition was based on the fact that in 1864 when coalition was possible, the parties were equally divided. However currently there was no deadlock in government, there was a majority, therefore union towards a single common cause – so-called good government – was not indicated. He charged that not a single member of the Liberal party had been brought into the federal government or into the local government and if the Conservatives were so strong on coalition, then why "had they brought out a Conservative to oppose me? ... he was not sorry to have a true blue Conservative opponent ... like one whose opinions were decisive and positive ... but this gentleman was brought out by the Government to oppose a Reformer in East Toronto ... the Government, in fact, did not seem to care one fig whether the man elected was a Reformer or a Conservative, providing he was bound hand and foot to support a Government about whose policy he knew nothing". He then charged that his opponent had not given him the slightest outline of what the Conservatives proposed to do. "And yet we are now asked to come forward and sustain the same phalanx which composed the backbone of the former bad government and which composes the strength of the administration now." The Reform candidate was able to heap ridicule and sarcasm on his tongue-tied Tony opponent.

Another reason why Aikins opposed the government was that Alexander Tilloch Galt was the head of the finance department. Because his policies were shaped by where his interest lay, namely in Portland, U.S.A. and in the city of Montreal, Galt's policy, Aikins charged, was against Upper Canada. "Did the Conservatives as well as the Reformers in this Assembly have confidence in Mr. Galt as superintendent of the expenditure of $15 or $20 million in the Lower Province on the Inter-Colonial Railway? If, Dr. Aikins were elected, that question would be put to Galt. He could not get over the fact that the head of the finance department was the same gentleman whose previous administration of the finances had been so loudly and so justly complained of, both by Conservative and Reformers ... If ever there was a time in the history of this country, when the representatives of the people should go to parliament free to act independently with reference to the government, it was such a time now. Their representative should be sent unfettered, so as to exercise their best judgement and intellect on the measures that would be brought before them". Touching on one hand the pocket and with the other the heart, Aikins was straddling twin election sure-fires.

He ended his speech by proclaiming his sincerity and altruism, reminding all that he was throwing himself on the intelligent support of the electors of East Toronto. No government influenced or aided him, no moneyed institutions backed him. Once again he was pressing the right levers.

During the campaign he continued to hammer at the fact that when the Conservatives were in the majority, they froze out any Liberal or Reformer appointees. When they were in the minority, they wanted coalition but at the same time to preserve for themselves the key cabinet portfolios. "They resisted representation by population as long as they could, but when they saw they were able to retain their position, they were for it."

During the campaign Aikins demonstrated considerable crowd savvy. Frequently he asked rhetorical questions such as "Was that fair?" The audience responded "No! No! No!" At times he was given "thunderous applause" when he charged the Tories with poor administration of public affairs in the past years. He showed graphically that he had been an active watcher of public affairs. He proclaimed that if he was sent to Ottawa as a member of the House of Commons, he would go there with a strong prejudice against the personnel of that Government. The crowd responded with a "We will send you there". But, in a spirit of fairness, he stated that if "these same men gave good evidence that they were sorry of the past and intended to do better in the future, and brought in good measures, I would not consider myself justified in giving them a factious opposition."

Then he appealed to the taxpayer's purse. He accused the government of extragavent spending. "They press very heavily on the poor man who has to maintain himself and his family on a dollar a day and has to pay for sugar double what he has had to pay previously". Next he attacked his Tory opponent. He was told that the electors of East Toronto should be represented in the House of Commons by a merchant, well they had been represented before now by merchants and if Dr. Aikins did not do more than they had done for the commercial interest of the city, he would have a very easy time of it in Ottawa. This evoked cheers and laughter. He reminded the audience that the elected man should be acquainted with banking interests. The Bank of Montreal, by its influence on the Goverment had got the other banks under its control, and the managers of all of the other banks were now trembling in their shoes. This evoked a hearty "hear, hear". Those who held shares in the Bank of Montreal were getting rich, while those who held shares in other banks found it very different. And who was responsible for this? Mr. A.T. Galt, the present Minister of Finance! "How could anyone have the confidence in what would be the commerical and banking policy of the country, under the control of that gentleman? (A further round of "hear, hear"). "

He ended his speech by re-iterating that he had no Government or Grand Trunk influence on him. It was to the people he appealed for support. This drew loud cheers and a voice "You have the working men at your back". Aikins grabbed the auditory clue and gave thanks to the working men of Toronto for their warm and generous support. He knew he was running in a working class riding.

Election day dawned with *The Daily Globe* editorializing "We expect for Dr. Aikins a great victory in the east end over Mr. Beaty". (Beaty had replaced Worts who withdrew after severe heckling over his owning a financial empire.) On the following day, it was reported polling in the East Toronto was rather slack with less than 1200 votes, however Aikins had a considerable majority. On September 2nd, it was a different story. *The Globe* reported "On Saturday, however, the government adopted the same tactics as in other ridings. Money was freely supplied. Agents of Mr. Beaty were furnished with great rolls of bills, and bought votes at any price which was demanded ... Government went to the Bank of Montreal early in the forenoon and handed a large roll of bills to a leading agent of the party in St. David's Ward, who was waiting outside ... never was there better proof given of party corruption, or more entire disregard for the fitness in the candidate. The work which the coalition of Macdonald, Cartier and Galt, and of Blair, McDougall and Howland is fittingly crowned by the election of Beaty. The friends of Dr. Aikins believe that they constitute a considerable majority of the unpurchasible voters of East Toronto. They were overpowered by Government money and by that alone".

The defeated and disheartened Aikins reserved future politicking to medical and University affairs.

REFERENCES

1. British American Journal, 1, March 1846.
2. Upper Canada Journal 1851; pp 158-168.
3. Mirror of Parliament April 11, 1860.
4 . Daily Globe May 4, 1866.
5. Canada Medical Journal, VI, September 1867; p 140.
6. Ibid 1867; p 170.
7 . Ibid 1869; p 568.

Chapter Six

The Teacher

The threat of cholera was ever-present in the province. The disastrous epidemics of 1832, 1834 and 1849 had sensitized both populace and governors to the necessity of preventing a recurrence. This state of alertness was heightened in 1851 when two American visitors, staying in Montreal, died from cholera on the 25th of August. The disease raged in Montreal until November and killed 271 persons. In 1852 there was a slightly less severe epidemic with lower mortality in Quebec City. Although these episodes were far down the river from Toronto and Kingston, the memories of the spread of the disease at earlier dates meant that something had to be done.

To fight the dread cholera a Board of Health (BofH) was appointed in Toronto but its term was one year and it did not do a great deal to control the scourge. Some garbage was removed, some drains cleared and a palanquin purchased to transport the afflicted to "cholera huts". Even the so-called isolation techniques were ineffective. The muncipalities, which often had to pay for the unproven protective measures, as government grants were insufficient, were not taken with the health edicts from the central authorities. In Toronto, the Executive Council, in a cost-containment effort, ruled that any assistance to immigrants should be on a basic level and only sufficient to prevent any spread of disease. Possibly the most salutary action of the BofH was its resignation, because politicians refused to accept the recommendations of the epidemic experts – the doctors. However the Council had no misgivings because it was obvious that as far as the medical community was concerned, there was no clear idea of contagion. There continued to be musings about miasmata and animalcules, but there was no sense that body fluids and direct contact were the chief avenues of infection. The citizens knew better. They objected violently to having a cholera hospital in their backyard. Even when the BofH pried funds from Toronto to build a centre for the "reception and treatment" of victims in 1849, the putative neighbours put a torch to the structure. Workman, who had worked in a hardware store prior to being appointed chairman of the Board, resigned. His action failed to alter the Tory-mind set of the Council.

During the typhus epidemic in 1847, when the province refused to pay for the care of the victims, citizens opened their purses. They had little choice as a by-law directed that any immigrant landing in Toronto was to "... be forwarded to their intended destination by the very first conveyance". Even though the city survived outbreaks of typhoid, measles, diptheria, small-pox, dysentery, consumption and typhus, no sustained effort was put into establishing a means to combat major epidemics. In those days of non-intrusive government, no common sense revolution preached that money should be spent on a problem that was imported on the backs of immigrants. The by-law passed in 1834 that read:

> No tub shall be removed from any privy or necessary house wihin the City, except between the hours of eleven at night, and three in the morning, from the first day of May to the first day of October under penalty of TWO pounds ten shillings for each offence; nor shall any person under the like penalty empty, cast or lay the contents of any tub or privy, in any Slip or Dock, or in any Street, Lane or Alley or on any public property.

had sunk long ago into the mire around City Hall. It cost too much to enforce such dubious directives, and the doctors failed to convince the electorate of their necessity.

In 1855 the Government of Lower Canada appointed a central BofH which reported to the Legislative Assembly with a series of recommendations that concluded that the "impossibility of preventing the importation of the disease to this country, whose extensive frontier and great and everyday increasing intercourse with the United States, would, were it deemed desirable by the advocates of contagion, render a complete and thorough quarantine impracticable, and many in whose minds the disease bears a contagious nature, are free to admit that its operations are so remote and inscrutable, that rigid quarantine or sanitary cordons would prove no counter-measures towards its introduction to a country so situated."

Although it was argued that sanitary measures, including drainage, sewage and ventilation, seemed to result in a marked and satisfactory result, the Board could not guarantee that this would be sufficient to stay the disease. It ended by recommending limited quarantine, especially of immigrants; sanitary and remedial measures; upgrading the reception area at Gross-Isle, including separate privies for male and female patients (to remove the shared accommodation), and removal of all the non-infected from the cholera sheds. The report ended with a table showing daily mortality and the course of previous epidemics of cholera, which gave a statistical basis for further planning.

Following the lead of its neighbour, Upper Canada, in view of an imminent epidemic in March of 1866, held a medical conference at the Bureau of Agriculture. Aikins was one of the leaders of the event which included Doctors Macdonell, Van Cortland, Dixon, Grant and Tache. This group produced recommendations similar to the Quebec report and stressed cleanliness in the town, with proper drainage of pit latrines and clean water. They also advised that government could not be expected to do all of the work and that prevention was also a matter of people participation. In fact, the report urged that government, in itself, could do only a minimal amount to prevent the spread .

But there was little new in the report as to the causes of the disease. It was agreed that it was contagious and there was need for isolation, but there was no concept of the real causes of the disorder. Although identification had been made of disease vectors in typhoid and jail house (typhus) fever, in Toronto the etiology of cholera remained obscure.

On this round the medical establishment showed that it had learned from previous unsatisfactory outcomes to its advice. In 1861 the newly-formed Toronto Medical-Chirugical Society had prepared the ground with a meeting on sanitation. By 1863 the Canadian Institute provided another platform from which various physicians could present their findings, as well as cite the experiences from England about how to prevent disease. *The Globe*, in 1866, joined the cause with a St. Valentine's day statment:

> Toronto has within its limits low, unventilated, and thickly populated districts, where miserable drainage, bad air, bad water, filth, dirt and refuse of the worst kind predominate, and which are the main causes of epidemic diseases; and in such places if proper precautions are not taken, the mortality will be frightful.

This threat of an epidemic led to the appointment of two medical health officers (MHO), Dr. William Tempest and Dr. Rowell, who were genuinely interested in sanitation. But after they had brought in their ideas on prevention, they were fired and replaced by non-medical inspectors, who could carry out the recommendations at a lower pay-rate. The Toronto physicians received more support when the Canadian Medical Association (CMA) strongly suggested that Ottawa should fund the collection and analysis of mortality statistics, which could be used as a basis for any discussion of the need for a science of sanitation. Eventually, this resulted in Toronto appointing a MHO and the Mowat government establishing a permanent provincial BofH.

In spite of these actions there was still resistance from local politicians because it had not been costed. Curative medicine and hospital assistance were the prime need that they saw in their community, unless there was a raging epidemic. Nevertheless Canniff was appointed MHO in 1883. With his enthusiasm, there was a strong argument established for trunk sewers on the basis of figures that were available from British and American cities showing that the death rate from preventable diseases dropped considerably with adequate sewerage. The capital investment non-plussed aldermen, but Canniff, Aikins and other Toronto MDs combined forces to secure the proposed constructions. To acquire more hard facts and convince the foot-dragging politicians, Canniff marched from house to house to determine disease incidence, prevalence and the state of sanitary conditions such as pure food, water, milk and garbage disposal.

To the taxpaying public, imbued with the philosophy that "One got sick, one died", any presentation of hot facts was greeted with lukewarm appreciation. After all, God's wrath, which resulted in punishment for transgressors, was as strong a disease vector as any unseen germs or dirty water. In time the sanitarians began to change some beliefs and were able, gradually, to persuade the public that prevention was more effective, or at least as effective as a cure. Their case was given a firmer foundation with the link established by microscopy and physiology in 1880s when European investigator Robert Koch, drawing from the work of Pasteur and Carl Rokitansky, published his results.

These findings were in open disagreement with those who considered epidemics the result of the miasmic state, which had been the accepted explanation for the pandemics of cholera which had swept the country over the past fifty years. The conflicting theories were resolved by a third explanation, known as the contingent-contagion school. This proposed that although infectious diseases could be due to contagion, they could not act except in conjunction with other elements such as the state of the atmosphere, condition of the soil or social factors. This conclusion gave many sanitary reformers the tools they needed to legislate cleaning up the environment, eliminating noxious trades and quarantining the sick. Their position was strengthened by the recently published reports by John Simon and John Snow in London in the 1850's. But money continued to be the root of inaction. Although successive MHOs and BofH recommended that the city be cleaned up by removal of waste, their recommendations were spiked by various civic divisions. The Works Department viewed most efforts of the BofH as an intrusion into their territory. It was an open secret that the municipality used various services for patronage appointments.

There were three major areas in the city, which had almost doubled its population in the 1880s, that required remediation. The quality of milk was highly suspect and Canniff and his officers continually pressed for a means to test it. Pasteurization was not being carried out and the only way of measuring quality was by taste. Even though a conscientious inspector was put in charge of the program, the safety level remained low. By 1884, under the Public Health Act, Canniff's span of control was enlarged to ensure the proper disposal of waste products. He began a campaign to improve the quality of sanitation in cow byres, pig styes and other farm areas, many of which were within the city itself. Gooderham and Worts, which operated a large farm in the east end of the city, dumped waste into the bay, close to a water intake. Eventually, this condition was partially repaired, however the water continued, in spite of Canniffs' efforts, to be well below par.

Aikins and the TSM were foremost in establishing courses to teach physicians and, in particular, special interest groups in the field of sanitation. In 1878, lectures in Sanitary Science and Practical Chemistry commenced, including twenty hours on microscopy. At the same time, there was some territorial pushing and pulling as the newly established School of Practical Science became interested in the engineering of water supplies and standards for installation of water closets, which were becoming more common, and felt it had a stake in any public health education. By that time the laboratory and microscope courses were providing the necessary tools.

Charles W. Covernton was one of the major figures in the sanitary movement in Toronto. He had received his medical training in England and after qualifying at the Royal College of Surgeons, in 1836, signed on as ship's surgeon and sailed to Quebec. After establishing a practice in Vittoria, he was elected to the CPSO in 1869. He remained as chairman until 1871 when he took up a teaching position at Trinity. His counterpart, William Oldbright graduated from the TSM and began to teach sanitary science and clinical surgery at that school, later becoming chairman of the Provincial B of H. Covernton set up a special committee to "survey the sanitary measures for maintaining and promoting public health", and sent questionnaires to various people in the province. Dr. Edward Playter was a major figure in preparing the final report which stated that there was public ignorance of sanitary laws and a lack of central supervision. From this, a strong recommendation was made for an extensive educational campaign in schools, public addresses and press stories. A group of Toronto doctors met with Mowat in December.[1] This deputation consisted of John Fullerton of *Canada Lancet*, Oldright, Canniff, Covernton, Playter and W.W. Ogden. Finally in 1882, the government passed an "Act to establish a Provincial Board of Health" and sponsored a sanitary convention in St. Thomas.[2]

Playter was one of the members of this convention. He was a TSM graduate and became editor of the *Sanitary Journal* in 1874 and Parkdale's first MHO. He was instrumental in forming the Canadian Sanitary Association in 1883 and the Toronto Sanitary Association in 1884. Dr. Peter H. Bryce, who graduated in 1888 and did postgraduate work in Edinburgh and Paris returned to the teaching staff of Toronto and was appointed to the Provincial BOH.

All these forces, plus the improvement in curative care, should have resulted in an enhanced curriculum. This was not necessarily the case because the prevention priests were constantly in controversy with the allopathic acolytes over the distribution of academic time and money. Sanitarians were openly hostile to primacy of animal experimentation, bacteriology and immunology. It was logical that if there were more hours per timetable to prevention, there was less need for the healing branch as fewer people became ill. This controversy confronted the Dean on one front, while on the other a territorial thrust by the clinical services was evident.

The anwer from the practising physicians could be heard in the wind. Osler remarked "I retain loud recollections of the buzzing ears of my boyhood from the large doses of quinine administered to us in the summer and autumn". Malaria was endemic in Southern Ontario and until the marshes were drained, during the mosquito season fever was common.[3]

Writing about malaria in 1897, Ross penned

> I know that this little thing
> A million men will say –
> oh death where is thy sting?
> Thy victory, oh grave?[4]

Smallpox was another contagious condition, in spite of Jenner's vaccination regimen. It held a major fear over the public – and the doctor. In 1881 *The Varsity* printed a poem "An Aesculapianarration". It began by warning the reader to have his handkerchief handy, and went on to describe Mary Smith who was a beautiful woman, courted by a physician, Dr. Felix Brown. He had:

> Within the study four degrees engrossed on parchment hung,
> They didn't cost so much, you know, when Felix Brown was young.

He wooed her not only with loving words, but also seduced her with many medical conditions.

He taught her how to diagnose the Rubellaceous Rash,
The moaning in her shell-like ear, the scarcity of cash;
He also showed her how to know, without the slightest doubt,
The symptoms of Pyaemia, of Colic and the Gout ...
He stored her mind with anecdotes and scientific facts
Connected with each malady the human frame contracts;
He taught her how to pull a tooth and lance a little boil,
And treat a burn with cotton-wool and soothing Carron-oil.

This torrid courtship led directly to the altar. However when he turned to face the bride-to-be he noted:

When on his Mary's lineaments a loving glance he cast;
He saw a red eruption there extending from her face,
All o'er her pretty features, to her popliteal space.

Dr. Brown was shocked and exclaimed that "the Smallpox dire has caught you in its clench;"

It was impossible for him to wed with a pock-marked girl, "for all of the Sultan's gold". He explained that he would accept somebody with a timber toe, or a vitreous artificial eye, or want of teeth or scarcity of hair, but "pock-marks are commodities I really cannot bear".

The pre-nuptial arrangement was shattered and he refused to marry. However, traditional Victorian retribution was at hand. The very next morning in the looking-glass he discovered that he had poxes. Many famous doctors were called upon and treated him with leeches, flies, blisters, emetics and Epsom salts. But all efforts were useless and the good doctor died. His creditors sold his corpus to the School of Medicine.

Fortunately, the poet knew enough about medicine to realize that some poxes were transitory, as was the case with Mary Smith. She made a complete recovery "Another man took up with her – a better man than Brown."

But despite the humour, the pox was serious, ever present, awaiting a carrier to start an epidemic. In Ontario in 1876, thirty-one cases were reported, but in 1879 there was an escalation to 195. Aikins brother, Moses, had to cope with an especially virulent epidemic in East Chinquacousy in 1880. Panic followed and hundreds of people descended on his office asking for vaccination. So great was the rush that Moses was allowed to take a medical student from the TSM as an assistant. Figures fluctuated until 1884 when there was a major epidemic in Hungerford township, north of Belleville with 202 cases reported and 45 deaths. This caused great concern in the medical profession, which was heightened the following the year when a major epidemic broke out in Montreal and 3,164 died. The epidemic was not halted until compulsory vaccination began in September. The decision by the city fathers to make this mandatory caused riots and threats to the MOH.

Ontario was able to secure a good supply of vaccine beginning in 1886 when Dr. Alexander Stewart, a graduate of McGill, established a vaccine farm at Palmerston.

While small pox was relatively rare, booze was everywhere. Inebriation was an endemic disorder which many doctors, including Aikins, struggled to control. He was a strict advocate of total abstinence. Other physicians felt temperance was the answer – not only for medical reasons. However, both schools were partially undermined in the 1850s when a study from Europe suggested that alcohol in moderation could do no harm. (It was unrecorded who sponsored the study). The debate continued in the 1860s with the philosophy that alcohol was a stimulant and was required as part of the nourishment process. Workman, who was in charge of the Provincial Asylum in Toronto, stated that "total abstainers should leave the domain of medicine". His successor felt that it could be used in disease with discretion and judgment, however he allowed that "alcohol as a beverage had done incalculable injury to society". This was brought home to the province on March 25th 1880. On that day George Bennett, an employee in *The Globe* office, was discharged by his foreman for "habitual tippling and gross neglect of his duties". He went to the office of the publisher, George Brown for a certificate of character. Bennett insisted that Brown should sign the certificate and when refused, Bennett pulled a pistol from his pocket. Brown attempted to grab the gun which discharged and the ball struck him on the outer side of his left thigh, taking a slanting direction, and passing through four inches below and towards the back of the leg. Brown was finally able to subdue Bennett and received help from other employees in the office. He was able to walk back into his office, apparently not seriously hurt and then went to his home, making light of the wound with the belief that a few days rest and care would set him right.

Initially it was felt that the wound was superficial as it affected only the outer part of the thigh. Aikins was called in consultation immediately. He concurred with Arthur Jukes Johnson that treatment should consist of rest and splinting. However in spite of the optimism of all concerned, daily bulletins were issued. Brown began to have rigors, fevers, disturbance of sleep, loss of appetite and drowsiness. At the end he appeared to have congestion of the lungs with severe difficulty in breathing.

At the post-mortem, performed by Thorburn, Daniel Clark and Aikins, "the skin and other tissues of the lateral aspect of the thigh and down to the muscles were mortified. The inflammation extended from this mortified part ... especially on the inside of the thigh destroying the tissues between the skin and muscles for a distance of nearly 12 inches along the length of the limb and several inches in width, necessitating four or five incisions in order that sloughs could be removed ... there is not the slightest doubt in my own mind that the Honourable George Brown died from the results of a pistol wound he received ...".

Although the full flourishing of physiology did not take place until after Michael Foster published his *Textbook of Physiology* in 1877, students were required to pass examinations for licensure before that time. The 1860 paper at the U of T asked, "Explain the general plan of the circulation and state the causes which assist the heart in its production." However, other tests requested more specific answers, requiring more current knowledge. "State M. Claude Bernards' experiments on the influence of the nervous system on the kidney." This query was drawn from his work published in the *Academy of Science Reports* and his discovery of the vaso-constrictor and dilator nerves and their effect on regulating circulation to the kidney, and other organs in 1858. Similarly, another question to explain the structure and function of the pancreas was based on his discovery of the digestive action of the pancreatic juices, which had appeared in 1859.

When Hodder examined for the symptoms, pathology and treatment of diphtheria in 1860, he did not have a differentiation of the "malignant, ulcerous sore throat, or angina suffocativa", or even an updated description of what Pierre Bretonneau had described originally in 1826. At that time, "diphtheritis" was a special type of inflammation of the mucous membranes. By 1888, C.H. Fagge's *Principles and Practice of Medicine* outlined reports from Germany of finding "bacterium termo" – single micrococci, some dumb-bell shape, in diptheritic patients, and began the process of identifying fevers by their cause, rather than the signs and symptoms. In the same fashion, Hodder had little new to expect when he asked for the "common sequelae of scarlatina." Most of the important works describing the condition were more than fifty years old – such as William Withering or John Fothergill. The cause of scarlet fever, and its sequelae, remained a mystery until the 20th century, although Edward E. Klein suggested that a streptococcyx was responsible for the fever in 1885. So the only answers Hodder received, although very general, still applied in the 90's when bed rest, purgation and occasional brushing of the throat with hydrochloric acid was routine. But by that time, the clinician could comment on albuminaria and a temperature up to 105° F. He might also differentiate the dry, hot skin from that of small pox and the desquamation which occurred 6 to 12 days with scarlet fever.

Diphtheria was a "well characterized, specific, acute, infectious disease, the chief visible lesion of which is a croupous-diphtheritic inflammation of the pharynx and upper air passages." The term croupous and diphtheritic denoted a certain form of inflammation which might occur in the mucous membrane in almost any part of the body. The croupous membrane was a grayish, white, rather firm, elastic material which could be lifted off with comparative ease from the mucous membrane, or it might be a diphtheritic infiltration with necrosis of the tissues. According to Strumpell,[5] "there is no essential difference between croup and diphtheria; diphtheritic inflammation is a severe form of the disease, croup is inflammation, the milder. The fibrous exantha can be formed in those places only where the cause which excites the inflammation kills the epithelium at the same time ... The diphtheritic poison is organized. However it is difficult to demonstrate this because of a great number of diverse micro-organisms, originating in the mouth and throat and really secondary to the diphtheritic process ... Loeffler's bacilli are little cylinders with a peculiar club-like swelling at their ends." They had been identified in croupous membranes and animal inoculations resulted in a disease similar to diphtheria. "They constitute the long-sought diphtheritic poison which is therefore probable, but it is by no means conclusively proved."

The 1878 examinations asked for more in-depth answers. The Surgery paper requested the differentiation of the varieties of erysipelas and treatment. The textbook said that the cutaneous or simple erysipelas generally resolved spontaneously and might leave a large vesicle from effusion of the serum under the cuticle. The cellulocutaneous erysipelas was characterized by a deeper redness which was not dispelled by pressure, as was the case in the cutaneous type. It noted the swelling was "hard, brawny and tense; and the pain is not only burning, but throbbing." The treatment was to diminish inflammatory action and allay local irritation, and was accomplished by emetics and purgatives and in some cases bleeding might be used. In addition, camomile could be used and "bark" (quinine) should be given in all cases as soon as the tongue became clear and the skin moist. Opium was also recommended to allay restlessness.

The examiner also requested the different forms of dislocation of the hip joint and asked whether the treatment would be the same in all types. This question was similar to the one asked thirteen years previously by Aikins when he queried the symptoms, diagnosis and treatment of the two most frequent luxations of the hip joint.

The last question asked for the clinical history and treatment of a case of psoas abscess, which was a recurrent query every ten years. Druitt had looked at this problem in detail and pointed out that it was vital that psoas abscess be distinguished from femoral crural hernia, as each dilated on coughing and diminished when the patient was recumbent. He felt the point of distinction was that since the abscess was generally more external, it fluctuated, it did not feel tympanitic and it was attended by symptoms of disease of the spine.

While the examination in Medicine in 1860 had stressed contagious diseases such as small pox, diphtheria, etc. the third year examination in Medicine in 1876 asked students to define the terms "hypertrophy" and "atrophy" and to state their causes. The paper repeated the question asked sixteen years previously for a description of scarlet fever and also asked for the symptoms of intermittent fever.

Physiology was assuming more importance and vaunted to be the coming wave which would truly lead to a new definition of medicine as a science. The test in 1874 was conducted by Macallum. He asked for a description of the spinal cord with the development of nerve fibres. This determined if the student had appreciated the work of Jacob Clarke who described the structure of the cord in *Phil. Trans., 1851*. Although the question required a keen knowledge of anatomy and histology, there were also some biochemical facts which could be included in the answer – for an Honours citation. In addition to such a specific question, the examiner included some "soft" ones such as "Name the different forces by which blood is circulated." The level of sophistication of the examination in this subject elevated rapidly and in 1884 Charles Sheard asked for the structure of an artery and its function; the function of the bile; and "How do you describe protoplasm?"

The exam question on protoplasm tested the student's knowledge of a war of words that had been waged over the past thirty years. In 1869 Huxley published a paper[6] in which he claimed that a nitrogenous semi-fluid substance called protoplasm, was the "physical basis of life." This material had been identified by the microscope earlier as being common both to plant and animal existence. Two botantists, Hugo von Mohl and Karl von Nageli, had proposed that protoplasm rather than the plant cell, which had been put forward by Matthais Schleiden and Theodor Schwann, was the fundamental unit of being. This challenge suggested that it was the contents, rather than the container, which was responsible for the physiological activities of living bodies. Acting on this proposal Robert Remak in 1852 used the term protoplasm to describe the yolk of an egg, and Huxley's article popularized the hypothesis as being the basis for a theory of living matter.

But the structure, whichever it was, was a background for a much more important concept. The cell theory was based on the conviction that vitalism was the main force of life. This accepted that the living body followed laws different from those which ruled the non-living universe, and permitted that Creation had been a Divine act. The protoplasmic theory, based on Cartesian writings, denied any forces other than those which could be explained mechanically. T.H. Huxley's paper was in keeping with his espousal of Darwin's theory of evolution. In Toronto, Bovell reacted strongly to this claim in his lectures.

The conflict between vitalism and mechanism continued well into the end of the century on both sides of the Atlantic. Some investigators felt that it would be impossible to prove the claims of vitalism, as any chemical analysis of the living cell caused its vital properties to disappear. This advice had a deleterious effect on further investigation by some scientists of the cell theory. It was necessary that a student answering the question have a full grasp of the argument.

Beginning in the 80's, some medical practice was gradually becoming less empirical and more "physiological therapeutic." Henry Croft, the examiner in Chemistry, gave some solid basis to practice when he requested the meaning of the terms "elements, halogens, haloid and ony salts, acids and bases." In addition, he asked the student to "Mention the properties of oxygen, chlorine, sulfur and carbon and how to prepare iodate of potassa, hypochlorite of soda, calomel, corrosive sublimate, arsenate of soda, pure carbonate of lime, and hydrated sesquioxide of iron." This was a beginning of the effort to analyze medications and their specific effect. Many physicians did their own dispensing and students were asked to describe the method of making oxide of antimony and tartar emetic. These were two of the shorter questions on a twelve question examination paper.

The Anatomy examinations required the student to identify and describe several structures, and it was necessary to know the abdomen well to answer the question, "Give the character of cases most favourable to the operation of lithotripsy and lithotomy." These procedures had not changed particularly since Aikins had made his notes during his student days some thirty years earlier, but Henry Bigelow improved on the method of breaking the stone in 1878 by using a stronger crusher while the patient was etherized. In addition, by the 1890's a cystoscope was produced which permitted the operator to see inside the bladder. "How would you treat wounds of the intestines?" suggested that more open abdominal procedures were being done on an elective rather than an emergency basis. And it was necessary that anyone doing surgery should know medicine as the examinee in 1890 was expected to "Give the causes, pathology, symptoms and treatment of acute tetanus."

This disease was attributed to two chief exciting causes. The rheumatic variety resulted from catching cold or getting a thorough wetting or "some similar mishap." The other occurred in persons who had some open wounds, "whether from injury or operation. It is more frequent in times of war and was, in part, due to the unfavourable influence of certain external circumstances, such as bad weather or bad hygienic surroundings."

The first symptom was a feeling of rigidity and tension in the muscles of the face, lower jaw and nape of the neck. This could result in a "sardonic grin," when teeth were firmly pressed together so it becomes impossible to open the mouth. Strumpell explained that the true character of the disease remained a matter of hypothesis. The brain and spinal cord never showed any lesions in tetanus, suggesting that tetanus was a specific infectious disease. He maintained it could be confused with acute meningitis, strychnine poisoning or hydrophobia. No specific treatment was suggested except for large doses of salicylic acid, bromide of potassium and calabar-bean. These remedies diminished the irritability of the nervous centres. Curare was mentioned, but little success had been reported.

In the 90's W.B. Nichol asked the student to give a brief account of the different food poisons, their sources, symptoms and treatments for the Medical Jurisprudence paper. Jurisprudence also dealt with the mentally ill and in one of the questions, asked "Mention the different forms of insanity." His course was one of the main pillars in the courthouse which is why he queried on "The various causes of sudden death and describe the manner of determining to which of them poison is to be attributed."

Nichol also examined in other areas. In Obstetrics he asked "Give the symptoms, diagnosis and treatment of placenta previa", and to describe the symptoms, diagnosis, prognosis, pathology and "treatment of phlegmasia dolens." This post-partum disorder was characterized by rigor and fever, with pain in the groin, hard, hot swelling of the leg and tenderness over the veins and lymphatics. "White leg" was felt to be due to inflammation from poison imbibed by the uterine veins. The recognized treatment was the application of leeches followed by poultices, opiates, turpentine stupes and blisters according to J.G. Swayne's, *Obstetric Aphorisms*, 1867.

There was several changes in the handling of birthing by 1884. A.H. Wright, writing in a *Canadian Practitioner* [7] objected strongly to the usual practice for parturition, which was that a woman should be regarded as a patient who was to undergo a capital operation. Secondly, it was argued that local treatment, in the shape of injections, suppositories, etc., should be carried out during, and subsequent to, labour. He believed that regarding delivery as a capital operation resulted in a great deal of anxiety and tension for the patient. He reported that he had seen several patients who were about to go into labour who were thoroughly upset by the idea that this was an "operation". Actually he had mastered the "watchful waiting" school of thought and reported:

> I attended a lady of refinement, but very hysterical, who was progressing favourly until the seventh day (hospitalization at that time was more leisurely). On visiting, I found her greatly alarmed and excited. She had heard the evening before an exaggerated report of the prevalence of puerperal fever. My assurances had little effect. I took possession of an easy chair, made myself as comfortable as possible, and determined to remain there until I became a master of the situation, although it happened I could ill afford the extra time required ... I made no changes in the medicine, but treated rather the psychical, or mesmeric influences, or whatever you call them, left her in a comfortable frame of mind, and found her in the afternoon comparatively well.

He also objected vigorously to the practice of prophylactic injections which commonly were given every eight hours. Suppositories of cocoa butter, containing three to five grains of iodoform were placed near the os uteri. In his opinion this did absolutely no good whatever. In addition, he argued, injections after delivery were useless.

Instead he insisted on strict surgical cleanliness with instruments being immersed in bichloride of mercury. Regarding forceps he stated "... look upon the forceps as an evil – not to be used unless actually necessary". He did not accept that it was necessary to prevent rupture of the perineum and was quite positive that proper expulsion of the placenta, with subsequent traction of the uterus, was the most important thing to be done after the delivery.

While the practice of Medicine and Surgery showed little change until well into the 90's, Obstetrics and Gynecology experienced considerable improvement. This was seen clearly in the casebook of James F.W. Ross, who maintained records from the early 1870's until 1891. By that time he had recorded 2850 deliveries and was able to characterize the position of the fetus, the results of the delivery and other general observations. In the majority the child was delivered without significant problem, however there were entries, "she died on the 29th from typhoid fever and diarrhea after she had delivered on the 24th without any problem." In a number of cases the delivery was "safe", however the child had been dead in utero. On a first delivery at the age of 20, it was found the mother had syphilis. In some cases although the delivery was safe, the child died within 24 hours.

Ross had studied at Aikins school and on several occasions after joining the staff, referred to the Dean as "Tom". Beginning in 1878 more chloroform was used (Queen Victoria had assented to its use for the birth of her son, Leopold, in 1853) and this could be given after the mother had been in labour for six hours. By 1880 Ross was using chloroform for every third or fourth delivery, particularly with primiparous and by 1890 he was using chloroform routinely.

His casebook, which included histories by his clerk, Herbert A. Bruce, showed meticulous attention to detail: "... Johanna Mcdonald, age 45, married at 16 years of age, has had 13 children, first child born 14 months after marriage, last child about six years later. All the labours were normal, had no medical attendance with any of them. Her menses commenced at the age of 12 were natural and regular until interrupted by a pregnancy and has always had one menstrual period between each of the two successive pregnancies. Her youngest child died when five months old and her present trouble dates from the following month ... One month after the child's death, menstruation recommenced. This differed from all previous periods. It lasted six days, two days longer, the flow very profuse, much blood came away in large clots ... Next period lasted eight days and came on in less than four weeks. For the first year after this time her periods came on regularly between three and four weeks, lasting six to eight days. She complained of pain for the last three years." His diagnosis was myoma of the uterus and he treated the patient with ergotine and noted that there was a vaginal discharge which he examined with microscope, but could not see any bacteria.

Other records included Gussie –. She complained of pain in the lower abdomen, more severe on the left and also pain in the back with radiation down the left side. She began menustrating at twelve years of age, two weeks and seven days apart. She used napkins daily. This became more of a problem by the next year at which time she required five or six napkins. Past history showed some leucorrhea. She was compelled to give up work. The pain decreased and the patient was able to resume work and did not have any trouble until one month before admission, when she had pain in the lower abdomen. Physical examination did not show any abnormalities. She left the hospital in May and returned in July for an abdominal section and the right ovary and tubes were removed. The latter was filled with pus.

Another patient of Bruce's, a Miss C.W., age 30, was complaining of occasional pains in the abdomen which resembled labour pains. She was pregnant and had felt movement for the past few weeks. On examination "stethoscope in vagine heard uterine souffle, but couldn't hear fetal heart." She was discharged without therapy, with a diagnosis of placentia previa.

A woman complained of weakness and burning pains in the head and dizziness with pain in the womb shooting down the legs. This was made worse on defecation. She had had an abscess a year and half previously, which broke and about two quarts came away. Six years previously she had had typhoid fever. Physical examination showed the cervix to be dilated. The uterus was found to be empty and in the second stage of prolapse. The right ovary was normal, and on the left there was a mass of adhesions. Evenutally the remains of an old abscess were discharged.

A thirty-nine old woman was admitted with pain in the back over the previous year and a lump in the left iliac region. On physical examination there was dullness and fluctuations over most of the lower part of the abdomen. The diagnosis was fibromyoma accompanying pregnancy. She was operated on and a drawing in the notebook showed a large tumour. The uterus was pregnant and there was a large edematous myoma bulging up to the left and rising from the left broad ligament.

Ross was an acute observer of his patients and colleagues and printed a poem for a festive occasion:

T.S.M.

OUR GREAT MENAGERIE
The greatest medical show on earth.

Poor Tommy Aikens and his bones,
Put on extensions til he moans
In all hexations use your tape,
Look closely to a change of shape.

There's Henry Wright, who often sighs –
In agony, "O, Lord", he cries,
"You all should learn the normal sounds,
For many a healthy chest abounds."

Shy Ogden with the woman deals,
Dysmennorhea oft he heals,
While Will, his brother, tells us tales,
About the sinful crimes of males.

Next Dr. R., the carver comes
All Darwin's theories he shuns,
But into muscle deep he dives,
And Moses on the same still thrives.

Pale Thorburn in due time appears
And on his brow some herb he wears.
Then Barrett with his taste divine,
Makes cats to bark and frogs to whine.

Then past George Wright, so small in size,
And Dr. Reeve, who cures sore eyes,
MacFarland next, so trim and neat.
Oldright and muse-um complete.

Now near the last the chemist shines
We crave your pardon for our rhymes,
For fear the microscope might prove
That we should all be on the move.[8]

He not only clearly documented his cases, but he also analyzed the results, compared his figures with others, and announced his findings in his inaugural address as President of the Ontario Medical Association in 1904.

"Thanks to the scientific part of our surgical work, the mortality has been diminished after operations and a more conservative attitude has been rendered safe in dealing with severe injuries to limbs and joints. And the period of post-operative convalescence has been shortened. Imagine a mortality of 65% following amputations for injury. How useless this work must have appeared to the surgeons and then compare later statistics of a mortality of 9% for all amputations. The principles of asepticsm and anti-septicsm have saved thousands of lives that must otherwise have been sacrificed. In 1878 when I was a house surgeon at the Toronto General Hospital nearly every patient on whom the operation of ovariotomy was performed died. Patients died after other major operations. It was a pleasant surprise to see a non-suppurating wound and now a cry has been raised that we are doing too much operating work, that we are not leaving enough to nature. Sir William Gull is reported to have said 'nine times out of ten, nature does not want to cure the man. He wants to put him in his coffin'."

But not all practitioners had an equal felicity of modesty. In cases of myoma of the vagina, Ross confessed that he had difficulty in making the diagnosis. "Of course you know no one but an electrician can diagnosis a myoma, they can feel that every time with certainty. All they have to do is pass the finger in the vagina and then can assert that any lump they feel is a myoma and then they start to use electricity. I used electricity on one case myself, until I came to the conclusion that I could not diagnosis fibroid ... tumours may suppurate after electrolytic puncture and they may suppurate when undergoing no treatment ... long ago you see long lists treated with electricity, some will be marked improved and once in a while they will be cured. But if you follow up these cases, you will find them with the tumours still. I do not think that tumours grow any more without electricity than they do with electricity. To look over the literature of the subject would make you tired."

Electricity was the current panacea. In Strumpell's text it was advocated in ascending spinal paralysis, acute bulbar paralysis, sclerosis, trigeminus, anomalies of the sense of smell and taste; articular neuroses, articular rheumatism; asthma, athetosis, cerebral hemmorhage, cerebral syphillis, cerebral brachial neuralgia, chronic poliomyelitis, cutaneous anaesthesia, diabetes, dilation of the stomach, epilepsy, exothalmic goiter and many other diseases, including railroad spine. Many Ontario physicians, and charlatans, became purveyors of sparks and shocks. Langstaff carried an "electric machine" on his house calls, and Dr. Jenny Trout, the first licensed female physician in Canada, operated the "Electro-Therapeutic Institute" in Toronto, a few doors away from Aikins home. She proffered galvanic baths to ladies, while gentlemen could experience the electric belt, for the cure of "weakness", at Dr. D. Sanden's office two blocks away.

"... Are our surgeons a bunch of butchers who cut and hack for the pleasure they may derive from it? Are we doing useless operations that we may pocket the filthy lucre. I hope not. I know this is not the case," continued Ross.

He urged that the use of aseptics must take first place in attacking the evil at it source, with strict attention to the laws of hygiene with regard to space, ventilation and general cleanliness. But it was acknowledged that immunity could be acquired, as Pasteur had shown, from a previous attack of an infective disease. This could lead to the exhaustion of some nutritive material necessary for the growth of the micro-organism. In contradiction to this, C. Metchnickoff felt that immunity was the result of certain changes that imposed upon the living cells, which acted as phagocytes. Others felt that although the phagocytes were important, they played only a secondary role and there was another substance in the blood of immune animals.

The philosophy which drove the enthusiasm for teaching Sanitary Science was the prevention of illness. Covernton, one of the pioneers of the subject, set the Honours examination in 1890. Previous papers had dealt with air and water quality, ventilation, sewage disposal, climatology, hygiene architecture, food values, sleep, exercise and sanitary legislation. This year the question was, "What diseases would you include as causes of a preventible death..Give the reason why certain occupations are classed as unhealthy." If the student had not studied the course text, *Diseases of Modern Life* by Benjamin Moore Richardson, Fellow of the Royal College of Physicians and previously physician to the Royal Infirmary for Diseases of the Chest (London), the answer to the question would have been difficult. Richardson surveyed all of the factors which could cause disease in the occupational area. He was able to identify lead poisoning and other chemical problems associated with industry, based largely on the work of Charles T. Thackrah. But in other areas he was not as acute. "After rigid analysis of all the facts in my possession, I doubt whether smoking can be adduced as a prime cause of diseases of the chest," he stated, based on data collected at the Infirmary. In addition, although he felt that consumptives should not smoke, he did not feel that tobacco was a factor in their disease. "Cancer was present for ages before tobacco was introduced as a luxury," he wrote.

The book was peppered with many historical references to plagues and blights and salted with a wealth of observations of daily life. Drinking tea could cause severe headaches, constipation, deficiency of bilious secretion, flatulence, unsteadiness, feebleness of muscular power and a lowness of spirits. Coffee was less injurious. Foods which were unduly acid caused rheumatic, neuralgic or gouty pain. Impure air, the result of exhalations of carbonic acid from persons in an ill-ventilated room, were dangerous and contributed to disease. The ammonia-sulphur compounds, resulting from exhalation after eating garlic and onions, caused a variety of symptoms. The gas emanating from sewers caused fevers and contagious ophthalmia.

While his description of the conditions associated with parasites and worms was excellent, he had novel explanations for "saline purpura." This was a scurvy-like illness which resulted from modification of the blood from eating highly salted foods. It increased the specific gravity of the blood with a reduction of the size of the corpuscles and resulted in bleeding into the soft tissues. No mention was made of the well-known prevention of scurvy by fresh vegetables.

But in addition to the physical factors that were a hazard to living, there were problems associated with lifestyle. Various occupations were hazardous, particularly brain workers. The higher class men of letters, who thought as they wrote, were subject to great peril. This was particularly so in cases where there was concentration with earnest and prolonged study of one subject. It was potentiated by "writing against time." These problems were clearly demonstrated in different professions. The clerical profession, because it was subject to the strain of visiting and preaching, the monotony of living and the strict, rigid rules of action demanded by society, frequently led to nervous tension manifested by "clergyman's throat" and melancholia. "Unless he belonged to the Church of England, and be blessed, even in her Service with church wardens of unusual and perpetual complacency" he was more subject to physical complaints. The legal profession, which usually laboured in dusty, badly ventilated "dimnest dens" suffered from derangements of the nervous and digestive organs.

Fortunately, medical men were "remarkably free from disease, when all the details of their lives are taken into consideration."

One of his most urgent warnings was that "the idea that excessive physical exercises is a sound means of promoting health is erroneous. Man is not constructed to be a running or a leaping animal like a deer or a cat, and to raise the physical above the mental culture was to return to the shortness and misery of savage life." A propos of this nugget of information he mentioned that the Jewish race had never taken part in sports or heavy physical exercise, had never sought distinction in military prowess and had a life expectancy of 48 years and 9 months compared to that of the Christian of 36 years and 11 months. These figures, drawn from the work of several European scientists, showed that the Saxons and Celts were, by comparison, physically feeble.

In the same year, for the final examination in Medicine, the question was: "In what disease is Pericarditis most likely to be found? Give it's symptoms, prognosis and treatment."

Dr. J.S. Bristowe of St. Thomas' Hospital, London wrote *A Treatise on the Theory and Practice of Medicine,* which was a U of T text. Under causation of pericarditis, he listed extension from an abscess on the muscular walls of the heart or the pleura, the precordium or cellular tissues of the neck or other neighbouring part which was the seat of an inflammation. He also noted local injury such as penetrating wounds of the pericardium or by the rupture of aneurysms, hydatid cysts and the like. The most frequent and important cause of pericarditis "is exposure to cold, especially if that exposure results in the development of rheumatic fever." He added that the inflammation could occur along with chronic albuminuria, scarlatina, chorea, pyaemia and occasionally in connection with tubercular, syphilitic and carcinomatous growths. These symptoms were those commonly associated with the malady in the course of which it arose and in many cases was a mild disorder with few symptoms. In other cases it was a "perilous malady." It was recognized by pericardial friction and some times pain or uneasiness with cardiac dullness. The most severe cases were associated with pain and tenderness about the heart with rapid shallow breathing and, occasionally, severe pain and tenderness. In the wet type, where there was an effusion the friction decreased to reappear with absorption of the fluid. Severe pericarditis ended sooner or later in death. Treatment consisted of abstention from all forms of violent and sustained exertion, avoidance of mental excitement, proper clothing to protect against cold and wholesome, nutritious, but not abundant food. In some cases iron and vegetable tonics were indicated and a combination of digitalis and iron were of value. Diaphoretics, diuretics and purgatives were useful to relieve the overloaded venous system. Shortness of breath or precordial uneasiness could be relieved with squills, ipecacuanha or other expectorants.

Forty years after Aikins had read of Druitt's treatment of hernia, Erichsen, who had been Lister's chief at University College Hospital, London, described several procedures for the treatment of the reducible type. He applied a truss, if the protrusion could be contained within the cavity of the abdomen. However, if the truss was not effective then a radical cure was an operation which was founded on two principles; either causing an "amount of peritonitis" in the sac, and by the tissue reaction to obliterate the opening, or to plug the hernial aperture by "invagination of integumental tissues." The latter could be accomplished by a technique described by C.W. Wutzer, of Bonn, "the patient lying on his back, and the hernia being reduced, the Surgeon pushes his index-finger up the inguinal canal as high as the internal ring, carrying before it a cone of scrotal tissues; a box-wood hollow cylinder, about four inches long, well oiled is then pushed up as the finger is withdrawn, so as to occupy its place in the inguinal canal. A flexible steel needle was then pushed through the shaft of the cylinder to transverse the invaginated scrotum, the hernia sac and the anterior abdominal wall, through which its point protruded. Then a concave box-wood case was passed over the projecting point of the needle and fixed at the other end by a screw apparatus so as to compress the enclosed tissues. This apparatus was left in site for six or eight days. When a discharge was observed, it was withdrawn and the invaginated scrotal plug was held in place by a tightly applied bandage." After a quiet fortnight the patient was allowed to move about wearing a light truss for three to four months. "This method of treatment is easy of execution and appears to be more successful than any that has preceded it," wrote the author. Alternatively, an operation proposed by John Wood of London, consisted of approximating the tendinous structures "forming a boundary of the hernial canal, by the application of a subcutaneous wire tissue through a puncture in the skin". The effect of the suture was to close the external abdominal ring and adhese the posterior and anterior walls of the canal.

The irreducible hernia was usually caused by adhesions and was frequently inflamed and swollen. Erichsen stated that it could be attended by peritonitis and advised the application of leeches to the sac and its neck, the free administration of calomel and opium and the employment of enemata. If the hernia was incarcerated, a "condition principally occurs in old people, from the accumulation of flatus, or of undigested matters such as cherry stones or mustard seeds." Treatment consisted of purgation, ice and then taxis which might be performed under chloroform. With strangulation of the hernia, taxis was to be attempted. Erichsen wrote that it was not infrequently followed by "a sharp attack of peritonitis, which might probably, in some instances, prove fatal." If taxis was not successful, then an operation was necessary. Such confidence had been gained that it was "often regretted performing this operation too late, but never having done it too early." The sac was opened, the stricture divided from within, avoiding injury to the intestines and pushed back into the abdomen gently. A suture or two was then applied through the lips of the wound with a few cross strips of plaster and a pad of lint and a spica bandage to retain proper position."

Although the antiseptic regimen permitted more abdominal procedures, the "radical cure of hernia" was not successful. It was not uncommon for a herniotomy to fail after four years. It was surprising that this state prevailed inasmuch as it was a technical problem that prevented recurrences which should have been realized from anatomical studies. Dr. Edoardo Bassini finally solved the puzzle and reported his technique to the Italian Surgical Society which was published in 1890. He excised the sac, separated the internal oblique and transverse abdominal muscles, restored the internal ring and preserved the canal for the spermatic cord. Although his method was circulated widely, Viennese professors of surgery such as C.A.T. Billroth continued to have a high incidence of recurrence and an unacceptable death rate. By the end of the century Bassini's technique was being used in Toronto.

A common examination question was the care of a fractured humerus, a frequent happening with large numbers of heavy manual labourers. One method was to encircle the humerus with a 3½ inch strip of plaster spread on strong calico, which was then looped around the chest . A second loop was then passed around the arm immediately below the axillary border and fastened at the elbow. It was sometimes necessary to stitch the elements together. A third strip passed around the shoulder obliquely, across the chest and below the elbow of the injured side to overlap for some five to eight inches. Dr. Lewis A. Sayre, of New York, who had devised this treatment, felt that the arm should then be strapped to the chest. Erichsen wrote, as in the case with any other fracture, extreme care should be taken to avoid any shifting of the fragments. He felt that the period of union and fractures of the humerus was about five weeks and the patient should have regained the use of his arm at the end of the seventh week.

The astute candidate would be sure to mention the possibility of using the Aikins splint. This had been devised in the '80s and consisted of a 2 inch strip of hoop iron ("readily procured from an iron monger") which was curved around the leg of a table or a bed post to be fitted to the fractured humerus, or radius. A set of 2 inch bandages was then bound around the arm, drawing it to the chest wall. In humeral fractures this was an early example of the hanging splint.

Although the skill at immobilizing fractures had increased there remained confusion about the microparasitic organs which caused inflammation and gangrene. Osler himself, although he leaned towards specific microbial infection, still allowed many other explanations in his text. The "fungoid" theory provided a good example of persons who were infected with typhoid without ever having seen the bacterium.

"The experience of generations of Surgeons has taught us that although inflammation and suppuration with febrile disturbances result from contact with the raw surface of the wounds, of such simple septic products as must form in all dead tissues or the animal fluid exposed to the ordinary air of a dwelling house, the graver infective processes are of extreme rarity in cases treated in pure air and in the isolation of a private house. On the other hand, it has been established incontestably that if the cubic capacity of a hospital ward be taken, and the rate of ventilation through it determined, a surgeon may with certainty foretell how many suppurating wounds it will require, in the absence of antiseptic treatment, to generate infective disease in it," wrote Erichsen, President of University College, F.R.C.S. of England, and Surgeon to Her Majesty the Queen in the *Science and Art of Surgery*. The first edition appeared in the early 1850's and by 1895, when it was a standard text for Toronto, it was in its 10th edition.

Glanders was described as a poison usually entering into the mucous membrane. It was common among equine animals and could be communicated to man. Farcy was a circumscribed nodule about the size of a pea which might be on a free surface or an indurated ulcer. Farcy-buds were a diffuse inflammation in various stages of degeneration, suppuration and ulceration. In acute glanders inflammatory nodules appeared in the mucous membrane of the nose, frontal sinus and the submaxillary or cervical glands. It was associated with fever and a muco-purulent discharge from the nostrils. Microscopic examination showed slender rods, smaller than B. tuberculosis.

T. Henry Green in his *Introduction to Pathology and Morbid Anatomy*, one of the recommended texts in 1890, wrote that hypertrophy could be the result of increased nutrition, regeneration or tumour formation. In hypertrophy there was no change in the structure of the mother tissue which depended upon an inherited tendency of the cells to grow; the supply of food, and the amount of waste. True hypertrophy was associated with increased function of power, for example, in the hypertrophied heart from valve disease or the kidney after the loss of its fellow. False hypertrophy was due to an overgrowth of an element of an organ often at the expense of another, such as pseudohypertrophy of muscle. In many cases the causes were unknown, but the clearest case was that there was an obvious increase of food. Repeated hyperemia from slight injury caused "the thickened epithelium on the labourers hand, and a corn raised similarly." It was postulated that the enlarged spleen of intermittent fever and the thyroid in endemic goiter was due to an active hyperemia. Muscle contraction against a load gave hypertrophy, however frequent contractions alone were insufficient. Frequent micturition did not lead to hypertrophy of the bladder, though if there was an obstruction to the urinary passage, enlargement resulted.

Excessive waste over repair led to atrophy. A simple atrophy resulted when fat was removed from the cells which diminished in size. All that was necessary for restitution of the tissues was an increase in repair or a diminution of waste. It was recognized that muscles rendered inactive by ankylosis, or chronic diseases of joint, showed atrophy. Diminution in the size and weight of bone was also recognized particularly in elderly females, who were prone to fracture of the femur with slight violence.

Associated with atrophy were degenerative changes by infiltration of various organs with deposition of fat, which might affect the heart, liver or other organs with serious results. Lardaceous degenerative process was characterized by the appearance in the tissues of a colourless, translucent, firm, lardaceous substance resembling boiled bacon or white wax. Chemical analysis showed that affected organs were deficient in potash and phosphatic acid and contained excess soda and chlorine. It was observed that this type of degeneration was more common in males and was usually secondary to a prolonged and profuse suppuration, due possibly to tuberculous disease of the lung, bone, joint or kidney. In his book *General Pathology*, Ernst Ziegler of Freiberg wrote that "lardaceous degeneration was in reality amyloid which is an albuminoid substance, with a glassy, homeogeneous appearance." This answer was accepted, in part, for the 1890 final examination in Medical Pathology.

Calcareous degeneration was an infiltration of tissues by earthy salts deposited from the blood. It was recognized that osseofication was distinct. "Calicification was to be looked upon in many cases as a salutary lesion, the impregnation with calcareous materials preventing subsequent changes in the part. This is especially the case when it occurs in caseous tubercular foci, as it probably imprisons the cause of the disease most effectively."

For a description of inflammation, in response to the 1890 Surgery examination question, it was taught that in most cases the escape of white corpuscles was far in excess of red. If the blood was in motion, most red corpuscles passed through the inflammed area while the stickier, white adhered to the wall. It was realized that in acute suppuration staphylococcus pyogeneous aureus was the common organism. Pus-corpuscles were seen in the presence of suppuration and many of them had the appearance of leucocytes. Causes of inflammation were usually due to some chemical agency, or might be due to exposure to cold or wet, which were termed rheumatic and reflex inflammation. "When a man gets conjunctivitis in the action of a draught through a keyhole upon his eye, the relation between the cause and effect is easily comprehensible." (The author did not explain the circumstances of the posture.) But it was difficult to realize how internal organs, such as the lungs or kidneys, became inflamed, apparently in consequence of cold acting upon the surface of wet feet, etc.

Green relied on the action of leucocytes which ingested cocci. "As to the weapons with which this war is waged, we do not know anything very exact ... it may be that the bacteria, as is usual with living things, secrete or excrete products hostile to their own existence and that these at least accummulate in such quantities as to check the growth of the organism." He then drew attention to the work of Koch which showed that tubercular baccilli were surrounded by "victorous leucocytes blended to form a giant cell." The only practical procedure available was to apply heat as, "the beneficial effect of moist warm in inflammation is due largely to the fact that it increases migration and strengthens the army of leucocytes upon which so much depends."

The wise student knew that there would be an examination question on constipation. The 1891 paper set by Dr. R. James Macallum, suggested that, "The use of drugs for the relief of constipation is capable of division into two parts," and requested the student to discuss. Remedies could be used, first to unload the bowel, which had become filled, and then to influence the intestines and cause evacuation in a normal manner. This was according to the recommended text for the year, *Lectures on the Action of Medicines, being the course of Lectures on Pharmacology and Therapeutics* by T. Lauder Brunton. He was a physician and lecturer to St. Bartholomew's Hospital in London, England and a graduate of Aberdeen and Edinburgh. Brunton began his lectures in 1870 and updated them yearly with numerous publications. He lectured that the condition of the intestines was affected by drugs which influenced either the secretions or the peristaltic movements. Basing his therapy on postmortem findings that the small intestine contained fluid fecal matter, he advocated that any medication which hurried the fluid contents of the stomach and small intestine resulted in diarrhea. If bitartrate of potash was used, the secretions were increased, but there was little influence upon movement. He was able to demonstrate this by putting ligatures around the intestines of an experimental animal. He then injected one loop with bitartrate. Upon sacrificing the animal he showed that there was a tremendous accumulation of fluid in that loop, but not in the adjacent loops. Brunton combined this finding with a dose of jalap, which affected peristaltic movements to produce an effective purgative. From these experiments he urged that constipation was either a problem in the intestines, with a failure to secrete from the mucous membrane and induce peristaltic movement, or a nervous disturbance which caused a slowing down of all vital elimination factors.

From this he taught prescribing principles of stimulation of mucous membrane or of movement of the intestines. He thought much of the underlying problem with constipation was because western man ate bread which was made with fine wheat flour. The constipation caused by lack of stimulation to the intestines could result in typhlitis, peritonitis, or even death. In general the prescription to prevent this was to eat whole meal bread on the basis that it was essentially indigestible and provided a mechanical stimulus to the mucous membrane. Other stimuli were in the small seeds of figs, raw apples, or tomatoes. In addition marmalade, which had small traces of orange peel and sugar was excellent to promote normal bowel movement. The sugar in marmalade or other fruit jellies did not provide the mechanical stimulus, but did stimulate the mucous membranes.

The nervous disturbances were best relieved by a regular regimen of a set time per day for evacuations, and could also be promoted by smoking a pipeful of tobacco after breakfast.

He separated medications into laxatives and purgatives. Laxatives led to more frequent formed stools. Medication for this was a mixture of sulphur and cream of tartar. The sulphur frequently caused flatus and he analogized its action as similar to a child's popgun. When the gas is under pressure, it explodes expelling the cork. Five grains of sulphur was the standard dosage. If this was not effective then senna was used or common licorice powder, which contained senna and fennel.

The next most powerful laxative was cascara sagrada, which came from the bark of a tree, native to New Mexico. Other laxatives could be compound rhubarb pill or croton oil. The last named was a dangerous medication unless the exact dose of a half to one minin was used. Brunton warned his students that, "The examination of medical students is not to find out what they do not know, but to find out what they do know, and ascertain whether they know enough to pass safely. If a man is not safe, he is rejected."

The profession, while agreeing that constipation was not a disease, was united in the necessity of regularity. It was vital to remove fecal substances mouldering in the intestines, otherwise the poisonous products of decomposition were absorbed. "We all know what a general dread is felt of sewer gas, and when anybody gets ill in a house, one always inquires; 'Are the drains in order?' But there are many people who carry a cesspool inside themselves. They do not get their bowels open as they ought to do, the fecal mass undergoes decomposition in their intestines, and then they wonder what is the matter with them."

While laxatives were sufficient most of the time, it was frequently necessary to use a purgative. This produced a liquid stool. Their action was confined to the muscular fibre of the intestines generally, and did not causes secretions from the mucous membrane. In order to induce an evacuation, croton oil was available or alternatively jalap and scammony which acted as hydragogues, could be used.

It was theorized that this type of drastic purgation drained blood from the brain to the intestines. It was seen as bloodletting into the abdomen and could be used to relieve headaches, on occasion.

All kinds of evil had been attributed to poisoning by resorption of noxious matters from the feces, stated Osler, but added "it is not likely that this takes place to any extent." In particular he suggested that chlorosis, which was attributed to fecal poisoning, was not always associated with constipation. He offered the logical argument, "if due to this cause, chlorosis, a common diagnosis in young women characterized by anemia, irregular menses and a pale greenish complexion should be in men, women and children, the most common of all disorders." He felt that the treatment of constipation was to develop systematic habits, particularly in the young. In older people, where the muscles were pendulous, he suggested the support of a bandage and also "a metal ball weighing four to six pounds, which may be rolled over the abdomen every morning for five to ten minutes." Alternatively, an enema with injections of soapy water or other various drugs could be used.

But neither Osler nor the other scientific practitioners could alter practice peremptorily. Dr. R.W. Bruce Smith, President of the Ontario Medical Association in 1895 claimed that;

> Professional interest has been considerably awakened in the subject of auto-intoxication. Putrefactive processes in the intestinal canal ... play an important part in many diseases processes until lately unknown.

The theme was recurrent from Egyptian days, through Greek and Roman history and into the middle ages. It was quite obvious to the olfactory senses that there was putrefaction in the bowels, and the modern science of the last half of the century demonstrated clearly that it was absorbed into the body. In 1869, the German physiologist Hermann Senator, published an article in the prestigious *Berlin Clinical Journal* that harmful toxins were produced by putrefaction of protein in the intestines. His article was followed by clinical investigation which established that the ingestion of tyrosine was followed by phenol excretion in the urine. This meant that certain elements were absorbed and caused a "ptomaine" poisoning which became a catch-all cause for the various diseases which resulted from constipation. Chlorosis, tuberculosis and other disorders were attributed to the auto-intoxication which resulted from stagnant feces. These concepts were given great support by Elia Metchnikoff, one of the foremost researchers in Germany. He predicated his thoughts on the known anatomical fact that man inherited useless rudimentary organs, which "fully developed may be useless." This meant the large intestine which served as a reservoir for waste. The weight of his argument was reinforced by his work in other areas such as the experimental transmission of syphilis from man to animal, his classic description of inflammation in 1892, and his demonstration of phagocytosis by leukocytes in 1874. For these, and other discoveries, he received a Nobel Prize in 1908.

Metchnikoff, in his zeal to blame the large intestines for many diseases, postulated and was able to show by a shaky statistical graph, that longevity in animals varied inversely as the length of their intestines. To prevent morbidity in man, he did an international survey and determined that drinking sour milk was one of the best means of prolonging life through reducing the putrefaction processes. Milk contained a bacillus which was noted, in one London publication, to have swept the nation into a frenzy of sour milk feeding, resulting in "monopolizing the conversation at the dinner tables of the great."

So messianic was Metchnikoff that he attracted an acolyte, Sir William Arbuthnot Lane, to the crusade. He was an expert surgeon who had developed many techniques in orthopaedic surgery including plating and screwing fractures, and had an impeccable record of the no-touch aseptic method in surgery. He became converted to the theory that disease skulked in the great intestine and began to do prophylactic removals of the iliosigmoid area in 1893. He felt that the design of the intestines was not suitable for the upright position. This caused the viscera to fall into the abdomen causing adhesions to form along the lines of resistance which obstructed fecal flow. Lane argued that the current habit of one bowel movement daily, with a lack of adequate roughage, led to a delay causing mechanical symptoms, ulceration of the stomach, skin changes, low blood pressure, loss of fat, stupidity, depression, tuberculosis and thyroid (indirectly). He also suggested rheumatoid arthritis could be prevented by an iliosigmoidotomy. Later, he carried out hundreds of total colectomies for the treatment of "chronic intestinal stasis." His success in performing this procedure was remarkable, particularly in view of the fact that frequently the operation was performed after appendectomies and other surgical procedures had been performed at a previous operation. So popular was his diagnostic ability, that it earned the title of "Lane's disease."

Gout was clearly described by Osler as a nutritional disorder associated with an excessive formation of uric acid. He quoted freely from the work of Sir Albert Garrod who had published a landmark study of the disorder in 1859. However, Osler also included the "nervous theory" that had been advocated by Sir Dyce Duckworth. This theory postulated that the gouty diathesis was expressed as a neurosis of the nerve centres associated with a peculiar incapacity for normal elaboration within the whole body of food, whereby excess uric acid was formed. Osler's text also mentioned Wilhelm Ebstein's theory, who felt that it was a nutritive tissue disturbance which caused necrosis and uric acid deposition.

Each of these theories showed an excessive uric acid demonstrated by immersing a thread in some of the serum from a blister. Within a few hours, this showed an incrustation of uric acid however, Osler acknowledged, that this was not peculiar to gout, but also occurred in leukemia and chlorosis. Changes in the kidney cortex and medulla, and bony changes particularly at the metatarsal-phalangeal joint of the big toe, were hallmarks. His suggested treatment was a modified nitrogenous diet with limited starchy and saccharine food. Lobsters and crabs were "to be eschewed." He approved of physical therapy including massage and heat and also a mercurial purge at the onset. Tincture of colchicium could be given until it had relieved the pain.

In his inaugural address to the Toronto Medical Society, James F.W. Ross said that the meetings would include papers on the indications for operations in spinal lesions; the methods of diagnosis of spinal diseases; the differential diagnosis of disease of the stomach with a demonstration of the chemical test recently introduced; summer diarrheas, their cause and treatment; the diagnosis of eruptive diseases of childhood; some important points in oral surgery; lessons in the post-mortem room; gonnorhea and the treatment of congenital club foot. He proposed a "paper" night and a pathological night alternatively.

"The system adopted for the support of our educational institutions is a bad one. The German system has done so much for Germany, it could be adopted with very little increased expenditure to the country if the Government would reduce the number of remunerative sinecures given to political trimmers; such men feed on our taxes and give us nothing in return," he stated.

Later, during a lecture on carcinoma of the breast, he pointed out that there were two types, scirrhous and encephaloid. He quoted Aikins' old teacher, the eminent Samuel D. Gross, that the average age of occurence usually was 40 and was most frequent in married women, which may have been due to the many changes in the breast with nursing. The production of cancer of the breast from eczema of the nipple was exactly identical to cancer below the jaw of a smoker's lip. Heredity was a factor in one third of the cases, usually going back one generation. If unoperated, scirrhous usually resulted in death in four years and encephaloid in two. However, in two cases, the patient had lived for 15 and 19 years. He disagreed that the axillary glands were affected because in the upper portion of the breast, the lymphatics ran to glands in the neck.

"There is no doubt that operation will prolong the life of a patient if the growth can be removed in an early period before much ulceration of the skin takes place," he lectured. If the skin was not adherent, life was prolonged to a greater extent. "Given a lump in the breast, the safest and simplest thing to do is to cut into it ... if it is a fatty tumour, it is far better out, if it is a fibroid, it is much better out." His method for the ideal operation was "the patient is lying on her back, I pull up the flap and let a little blood run into it and I watch where the deepest place in the pool is and I select that point for a puncture. I then take a knife and stick it in, and insert the long drainage tube."

In describing typhoid fever, Osler quoted a report from Graham which noted that of 1381 cases treated during 12 years at the Toronto General Hospital, 761 occurred during August, September and October. This was similar to the observations at the Montreal General Hospital and resulted in the term "autumnal fever." The disease was marked by a short, thick, motile bacilli with rounded ends which could be grown on nutritive media and fulfilled two requirements of Koch's law but could not cause the disease in animals. By the time of the first edition of Osler's text in 1892, infection by contaminated water was accepted as the most common mode of contagion.

While discussing general management, he complained that the profession was long in learning that typhoid was not a disease to be treated by medicines. "Careful nursing and a regulated diet are the essentials in the majority of the cases." With the fever, Osler felt "no treatment so efficacious as that by cold water ... the patient is placed in a bath at 70 degrees F ... and remains from 15 to 20 minutes ... the patient often complains bitterly when in the bath, shivering and blueness are almost a constant sequence ... I sympathize with those who designate it as entirely barbarous." In general he disagreed with medications such as carbonic acid, iodine and mercurials, but did agree that a starch and opium enema could be given for the diarrhea or possibly Dover's powder. A description of the treatment was called for in the final year medicine examination of 1895.

He described dysentry as one of the four great epidemic diseases of the world. In the tropics it destroyed more lives than cholera and had been more fatal to armies than powder and shot. He differentiated the clinical forms into acute catarrhal, amoebic, diphtheritic and chronic. While he acknowledged that some medications such as opium, corrosive sublimate and bismuth could be effective, he felt that treatment by topical applications was by far the most rational plan. This consisted of cocaine suppositories to reduce the irritability of the rectum, then injection of warm water into the bowel with various astringents such as alum, acetate of lead and nitrate of silver.

With diabetes, Osler admitted "we ignore the nature of the disease." However, he did recognize that whenever the sugar in the systemic blood exceeded a definite amount it was discharged producing glycosuria. He theorized that the condition could be induced by ingestion of large qualities of carbohydrates; disturbance of liver function or defective assimilation of glucose in the system. Under treatment he recommended, in addition to personal hygiene and eating food of easy digestion, that carbohydrates should be reduced to a minimum. "Opium alone stands the test of experience as a remedy capable of limiting the progress of the disease."

Forty years after Aikins and his colleagues, had undertaken to raise the level of medical knowledge there were some examples of improvement. Evidence of such changes was seen in the reports of the Toronto Medical Society which was formed in 1888 and included most of the prominent teachers in the city, as well as some family practitioners. One of the most impressive features was that the Society met on a regular basis for discussion of cases, illustrating a maturation of the profession. The meetings were vigorous. Although in many cases members exhibited a lack of understanding of basic disease processes, this was the beginning of peer evaluation.

In February of 1888 Dr. Machell gave a history of a nine year old child who had been "afflicted with eruptions of a pustular nature, scabby and bleeding in some places with serpiginous edges. The surrounding skin was thickened and the patches were itchy and gave a watery discharge." He also noted that these tended to occur in the flexures of the arms, the hollow of the back, the inner aspect of the thighs and behind the knees. The diagnosis of eczema was made and he was treated with zinc ointment with improvement.

Although a known entity, such as atopic dermatitis had been

described clearly by Robert Willan in the early part of the 19th century, it was not considered by the group.

Another skin problem, reported by Dr. Carveth, had extensive ulceration of the nose, cheek and throat. Discussion followed the presentation as to whether this was a case of syphilis or rodent ulcer. It was recalled that the patient had been seen six months previously and had "progressed favourably" under specific treatment. No microscopic findings resulting from a skin biopsy were provided to help delineate between the diagnoses. But, at least a differential diagnosis was considered.

While it was possible to diagnose tinea without great argument, the treatment was varied. Machell, who saw a number of skin cases, washed the head with soap and water and then applied raw turpentine which was rubbed in with a flannel until there was a "stinging pain". Then mercury was applied to the region. He opined that turpentine destroyed the bacilli with recovery in a few days. In fact, this was a traditional remedy, emperically proven, but lacking any professional component.

It was not possible at that time for these physicians to use microscopic examination for the identification of various bacteria. Fernand Cohn (in Europe had published papers on the fixing and dyeing of bacterial films on cover slips for positive identification. In addition Karl Weigert had demonstrated the use of anilin dyes to stain microscopic preparations. Many of these discoveries were published by R. Koch in 1878 when he described the etiology of traumatic infectious diseases with an identification program for six different kinds of surgical infections. However, these techniques did not reach Toronto for some years later.

Meanwhile Dr. Cuthbertson in 1888 asked the advice of his colleagues on what should be done with a testicle which had become enlarged with the formation of an abscess which ruptured. He stated that there was a "marked tubercular history which was obtained from the patient." His colleagues favoured the removal of the testicle, although a clear identification of the causative factor had not been given. It was always easier to remove the offending organ.

Tubercular lesions were commonly considered. Dr. Spencer presented a case of a previously healthy young male of 14 years of age who developed a dull appearance and began to walk in a stooping posture. Upon occasion he fell forward suddenly, frequently injuring himself. His memory was "fair" and he could write, but could not read, which was a change from his previous ability. He did not speak spontaneously and answered questions in a "stupid, abrupt way." His pupils were dilated, and did not respond to light. His taste was defective and there was no appetite. "Occasionally he takes wildish fits, but generally is quiet, well behaved and cleanly. The fingers and toes twitch occasionally ... the gait was shuffling, the left leg being thrown out. The patellar reflex was present in the right leg, absent in the left. When the eyes were shut and knees together, he swayed a little, but maintained his equilibrium and could turn around." The summary of his diagnosis was "believed to be tubercular."

While it is quite possible that this was a brain abscess , it appears that "tubercular" was being used as a general label without any specificity. Given the ubiquity of the tubercle bacillus, it was reasonable to reach this conclusion, but no opinions were given as to the site of the lesion, although the central nervous system had been well mapped.

The procedure of lithotomy had changed considerably over the preceding 40 years. Cameron, in discussing suprapubic lithotomy favoured the "Paterson method" of injecting at least 12 ounces of fluid into the bladder and 10 ounces into the rectum so as to raise the peritoneum out of the way. He followed the procedure developed in Edinburgh of elevating the stone with a lithotrite and bringing it against the vessel wall, and then cutting down upon the stone. He found that hemorrhage frequently resulted. He advised not to suture the wall of the bladder to that of the abdomen. Cameron's procedure was criticized by Dr. Atterton who argued that the perineal operation would eventually be the favourite, especially in children. The procedure appeared to be carried out often with children as it was reported that incontinence commonly resulted in the post-operative state.

Cameron, who was becoming acknowledged as one of the chief surgeons of the province, demonstrated an ideal example of case history and pathological findings. "A 19 year old servant girl, while washing up after dinner, was seized with an agonizing abdominal pain followed by vomiting. The pain radiating below the shoulder blade. She collapsed and died 21 hours after, during which time she vomited frothy stomach contents tinged with blood. There had been no history of gastric trouble or vomiting. An autopsy found that the stomach had a round perforating ulcer on the anterior surface and the abdominal cavity was distended with fluid."

The ability, and desire, to have a post-mortem showed clear evidence of a self-validation process. Theodor Billroth (1829-1894) had described resection of the stomach in the 1870s, but Cameron had no diagnostic tools to make a sound diagnosis, which was mandatory before an abdominal procedure.

But at other times there was not a clear connection between the diagnosis and the history. A Dr. Smith presented a case of a 22 year old male who had struck his elbow at nine years. The following day he experienced pain and an abscess appeared over the elbow four years later. He continued to have trouble with the forearm, characterized by the sudden onset of pain without any particular further trauma. The elbow would become swollen which could last for a week and then disappear without any treatment. He had ten such attacks in the two years previously. About the beginning of that time a lump had appeared over the elbow which began "to soften." However he was able to play baseball all summer. After he stopped playing, the lump reappeared.

No diagnosis was made, and until the availability of x-ray, ten years later, it is doubtful that there could be a clearer understanding of the pathology. Alternately, incision and drainage of the lesion, with microscopic examination might have been of use. Unfortunately, the temperature, tenderness and transillumination were unrecorded.

Graham related a case of ataxic paraplegia. "F.T. age 36, married, after birth of first child was troubled with headache from time to time at short intervals. Two months before second confinement it almost completely disappeared. Four months ago she noticed a pain in her back and limbs after exertion, gradually lost power in limbs of left side, pain in pelvis shooting down thighs, patellar tendon reflex increased, cannot stand steady or carry forefinger of left hand to nose with eyes closed, spastic gait, marked ankle clonus, numbness in upper extremity, double sight left pupil does not respond to light as promptly as the right, ophthalmoscope shows atrophy of optic disc on left side and commencing atrophy on right. Treatment, direct galvanism."

This was an excellent description of disseminated sclerosis which had been described by Jean Cruveilhier (1791-1874) in his text on pathological anatomy in 1842. Further to that Jean Charot described the histology of sclerose en plaque in 1880. However the diagnosis was not mentioned in this case and the treatment had no empirical or scientific basis.

Dr. N.A. Powell presented a "specimen of serofibrinous fluid removed by aspiration from the left pleural cavity of a lady 30 years old. The entire axillary and infra-axillary region was flat upon percussion while marked dullness extended up to the third rib in front ... As usual, this rose highest toward the axilla, reaching there a point three inches higher than it did near the spine. Only a small quantity of fluid was removed, the object being to reduce the intra-thoracic pressure and promote absorption. In the practice of one large hospital, not situated in Toronto, in nearly every case when aspiration was performed in the treatment of sub-acute pleurisy with effusion, empyema developed. After a time, the plan of purchasing a new needle for each operation was adopted, and the series of cases of empyema came suddenly to an end. The speaker had not himself seen empyema follow thoracentesis. He was in the habit of sterilizing his aspirator needles by scrubbing them in hot water with green soap, boiling them in a closely covered vessel after each use and also before they were used again, and finally just as aspiration was about to be done, the needle selected was dipped into alcohol and flamed in a spirit lamp. So treated they were reliably aseptic, inside as well as outside, would stand any gelatin culture test, and could be depended upon not to convey germs and cause purulent decomposition in fluids contained within any of the serous cavities of the body."

This was a classic description of tubercular pleurisy, with a splendid physical examination. In addition to showing the lack of specific therapy, it revealed an appalling infection rate following thoracentesis – and an excellent result in Powell's hands.

REFERENCES

1. The Mail, December 31, 1879.
2. Canadian Journal of Medical Science, 7, 1882; pp 344–347.
3. Osler, W. Homebred Malaria. Lancet 2,1917; p 621.
4. Ross, R. Memoirs, London 1923; p 226.

5. Strumpell, E.A. *A Textbook of Medicine*; 1883.

6. Huxley, T.H. On the Physical Basis of Life, The Fortnightly Review, N.S.,1869; pp129-145.

7. Canadian Practitioner Volume IX, 1894; p 229.

8. Ross, James. Book of Obstetrics, no. 2, 1877 and 1890-1893. Robarts Library.

Chapter Seven

The Surgeon

"... there was a board which was strewed with glittering instruments ... Two young men lounged in front of this; one threading needles, the other doing something to a brass coffee-pot-like thing which hissed out puffs of steam ... 'it's Lister's antiseptic spray, you know, and Archer's one of the carbolic acid men. Hays is the leader of the cleanliness-and-cold-water-school, and all hate each other like poison'" – Sir Arthur Conan Doyle wrote in *Round the red lamp; being facts and fancies of medical life.* (1894).[1] This controversy was the initial step by surgeons such as James Syme, Robert Lawson Tait and Thomas Spencer Wells towards controlling sepsis in the mid-century.

In 1867, Joseph Lister announced a radical theory of the causes of wound putrefaction. He wrote that microscopic organisms in the air – germs – entered a wound with resultant putrefaction and possibly death. He proposed that the use of carbolic acid and a regimen of bandaging and care would prevent this process.

His paper, which appeared in *The Lancet,* gave acknowledgment to the research of Louis Pasteur, who had demonstrated that wound infection was not the result of spontaneous generation, which had been the accepted view, but because of air-borne particles. There had been controversy during the 1860's as to whether disease was caused by a fermentation of yeasts, as suggested by Liebig or was the result of the action of toxins secreted in the body which acted on albumen. Some researchers invoked various non-organic particles, but Lister, drawing on the work of John Burdon Sanderson of London, concluded and showed that germs caused putrefaction.

... bearing in the mind that it is from the vitality of the atmospheric particles that all the mischief arises, it appears that all that is requisite is to dress the wound with some material capable of killing these septic germs, provided that any substance can be found reliable for this purpose, yet not too potent as a caustic.

Drawing on his experience Lister deduced that carbolic acid facilitated wound healing and did not cause any objectionable side effects. He chose carbolic because it had been used and found effective in combatting the odour of sewage. His experience, and his nose, told him that infection had a peculiar stench. It wasn't until much later that he was able to acknowledge the "four horsemen of infection – septicaemia, pyaemia, hospital gangrene and erysipelas". The last named was odourless.

His method was to apply a piece of acid-soaked lint to a wound, then a layer of lint in a watery solution of carbolic and change this dressing in five days time, using another soaked in carbolic acid and olive oil. He found that over six weeks a wound, or fractured bone, healed without complications. To prevent the acid from evaporating through the dressing, he applied a cover of sheet-tin. Over the next few years he modified his technique and at one time used carbolic acid in linseed oil mixed with carbonate of lime which formed a paste, or sealed the dressing with a "light form of Macintosh termed 'hat-lining' by the India rubber dealers". The whole thrust of his regimen was to remove the germs that were in the wound and prevent others, present in the air, from entering. In 1871 he introduced a carbolic acid spray which was used in the operating room to kill any airborne germs.

His initial papers caused great excitement in the medical world but there was considerable scepticsm by many scientists. One of the main contradictions was why all wounds did not putrefy – or how did Pasteur or Lister, explain why some wounds healed without problem. In addition, carrying the concept to the extreme, if germs were that common, how could we continue to survive? This dissension created two opposing, vehement camps. Some surgeons argued suppuration was common to all wounds and was part of normal healing, Galen had named it "laudable pus". Even into the '80s some surgeons believed that under the layer of laudable pus, the wound condition was satisfactory.

Although there were no research giants in Canada to match or even emulate the wealth of talent in Britain or Europe, it was perfectly reasonable to read the literature and try the theories. Hodder reported in 1868 that he had removed a tumour and then wiped the cut surfaces with carbolic acid and oil and had applied a strip of lint soaked in carbolic acid and oil over the cut edges.[2] While he may have been attempting to follow the Listerian regimen, James Connor pointed out that there was little resemblance to the antiseptic system of surgery which Lister espoused.[3] This report was one of many from across Canada from surgeons who were applying part, or all, of the Listerian protocol. Dr. Archibald E. Malloch wrote,[4] while Professor of Anatomy at the TSM, the use of the exact technique he had learned while a dresser for Lister at the Royal Infirmary in Glasgow from 1865–7. Aikins, while travelling in England with his wife in July 1873, was able to see the procedure at first hand. During that year Dr. Fred Le Maitrie Grasett of Hamilton was Lister's clerk, before returning to Toronto, to write a description of the technique. [5]

However, like many of his colleagues, Aikins had his own interpretation. In 1882 when reporting on the removal of an epithelioma of the tongue by galvano-cautery, *The Canadian Journal of Medical Science* wrote that "the posterior two-thirds on the left were removed with cautery wires." The operation was tedious (occupying about three hours) and it was found very difficult to get well behind the growth. There was little or no bleeding and no mishap of any description. The after treatment consisted simply in washing the mouth with carbolized water. In a follow-up examination performed four months later, the condition of his mouth was found to be most satisfactory in every respect. "The wound was thoroughly healed and looked perfectly healthy".

Another case reported in the same year, was of a 49 year old male who had an attack of jaundice, accompanied with symptoms of gallstone. He had begun having night sweats two months earlier but by the end of 1881 was having increasing weakness with loss of weight. At that time he began complaining of severe pain in the left abdomen. The night sweats increased, Aikins detected a prominent swelling, tympanitic and "evidently pointing" about 1½ inches to the left of the umbilicus. "Aspiration was accordingly performed under the carbolic spray, and from 10 to 12 ounces of extremely foetid, thick, and grayish pus were withdrawn, preceded by a quantity of foetid gas ... the sac was subsequently washed out with carbolic solution and this was repeated daily ... in the course of ten days a cessation and improvement was observed but another purulent collection was taking place a little below the point of the xiphoid appendix on the left side. This was evacuated and improvement set in with daily injections ... since the first aspiration there was a regular discharge of about a drachm of matter which still continues up to the 119th day, the time of writing. The patient has never been subjected to any tropical influence whatever, but he had always been a pretty free liver".

While a truncated Lister routine was reported in 1882, in 1872 two operations failed to mention any use of carbolic acid, pressure bandages, etc.

Dr. Herbert A. Bruce wrote that he had assisted Aikins in an operation in 1891:

> The surgeon removed his coat, turned up the cuffs of his shirt, washed his hands and dipped them in a solution of bichloride, put his instruments in a solution of carbolic acid and after a few minutes transferred them to a dish of boiled water. He then proceeded to operate ... he closed the skin and covered it with a dressing. Although observing some of the Listerian methods of antiseptis, whenever Dr. Aikins wanted to 'park' his knife, he put it between his teeth.[6]

The operation was lengthy and while Dr. H. Wilberforce Aikins kept the patient anaesthesized with ether, the remainder of the operating team had an hour long lunch. In all the procedure lasted 5½ hours (excluding the luncheon break).

But, as with any innovation in medicine, there were some who reported to the contrary. Canniff, who was now Dean of the Victoria Medical College, rejected Lister's assumptions of the causes of wound problems on the basis that healing occurred because of the production of fibrin by the body. This fibrin led to granulation which was part of the process of healing which could be delayed by improper dressing of the wound. He had described this process in his textbook *A Manual of the Principles of Surgery Based on the Pathology for Students* (1866). His arguments, which were based on his experience as a surgeon in the

Federal Army during the American Civil War, influenced many colleagues as, in addition to his deanship, he was Secretary of the Canadian Medical Association and a member of the Council of the Royal Canadian Institute. He wrote, and taught, that "a healthy sore requires nothing but protection from the air and other objections of irritation". He contended that nature did the healing and the practitioner should not be medically meddlesome – a contradiction of the time-honoured ethic that a doctor should do something. Although he agreed that "germs" existed, he denied that they caused disease and were killed by carbolic, instead he postulated that the carbolic delayed or halted the passage into the body of poisonous elements produced by the wound.

Listers' pronouncements spurred many practitioners as they were aware of the terrible mortality with infection, particularily in childbirth. Aikins' and Rolph's students who purchased tickets to the Toronto Lying-In Hospital in 1869, read on the reverse side:

> The Lying-In Hospital of Munich, despite its excellent ventilation and many admirable arrangements has been very unfortunate for the prevalence of puerperal fever, which broke out among the inmates in December, 1856, a few months after the hospital first opened ... An investigation showed that both these patients had been examined by one of the Assistants, who had just come from making a post-mortem inspection of an infant, having previously washed his hands in a solution of chloride before leaving the deadhouse ... Here, then, was clear proof that cadaveric infection was one specific cause of the outbreak ... All of these facts proved the correctness of the theory of Semmelweis of Vienna, that puerperal fever may be originated, and propagated by inoculation of the maternal passages with putrid animal fluids. Nay, further, that it may be induced by the mere presence of cadaveric odours imported into the atmosphere of the Lying-In chamber on the clothes of the accoucher; ... The moral of the whole story is just the truism that no accoucher is justifiable in going to a case of labour, who has recently been engaged in dissection of dead bodies, or attending cases of erysipelas, or of surgical or typhoid fever.

Aikins, Hodder and Malloch were present at the International Medical

Congress in Philadelphia in 1876, which was chaired by Lister when he was lauded by the Assembly. As a result of the acceptance of his theories by the staff of TSM, the students at Aikins' school received lectures on Listerism. On the other hand, students at Victoria were discouraged from considering the new regimen as it was considered not proven and, in any case, Canniff and his group were satisfied with the traditional procedures, but were more conscious of the necessity to be sanitary. This followed the lead of several British surgeons, such as Lawson Tait and Thomas Keith, who argued that cleanliness was the best way to avoid infection. The argument continued between the two schools of thought with Caniff challenging the enthusiastic Malloch, with the statement that his mind " ... was so intensely fixed upon the germ theory that he cannot discover my meaning of disease causation".[7]

So bigoted were some that Dr. Clarence Starr, when Professor of Surgery recalled that when a student of Aikins " ... he had few equals, his style was impressive, his advice good and his methods of teaching practical ... was the first man in Canada to adopt Lister's views and practice antiseptic surgery ... In the carrying out of antiseptic surgery, as you may imagine, he met with much opposition and even with dishonest and underhand treatment, in so far that one man, who shall be nameless – and may he rest in a nameless grave – would go to his cases, after their removal to the ward, and infect the wounds with pus taken from other cases".[8]

Others, such as Dr. Abraham Groves, practiced their craft in a more pragmatic manner. He wrote in *All in a Day's Work*, in 1934 that two of his greatest teachers were Bovell, who taught Physiology and Aikins, lecturer in Surgery. "Dr. Aikins was practical in everything. His teaching made surgery educated common sense. With him everything was reasoned out; there was no *ipso dixit*". Groves practiced in Fergus over the next half a century. Frequently his operating theatre was in the kitchen, which held the only large table in the house. Chloroform was the anaesthesia and hair from the tail of his horse was used for sutures. Later silk was used. and much later catgut sterilized by Lister's carbolic acid was available. His first major operation was in 1874, two years after his graduation, when he removed an ovarian tumour. This ability of newly qualified graduates to do major surgery attested to the level of Aikins teaching; a cavalier disregard of postoperative morbidity or mortality, or the good fortune to be in that state of Grace. The following year he performed a vaginal hysterec-tomy and in 1878 he removed seven calculi by a supra-pubic lithot-omy. He did a lithotomy rather than the newly developed technique using an evacuator which emptied the bladder of stones in one opera-tion, described by Dr. Henry Bigelow in the *American Journal of the Medical Sciences*, which changed the whole outlook of lithotrity, as had been taught at the TSM for many years. Groves did not have the instrument which first filled the bladder with water, then crushed the stone and evacuated the fragments with a specially shaped lithotrite, followed by removal of all the fluid and debris by suction. The proce-dure was called lithopaxy. It had the advantage of clearing all the stone and fragments in one step, thus avoiding repeat procedures with the attendant high morbidity and death. In truth Groves used very few instruments at any time, a needle and scalpel sufficing and these rarely required supplementing.

In describing the hysterectomy he reported:

> The operation was done at an old log house in the country without a nurse or modern appliances, and with very few instruments; my only assistants, being two medical students. An incision having been made through the mucous membrane so as to encircle the cer-vix, the bladder was separated from the uterus; the Douglas pouch being opened, and the fundus of the uterus brought down, the broad ligaments were ligated in sections, ... my usual carefulness in boiling everything was adhered to; and to that I attribute in great part any success I have had in operative work, although at that time my boiling and endless scrubbing (using six different brushes for five minutes each) were by many considered useless refine-ments.

Although Lister's technique was well known to the TSM faculty, the teaching was to select only certain elements. The dressings suggested by Lister were changed when Robert Wood Johnson in 1885 developed a soft, absorbent cotton and gauze dressing. He drew on the experience of a German surgeon, Dr. G. Neuber, who in 1881 had used sphagnum moss as an absorbent. This moss was used during World War I for many wounds.

Groves rarely had infections in spite of the fact he did many intra-abdominal procedures. In dealing with septic abdomens he stated:

> Sucking out infected or any other fluid by means of an aspirator is ineffective because it is impossible to remove all the foreign fluid in that way. Wiping it out with sponges is as ineffective as it would be to try to clean the dinner dishes with a dirty cloth ... putting in drainage tubes is not only useless but also dangerous; ... the quantity of fluid injected, of course, depends on the condition, but I have used five or more gallons. I have used this methods in three cases of ruptured bladder, two of ruptured gall bladder, one of a ruptured pancreatic duct, one of ruptured abscess of the ovary, and in my last 98 cases of ruptured appendices, without a death in any case.

Even as late as 1898 echoes of the debate were sounded. Lord Lister (he had been knighted) after receiving an honourary Doctor of Law from the University of Toronto received another evaluation from his long-time critic Lawson Tait, gynecologist in Birmingham. *The Lancet* published:

> Let us hear no more of the nonsense of the bad results in surgery in the pre-Listerian times as having been cured by Lister. It is not the truth.

Carbolic continued to intrigue the medical – and non-medical world. The fame of Lister was capitalized by many opportunists including "Listerine" and the "Carbolic Smoke Ball Company". The latter, utilizing the death of Prince Albert Victor, (second in line to the Throne of England) by influenza in 1892, advertised their product with a guarantee that it would positively cure a variety of disorders and prevent influenza. So blatant were the advertisements that a £100 reward was offered to anyone who contracted influenza after using the smoke balls. The apparatus consisted of a container from which carbolic spray could be inhaled through the nose. The success of this enterprise was practically guaranteed because of the great influenza endemic which had swept through Europe in 1890 – and the skilfully written warranty which could not hold up in court.

By the 1870's Toronto had become , according to Conyngham C. Taylor, a very important commercial centre. "The principal streets were an aspect of stately, unpretentious prosperity". [9]

> King Street is honoured by the daily presence of the aristocracy, while Yonge is given over to the business of the middle class and the beggar. Amid the upper classes, there is a performance that goes on daily, that is known among habitues as 'doing King'. It consists principally of marching up and down a certain part of that street at a certain hour, performing, as it were, 'Kowtow" to the goddess of fashion, and sacrificing to her sister divinity of society ... these consists principally of young ladies whose proper place should be at school, and young men attired in the height of fashion. By the time these ardent devotees have paraded a few times, the regular habitues make their appearance until 6 o'clock in the evening one side – for only one side is patronized – it's crowded to excess.

The population of the city was 56,000 and over the next three years there was an era of expansion in both the economy and in the size of the medical schools.

Dr. James E. Graham who graduated from the TSM, was one of the first to be designated a specialist when the Toronto General Hospital published a set of by-laws in 1889, recognizing specialties. Graham had worked with Osler and Bovell and was taken on staff at the TSM and in 1887 became Professor of Clinical Medicine and Medical Pathology and Lecturer in Dermatology. The Graham family had donated the land for the Wesleyan Methodist Shiloh Chapel of which James Eakins had been a Trustee. James Graham married a daughter of William's brother, J.C. Aikins.

In order to put more teeth into the concept that homeopaths were not suitable to practice medicine, the Canadian Medical Association frowned on any collaboration. In consequence, Canniff felt it necessary to report that he had inadvertently consulted with a homeopath while doing hospital work on the battle front. This pattern of confession had been set in the U.K. when James Syme and James Simpson, two pillars of the Department of Surgery in Edinburgh, were embarrassed to report that they had consulted with Dr. William Henderson, who after being appointed Professor of Pathology, came out of the closet and confessed to being a homeopath – and even published a pamphlet praising its merit.

Dr. William Clark, who was nominated for President of the CMA in 1869 was accused by Orton of consulting with homeopaths, to which he admitted after a prolonged discussion. Fortunately, the President of the CMA came to his rescue. In spite of this attitude of the CMA, homeopaths had a great deal of influence in the Ontario Medical Council. Duncan Campbell, George Logan and George Henderson, all homeopaths, occupied the President's chair in the late 70's and 80's. In 1893 Clarence Campbell, homeopathic physician, was elected President and Leonard Luton of St. Thomas became President in 1898. In order to face reality rather than stand on principles, the President of the OMA in 1883 opined that it was permissible to consult with homeopaths even if the CMA said it was not.

Part of the difficulty of working with homeopaths was that there was no Canadian training school which could be assessed by the allopathic physicians. The homeopaths opened a small hospital at Huron and College Street in Toronto which operated from 1890 to 1892 and also served as a school for nurses, known as the Grace Homeopathic Hospital. It had a powerful clientele including Sir Casimir and Lady Gzowski. It expanded and by 1896, the "Grace Hospital", was the first to have x-ray-assisted operations in Ontario and published a monthly journal *The Homeopathic Messenger*. The Board of Directors included Judge MacDonnell, John Ross Robertson and W. Gooderham. However the hospital was not successful financially and in 1892 the designation "homeopathic" was abandoned and a new charter drawn up in 1902, which established a "non-sectarian" treatment institution which amalgated in the 20's with the Toronto Western Hospital.

One of the main motives in forming an association to be the "Doctors Parliament," i.e. the CPSO, was to attempt to control overcrowding in the profession. Competition by the schools for students had resulted in a lowering of standards and a flood of practitioners into the market place. In consequence, fee cutting, guaranteed cures and extravagant claims for treatment outcomes were common, forcing medical leaders and "Parliament" to implement a code of professional ethics. The College had a Registrar and was charged to set the standards for curriculum and licencing. The Treasurer, once again, was Aikins who kept the financial records and added many other functions until his death. In point of fact, he became advisor to each of the Executives for over thirty years, a power behind the throne and even a cash resource. "Up to the present," he wrote in the initial years "I have received about two hundred dollars and therefore am out of pocket about $500.00." Fortunately his professional income, plus an inheritance from his father and cash from his father-in-law enabled him to act as benefactor to the fledging society. The source of funds at that time was examination fees. But to hold the examinations it was necessary to pay for invigilators and have a suitable hall for writing papers and taking orals. The College appealed to government in 1874 for funds, and was refused but, in recognition of the need to maintain quality, was given the right to levy an annual registration fee of $1.00 or $2.00.There was some opposition to this by many country doctors for years.

Although this revenue gave temporary relief the CPSO complained of the difficulty of maintaining its records and having a proper examination room for candidates. The Executive felt that if it owned premises it could manage more economically, but the College was not permitted to hold property. The problem was taken to the Legislature and finally in 1878 a new Act allowed the CPSO to acquire a permanent home. After many protracted arguments with Council members and some outspoken practitioners, who maintained that they were in the business of medicine not real estate, a building was purchased on the south-east corner of Bay and Richmond Street, Toronto for $13,500.00. Unfortunately the planners did not take into consideration all their space demands and soon found that the building was inadequate. Fortunately the location was excellent, so the premises were put on the market and sold for $100.00, on the provision that the purchaser removed the building. Following this, a new office was built, complete with an elevator, speaking tubes and elaborate facade. It gave Aikins great pleasure to read the brass plate facing Richmond Street with the notice "Medical Registraton Office". It gave more ammunition to those practitioners who had objected to the original purchase, and saw the registration fee as gross evidence of taxation, without representation.

But there was a cost over-run for the new building and the final figures came out at $80,000.00 in spite of Aikins continual urging that the CPSO should stay within its means. The Executive applied to the government for assistance and on being refused, proposed to rent part of the building for $8,000.00 per year. This optimistic forecast was pared by maintenance and operating costs, and the income generated was only $3,000.00.

In the early 1890's there was a considerable downturn of the economy and the shortfall of revenue drove the College further into debt. In addition there were unforseen expenses when the fire department ordered installation of proper fire escapes and the central heating system required more radiators. Once again physicians outside the Toronto area grumbled at the cost of maintaining a building which was a fringe activity to the needs of caring for the sick.

Even though the Treasurer kept impeccable accounts of all expenses such as fees paid, and disinfectants used in the "closets", someone had failed to instruct the architect, E.J. Lennox, that there was need for more than the single washroom, which was entered through Council chamber. This barely took care of the male members, and with the influx of more female workers, who prevailed and it was necessary to open an alternate male lavatory in the basement, for males. Nature's call was sometimes drowned out by the noise of the gasoline engine which powered the elevator, and was eventually replaced by an expensive electric motor.

All these financial problems which were not really conceived to be the role of a College established to examine on a physician's competency, led to embarassing questioning by reluctant dues-paying physicians, with Aikins constantly fending off disgruntled doctors. A query was raised of the legality of property speculation. Dr. McLaughlin declared these ventures had led to "loss, loss, loss, eternal loss, nothing else but loss". He insisted that it was time for the profession to stop carrying a burden of this kind.

The CPSO functions, in addition to conducting examinations for registration, included policing of the unauthorized practice of medicine. Unregistered practitioners could not be appointed to the provincial service or any hospital or militia and they could not sign medical certificates. A $100.00 fine was legislated to be paid to the Treasurer of the Council for practice without a license. However many physicians refused to be registered after the 1868 Act since they had registered under the ECMER in 1865. This stubbornness resulted in a conviction against a Victoria graduate on November 23rd 1868 of practicing without registration. He was fined 25 cents. He refused to pay and was served with a warrant of committal in quick time. Fortunately for the profession, and himself, the Council decided to drop the charges after some behind-the-scenes negotiations.

The annual levy on all registered practitioners irked many physicians. So intense did the feelings become that in the early 90's, one thousand organized themselves into a Medical Defense Association (MDA) whose purpose was to object to the fee raise of $2.00, and register complaints with the way the moneys were being spent, such as real estate adventures and payments and travel fees to examiners. Sangster led the group and was able to draw on the pervasive sentiment that general practitioners, particularly in the rural areas, had lost control of the profession, which had been taken over by homeopaths and University representatives. This was not without foundation as only sixty homeopaths were in practice at that time and it had been legislated that they had five seats on the Council. Those seats, plus the ten educational delegates, meant that the territorial delegates were outnumbered. Feelings became hotter with an escalation of town versus gown prejudices, fired by charges that the University representatives were attempting to increase enrollment in the schools, in spite of the crowded medical market place. The College register showed 139 new registrants in 1886, and 161, 134, 158, 160, 117 and 139 in successive years. Sangster, who was elected to Council in 1892, argued that the matriculation examination should be toughened in order to reduce the number of students. Overcrowding had been partially controlled in the 1860s but became uncontrolled by 1880.[11]

The MDA cause drew re-inforcement from a strange source. About the third quarter of the century there occurred a rising tide of rural protest on the basis that farmers were living in poverty because of excessive profits by financial houses, grain elevators owners and the railway share holders. This wide-spread grievance reached its zenith in 1889 with the formation of the Grand Association of Patrons of Industry. Its credo was deregulation, a free trade philosophy, which would remove power from the capitalists, professional classes and middlemen. This anti-protectionist philosophy, allied with a demand for simpler government was attractive to thousands of voters who objected to tariffs, duties and subsidies to businesses, which generated great profits. These discontented citizens formed local organizations but specifically banned membership to doctors – "a prominent feature was obnoxious opposition to all kinds of class legislation and the doctor was labelled a parasite in the community."[12] The Patrons gained 15 seats in the House in 1893.

Dr. Walter Meacham in the House felt that the MDA had considerable merit and introduced a Bill to reduce University representation on Council, but his attempts were thwarted by other physician Honourable Members. Sangster responded by circulating a notice to all members which was highly critical of the Council, with the result that Meacham, sensing an obvious wave of protest, introduced another Bill, which drastically changed the composition and powers of the Council. Eventually this led to a Parliamentary review, with Mowat in the Chair. The outcome was that although the University representation remained as before, there was an increase in delegates-at-large, drawn from the smaller centres, with 17 territorial representatives. In the election of 1893 of the territorial representatives, six were members of the MDA, and were from small towns. Commenting on this, the *Canada Lancet*[13] remarked "the June meeting may be expected to be musical to a degree."

But the College maintained that the annual fee was reasonable as the chief beneficiary of the its activities was the medical profession, which chronically complained of the number of unqualified practitioners, charlatans and others who were competing at the patient level. There had been a more active pursuit of quacks and a rigid interpretation of the Medical Act as far as unregistered physicians were concerned. To enforce this regulation, it was necessary to hire an Official Prosecutor, whose salary was paid from the fines levied by the court. Although these added up to only small amounts initially, by the 1890's they ranged from several hundred to thousands of dollars. Unfortunately, it was difficult for the College to enforce collection and the Prosecutor reported that he was barely able to cover his expenses of $50.00 a month. He resigned and was replaced by a long term employee, the College caretaker, a Thomas Wasson. Aikins was aware of the fact that he had been employed by Pinkerton's previously and was also President of the Provincial Constabulatory Association. This action put teeth into the collection process and Wasson was able to report a large number of delinquents to the Discipline Committee, which had been formed by an Act of Parliament in 1887. Their transgressions ranged from simply failing to pay the registration fee to "gross indecency with a male person" and "sexual misconduct of a doctor to a patient".

Sangster took the increase of territorial representation as a signal victory and pressed for even greater changes, but he was tempting the wrath of the Council because he had refused to pay his annual $1.00 fee for the past eighteen years. Several other MDA members had withheld payment as well and Aikins reported the outstanding total, was something like $5,500.00. The Port Perry practitioner prodded his way through Council meets, which were normally decorous and gentlemanly. He caustically challenged the mechanism of selecting a President and Treasurer, but was defeated. He derisively demanded recounts of votes and showed an annoying antipathy to an "inner circle of selectees" who "had usurped the democratic role of the Council and were conducting the medical business of the province without regard to the welfare of the country."

In May 1892 he wrote a peremptory letter to Aikins, directing an early reply of the details of expenditures of College activities over the previous five years. Aikins replied that he was a servant of the Council and could not release any information without permission. Sangster then demanded that Dr. Fife Fowler, the President, instruct the Treasurer to comply. Even though Aikins received such instructions, he still refused on the basis that the President had exceeded his authority, most likely in ignorance of the By-laws of the CPSO. Aikins snidely added that the place for such questions was when the reports were presented, and accepted. Although he had been refused, Sangster now prompted several other requests for similar information from members of the MDA and at the same time fired off a third demand to Aikins. By now the Treasurer was losing patience and the "Dear Doctor" letters were becoming barbed, "I caused to be prepared at very considerable trouble and much loss of time, statements ... covering the 26 years of its existence ... copies were sent to each registered practitioner, no dissatisfaction whatever with the information was expressed ... my refusal to furnish the information, should not be construed to mean that there must be something to hide."

Of course, Aikins did not mention that members who were in arrears of payments would not receive the reports, but he did send a printed copy of Sangster's letter to the entire College membership and asked their opinion whether he should answer the request. Fowler was icily cold in his follow-up letter to Aikins, but Council never did vote to send out the material.

Although he was stymied on the financial accountability fairways, Sangster changed his course and led the MDA in a contest to reduce competition resulting from the overcrowding of the profession. "Many physicians in Toronto were hardly making a living!" He proposed raising the standards for matriculation and making zoology, botany and chemistry mandatory rather than optional. Aikins, although still anxious to elevate the qualification, cannily held back his vote for he was keenly aware of the attitude of the Minister of Education, who had joined the meeting as Patron of the College, and was all too aware of his insistence that young men of less privileged families would not receive such preparation. In addition, Ross did not feel that the University would require those qualifications for several years. The Council agreed with the general principle that "no educational standard (should be) raised to such an extent that it would shut out the poor man, who is honestly pushing his way to get into the profession."

However, once the candidate had entered the school, Aikins, as ever, was interested to make the course as tough as possible. In 1892 he urged that there should be only one examination per year, instead of allowing repeats by below-liners. At the same time he pressed for a longer school year. "Surely if little children can stand a full term, grown men should be able to manage a full six month term, with not more than 50 lectures per subject." The 50 lectures per subject was suggested as result of a survey carried out by Dr. Darby Bergin, who chaired a curriculum committee. In making the report, he was fulsome in praise of "Dr. Aikins, Dr. Wright ... made an effort to raise the profession from the slough into which it had sunk ... they laid strong and deep foundations for a wise, prudent, dignified and learned profession ...". His recommendation was to reduce the number of lectures to 50 per subject "... to leave time for practical study."

Undaunted by Geikie who disagreed, Bergin and Aikins continued their campaign as they had completed a systematic review of different teaching bodies in Europe and had discovered they were in "thorough accord" with a change from the past. For example Mr. Mitchell Banks, a prominent surgeon in the U.K. observed "he had heard of being preached to death by wild curates, but an even more terrible disaster was to be lectured to death; he himself had narrowly escaped that fate, and only attributed it to a strong constitution resulting from surviving the course of lectures in Botany, Zoology and Chemistry, which were inflicted upon him."

> He knew many friends who bore indelible marks of the infliction and whose days had been and probably would be shortened thereby; he urged therefore that some restriction was indispensable.

Sir John Simon, of Edinburgh, observed that "the unhappy student should have an alternative, not to be bored to death by tiresome professors". This comparison with English schools was matched with schools in France, Switzerland, Italy and Sweden where there was a similar opinion as to the value of lectures. It took some years before the Ontario colleges and universities agreed on this matter.

Although Sangster was a thorn in the shoe of the Council which was on the march to an improved brand of medicine, other forces caused more pain. The Patrons by the 90's had gained popular support and now had ten seats in the House - enough for a proposal to change the path of the Council. Part of their mission statement had been to exclude all persons of proven immoral character, lawyers and doctors, so there were no surprises when their demands were put to the Legislature. In keeping with the general philosophy, they demanded "free trade in medicine," which when translated meant that if an examination was necessary to protect the public from incompetent practitioners, it should be conducted by the Government and not by a group of doctors, which might include some incompetents, who had a long agenda, aside from protecting citizens. In addition it was urged that the $100.00 examination fee was "a system of protection, as much as a 20% duty on cloth", and both should be abandoned. The appointed task of the Council to discipline its members was labeled as nothing short of a "star chamber court" and should be replaced by public trials before a judge.

Furthermore, they argued that the contentious annual registration fee of $2.00 should be cut to $1.00. This released the drain on the rural family physician and trimmed the wings of a Council which could not see the problems of the annual fee through the euphoria of an expansion ethic.

It was not surprising that some of these items were on the MDA docket as each institution was resolved to alter the face of organized medicine. But while the Patrons sought to change the powers of "private" governance, the MDA urged a change of policies and personalities. The Bill, when introduced, had few surprises. One item which suggested intervention by the Government if medical treatment cost too much, shocked most of the senior members present, but this jolt was forgotten when it was revealed that the Patrons wished to license "women of good character" as midwives. This clause struck at the source of a physician's practice, which began with birth and reached well into school leaving age, and in effect, threatened the basic structure of family practice.

Mowat responded that the Bill was "... revolutionary ... not in the public interest". The Conservative opposition accused the Patrons of promoting class clashes. The Council mounted a special group of lobbyists, including Aikins, which succeeded in persuading the members of the Legislative Assembly to give the Bill a six month hoist. Angus Mackay, previously a member of the Council, while quoting Aikins as a protestant, introduced and shepherded through the House a private member's Bill which mollified some of the Patrons. This resulted from a deal that was made by the special lobby group, which although it did not affect the CPSO's revenue, did disgruntle some practitioners, who tried for several years to reverse the Bill, but were not successful until the 1900's.

The wisdom of delay and gradualism paid off as the MDA lost its impetus and finally disappeared with Sangster's death in 1903. Similarly the Patrons were a spent force by the turn of the century.

REFERENCES

1. Connor, James Thomas Hamilton. Joseph Lister's System of Wound Management and the Canadian Medical Practitioner, 1867–1900: MA Thesis, UWO, 1980.

2. Dominion Medical Journal. 1, 1868–9; pp 137–38
3. Connor Ibid
4. Canada Medical Journal. 6, 1870; pp 155–59.
5. Grasett, F. Le M. Antiseptic Surgery. The Canada Lancet, Vol. IX, December 1, 1876; pp 99–104.
6. Bruce, H.A.: Varied Operations, Longmans, Green, Toronto 1958.
7. Canada Medical Journal. 6, 1870; pp 406–409.
8. Can Pract Nov 20, 1901; p 27.
9. "Toronto Called Back", 1892.
10. Canadian Practitioner, September 1888.
11. Canadian Medical Review. 8, July 1898; p 9.
12. Canada Lancet, Vol 27, 1894; p 127.

Chapter Eight

The Dean

Whether Thomas Henry Huxley, if he had been appointed to the Faculty instead of Hincks, would have established a compatible relationship with Aikins is questionable. While each had a boundless absorption in science, Huxley was not content to explore within the bounds of "accepted wisdom." In 1866, he lectured the London Mechanics Institute on "Improving Natural Knowledge," stating "there is but one kind of knowledge, and but one method of acquiring it."[1] In doing so, he countered the traditions of avowed truths, maintaining that the only route was by the scientific method. While Aikins was an enthusiast for science in medicine, the via dolorosa taken by Huxley, and later, by others including John Tyndall, Herbert Spencer and Sir James Galton, which eventually led to the concept of scientific naturalism, was perturbing for the devout, Methodist physician. Embracing this new concept meant accepting a wholly secular philosophy which postulated that Nature had been created by science and could be interpreted only through science. Such a denial of the glory of God in Nature resulted from the inability of the tenets of the Church to explain, categorize and contain the theories of science and the miraculous results, which had evolved since the beginning of the century. No longer was it possible to accept Christian faith as an explanation for the flood of new facts which were brought forward by scientists such as Darwin, Ernest Haeckel, Alfred Russell Wallace and others.

There was a bitter irony for Aikins in the 1880's. He was a strong disciple of Wesley, who had challenged the body of the Church and then placed all his life-meaning on the conviction of faith. Aikins, in his vocation to improve medicine, had challenged the corpus of mid-century medicine and then placed all his soul-substance on the faith that science was the only way to explain disease and its treatment. By the last quarter of the century it was obvious that science was not solely a medical tool but was uncovering facts that contradicted the whole philosophy of Christianity by undermining the basic concepts of the creation and God's place in daily life. Although the ideas of the new scientists were seductive at the mid-point of the century, by 1880 the questioning of God's existence posed by Huxley was clearly unacceptable to a church trustee.

This was not a fiction drawn from Mary Wollstonecraft Shelley nor an abstruse, ecclesiastic discussion. Physiology, based on the methodology of laboratory testing, was the cutting edge of why time-honoured beliefs could no longer be accepted. The debate – "crisis of faith" – which burned for many years in England and Europe, seared the University of Toronto. However, there was no hesitation in the appointment of Robert Ramsay Wright to be Professor of Natural History in University College in 1874. Over the next thirty years, his brilliant teaching of physiology gave much credibility to those who maintained that the great chain of being could be explained totally in scientific terms.

In the first half of the 19th century, most of the teachers in colleges and universities were recruited from their own graduates. In addition, many of the regular staff lived, and taught, to an advanced age, as there was no mandatory retirement. In the third quarter, the U of T began inviting applications from overseas. Huxley, on reading the advertisement in *The Atheneaum* applied without success. A year later John Tyndall sought, and was rejected from the Chair of Natural History. He did not lose on account of merit, but because the successful candidate was nearby.

A third aspirant, Robert Knox, applied and was refused. He was the most popular anatomy teacher in Edinburgh, attracting medical students, as well as barristers, clergy, noblemen and men of letters. He became the innocent accomplice of Burke and Hare, two Irishmen who supplied bodies for dissection by first murdering and then selling the corpses to porters of the various anatomy rooms. Although Knox was only a teacher, he received considerable adverse publicity. He was not directly implicated and proved his professional mettle by the publication of several excellent anatomical texts, and pioneering new teaching techniques. Historians could conjecture the course of the U of T if this trio had been accepted!

When Wilson succeeded John McCaul, as President, in 1880, any applicant from Edinburgh was welcome, even though he was not homegrown, as he most likely had the basic requirements of possessing "Scottish Common Sense". This philosophy which had developed in the capital of Scotland in response to the skepticism of David Hume's ideas of causality, was the accepted school of thought with Ontario, as well as American intellectuals. It was particularly apposite to the times, with the challenge to traditional knowledge by scientific discoveries. Scottish Common Sense was able to accept and promote the new findings on the basis that "a properly conducted inquiry into the world of nature, whether physical or human, would reveal the wonderful handiwork of God."

Thus science instructors such as Croft, Hincks and Chapman continued their courses, which usually meant a repetition of the previous year's content, without reference to the emerging hypotheses springing from the *Origin of Species*. But, intellectually, teachers were caught up in the general discussion of evolution. It was not possible to ignore the implications of Darwin's thoughts, and the churches, newspapers and dinner tables hummed with arguments. On the one side, acceptance of the Darwinian descent was seen as gross heresy, meriting excommunication from any of the various congregations. Opposed to this was the adaptive model of belief, where science and the church could live together. The devout Aikins was keenly aware of the advantages which could accrue from more science in medicine. He may well have wondered if the genie he had uncorked with the provision of science in his curriculum, could be contained within the bounds of theology, or would fly over the land spreading doubt - the agnosticism of Darwin's bulldog, Huxley. Beyond acceptance of the fact of evolution lay an even greater jump of "faith", namely the mechanism of evolution, natural selection.

However any trepidation over a general change of common belief was tempered by the actual standard of science instruction. For example, Hincks simply required that his students regurgitate his out-of-date lectures and delighted in reporting off-beat items. W.M. Biggar[2] reported that he was a kind and gentle man and entertained his classes with impish asides such as "these molluscs – properly prepared – and served – form a delicious dish" during his lectures. His published papers dealt mainly with descriptive botany and had little relationship to the work being done by Ernst Haeckel, Herbert Spencer or other Lamarckians.[3] Bovell was more interested in the Christian message of his lectures than any prosaic content and according to the *Trinity University Review XV*, gave only one lecture a week, without any apparatus. It wasn't until 1875 that the newly appointed Eugene Haanel began to encourage practical work at Victoria. As with other instructors, he used his personal equipment because there was little money available for experimental apparatus.

The level of the University lectures was determined by the preparation of the students for matriculation. It was not before 1882 that high school teachers urged that science should be on the program for university matriculation.[4] Minister of Education Ross then instructed that laboratories in high schools should have the necessary chemicals and apparatus for the teaching of elementary science and that teachers should be upgraded in their training. This improved instruction so that by 1897, he was able to report that high school courses had been greatly enlarged: "In the last ten years every collegiate institute has been fitted up with chemical and physical laboratories that would do credit to a university."

From the time Aikins joined Rolph and the TSM, until he was appointed Dean of the University of Toronto, the whole world – both temporal and medical – changed. In the 1850s the practice of medicine was a succession of established procedures used in a set sequence. Whether a patient was treated from the depletion standpoint or from the stimulation was determined by the particular circumstances during the presentation of that particular illness. The "scientific" basis for this was empirical, what had worked previously, with a framework of beliefs which were handed down from the "experts" of the previous age. These authorities had founded their approach on a world which was relatively static. Newtonian science was accepted and appreciated, but did not change the place of man in the firmament. But with the publication of the *Origin of Species*, a violent turbulence shook all faiths and beliefs and in particular impinged upon the Toronto university scene. The refusal to accept the logic of Darwin's thesis was led by Wilson, Croft, Hincks and Chapman. Although Wilson conceded that there could be some evolution of animal forms, he and his colleagues did not accept that this extended to humans. Bovell, the pre-eminent scientist, was more interested in the theosophy than the science of Darwinism. The defense of tradition and of God's place in the universe was a relatively easy task for these professors in the sixties. Neither Darwin nor his proponents, such as Asa Gray, ever went to the lengths that Huxley achieved, when he established the philosophy of apostasy. However, in spite of the fervor of the defense, the current of evidence which was being generated by science was a constant erosion of the rock on which faith was built. Granted that eternity offered everlasting joy, the allure of science offered a better life, here and now. This was acknowledged by many Ontarians including Nelles and Nathaniel Burwash, two Victorians who influenced Methodist theology. In addition, the fruits of science were totally in harmony with the Scottish Common Sense approach, which agreed that science should be accepted and given a place in the world of nature.

All this discussion and argumentation on the plausibility of the *Origin of Species,* took place in academic and the higher religious circles. While the man in the street had some concern, he was unable to get an objective view of the evidence which was being produced, in large amounts, by research endeavour. In spite of the availability in the Mechanics Institute of the books which gave rise to the controversy, the average parishioner agreed with Dr. McCosh of Princeton, who said "... be grateful to anyone who would help them keep the old faith in God and the Bible with their faith in science ..." Tyndall responded to this with, "the idea of a being standing outside the nebulous, which fashioned as a potter does clay ... was opposed to the very spirit of science."

Meanwhile it was suggested that other non-academic influences were mobilizing against the cohort of Christians, who were guarding the tabernacle. The *Christian Guardian* in 1865 proclaimed that "it is certain that immigration every year brings thousands to America of those who are infected with the poison of infidelity." These reinforcements called up greater defence from J.W. Dawson, Principal of McGill, who steadfastly held that there was no truth in the evolutionary concepts, and eventually led to his publishing the *Handbook of Zoology.* This became a standard text at McGill in the 1890's, and showed without equivocation that man had not evolved from any other order.

The intensity of the call to defend the Church was given some relief when a satire of Huxley's position was published in Toronto in 1871. *The Fall of Man*, or the love of the gorillas, was billed as a popular science lecture on the Darwinian theory of development by sexual selection. The gist of this tract was that a meeting of gorillas was addressed by a Huxley-faced elder who explained that the simian race had, through misadventure, contributed to the bastardization of the species and produced a much lower form, namely man. There was a formal dedication to Charles Darwin as a "faithful report of a humble attempt to confirm, explain and elucidate the wonderful and irrefragable theory of the promulgator ... look with a generous eye of exulted genius upon the honest and simple effort of a true labourer who strives, with you, to convince the world that Shakespeare may be but an oyster raised to the one thousandth power, or even a Darwin the cubed root of a ring-tailed monkey!" The book was illustrated. While this delighted strong church advocates such as Aikins, more hard evidence was required. This was provided in part by William Hincks in 1863 in a highly critical review of a course of *Lectures on Evolution to Working Men*, delivered by Huxley, who was intent on converting the masses to Darwinism. "Darwin's special views will be resisted by all those who view nature, as part of a perfect divine plan proceeding from Divine intelligence, which it is the object of our efforts to understand and interpret" wrote the University College professor.[5]

Standing shoulder to shoulder with his colleagues was Daniel Wilson. He denied that the divine creation of man was compatible with any evolutionary process, although he did agree that there was evidence of changes in lower species of the plant and animal kingdom. By a thought process which combined the artistic works made by man, with the findings of his study *Prehistoric Man: Researches into the Origin of Civilisation in the Old and New World* (1862) he concluded that humans were complete and perfect and did not evolve. But it was necessary to explain the mass of findings which supported some evolution in lower animals with man's presence. To do this he provided a "missing link", Caliban, of Shakespeare's creation. This half-human, half-animal creation provided Wilson with a concept whereby he could hold his conviction about the divine origin of humans, which was separated from the animal kingdom by the grotesque of a *Mid-Summer Night's Dream*.

With the retirement of Hincks from the Chair, his replacement, Professor H. Alleyne Nicholson, once again an Edinburgh graduate, maintained his predecessor's theme and argued "man alone has free will." This was the result of a struggle between man's animal and Divine Principle and "of the means vouchsafed by the Creator for his relief." Even though this discussion was rife in the University group, it did affect others such as at Aikins' school.

· · · · · ·

Albeit Aikins and his colleagues reiterated the need for more science in the school curriculums, they were all limited by the quality of available information. During his student days at Jefferson, he had used Dunglison's *Text of Human Physiology* which had been published in 1832 and remained a standard well into the sixties. Both Dunglison and S. Weir Mitchell taught in the didactic manner, the latter pioneering the demonstration type lecture, necessitated because of the increased number of students in classes and the impossibility of providing physiological apparatus to each student. Physiology was the most important of the science subjects, which included botany and zoology, and was a late bloomer in all of the medical schools. Bernard in France had joined with the "1847 Group" in Germany, which included Hermann Helmholtz, Emil DuBois-Reymond, Ernst Brucke and Carl Ludwig, – all pledged to revitalize the study of physiology. Part of their creed was to free physiology from its anatomical basis, which stagnated physiological research by stressing the importance of structure over function and urged that the future of the specialty laid in physics and chemistry. Each of these nationalities had a different emphasis in the approach to physiology, but both agreed on the necessity of the experimental method in the science of vital phenomena.

English workers at mid-century remained convinced that answers were to be found in the anatomical approach, which was combined in most laboratories with religio-philosophical issues. The standard text for England, and to a certain extent in Canada, was by William Carpenter which, while teaching a certain amount of physiological knowledge, always included references to man's soul and the Creator's presence. His textbook was superseded in 1857 by that of Todd and Bowman, *The Physiological Anatomy and Physiology of Man* which went even further in distinction from continental physiological texts by urging "a greater degree of prominence than had been usual in physiological works" for anatomy. The English approach was echoed in the works of Bovell in Toronto.

This state of affairs was challenged by Huxley and his protégé Michael Foster when the latter, wrote to Huxley:

> "speaking of emancipation, don't you think science wanted a little heroic striking off of fetters. I mean of course you do, but don't you think something useful might be done by comparing in print the scientific work done by an Englishman with that done by Furriners during the last thirty years, showing the influence of fetters? In physiology at least we should look very small."[6]

This challenge to Todd and Bowmann, who maintained that the only legitimate goal of physiology was to demonstrate that each and every structure had been perfectly designed by the "Creator to subserve a function" resulted in a major change in teaching. Following a number of similar declarations by other teachers and researchers in England, Foster left University College in London with the hope that Cambridge would metamorphose and emerge as a major research centre. Aided and sponsored by the Professor of Human Anatomy, Dr. George M. Humphrey, he promoted the ruling by the College of Surgeons which required all candidates for Membership to study "practical physiology". Although this ruling did not appear to have a great application in the practice of medicine, it was the chosen course of Huxley, who was a College examiner in anatomy and physiology.

But Foster's campaign, which was the flagship of scientific medicine in the United Kingdom, was launched under dark clouds. *Nature* editorialized that the backward state of physiology, and biology, suffered from a "glut of facts and disconnected minor theories" and "may after a lapse of thirty or forty years ... be on a level with a second rate German university."[7] Unblenched, Foster assembled a team of researchers who proceeded to surpass their continental rivals. Although he himself did not produce a mass of discoveries, he demonstrated a particular skill as a discoverer of men, rather than facts. Aikins too, brought keen minds into his faculty, including J.E. Graham, who, with others, took some training in German laboratories.

Foster realized at an early stage the incompleteness of the data coming from his laboratories and admitted "the answers which we can give at present can hardly be called answers at all." At the same time Ramsay Wright, who was completing his studies in Edinburgh was keenly aware of the dilemma that in spite of Herculean efforts, there was little to show. Even by the end of the decade the S.P.S. students could answer some questions in biology and do some simple experiments, but there was no overall theory which synthesized these isolated findings

Of particular interest to the physician, as well as the scientist, was the mechanism of the heart. Many clinicians had developed a theory of the significance of various heart rates and rhythms. However, Foster was the first to admit that, "our knowledge of the exact nature and of the causes of the cardiac beat is not very largely understood." His studies, which pioneered laboratory investigation, had looked mainly at the hearts of cold blooded subjects, such as frogs, and he had measured some endo-cardiac pressures. But he was unable to answer "why does the cardiac cycle begin with a sinus beat?" and "why is the contraction wave broken into sinus beat, auricular beat, ventricular beat." This problem intrigued Foster for most of his academic life, but he was not able to solve the enigma, even though there existed some evidence based on earlier work that electrical transmission was involved. "We have no satisfying evidence of nerve cells as being the main factors in the matter," he stated.

By the 1880's there were competing schools of thought within his research cadre, a circumstance which he fostered, because of his commitment to true scientific research, which accepted no conceptual limitations. With his appointment to the Chair of Physiology in 1883, more investigators were recruited, and although they worked on different problems, the heart-beat question continued in its regular rhythm. These schools ranged from an unclear connection between cause and effect, as proposed by W.H. Ransom and H. Newell Martin, to those who argued there was a direct influence on the heart. This could happen by an integrative nervous system action of a glandular secretion mechanism, proposed by J.W. Langley. W.H. Gaskell, who directed the laboratory, proposed a sympathetic nervous system and in a land-mark paper in 1883 finally solved the problem that had intrigued Cambridge for two decades, using as his model the tortoise. However, even with this breakthrough, it was another ten years before the full impact was felt in Toronto.

Although Foster's text was a monumental work on physiology, he was still limited. For example, he stated "certain structures which, though they differ in many ways, we may conveniently treat altogether, such as the thyroid and pituitary bodies, the supra-renal capsules, and the thymus, appear to play not unimportant parts in the metabolic processes of the body." He described the muscle tremors, spasms and tetanic convulsions following the removal of the thyroid in the monkey "all indicating mischief in the central nervous system." He inferred that the passage of blood through the thyroid resulted in some "special changes." From this he was able to describe myxoedema, goitre and cretinism. He admitted however, that about the pituitary gland "we know absolutely nothing." In addition in describing the action of the supra-renals, he acknowledged the bronzing of Addison's disease, but admitted "several links of the chain are as yet unknown." The best he could describe about the thymus was that its functions were in some way associated with events taking place before birth or in early life. While he demonstrated that sugar in the urine was consequent to injection of sugar into the jugular vein, he was unable to determine the action of the pancreas. Perhaps the greatest contribution by Foster was the acknowledgment, which was frequently written, "we do not possess at present experimental or other evidence of so clear a kind as to enable us to decide dogmatically between these two views."

There was little possibility that Toronto could compete with London or Cambridge in the physiology forum, even though there had been a long history of science teaching in University College and the proprietary schools.

The first Professor of Chemistry appointed in 1843, when a department was formed in King's College, was Henry H. Croft. He had studied with Michael Faraday who described the laws of electrolysis and, among many other findings, discovered electrical induction. Croft had been also a pupil of Albert Mitscherlick who propounded the law of isomorphism. While working in the laboratory of Jons Jacob Berzelius in Berlin he described many other chemicals and pioneered the research on benzin. Mitscherlick applied his chemical ability to medicine with the discovery of grape sugar in the urine in the 1840's. Croft, with this training, became editor of *The Chemical Gazette* and a charter member of the London Chemical Society. On being appointed to the Chair in Toronto he introduced methods of toxicology and, at the same time as Liebig, he was laying the foundations for laboratory medicine. Croft advised that the University College laboratory should be built along the lines of the Old Monk's Kitchen at Glastonbury. His publications were on various chemicals such as magnesium, thallium and the oxalate of iron, but there was little that could be applied to the medical practice of the day. In addition to his work in the field of chemistry, he was a leader in the Entomological Society of Ontario, organized in 1863. His collection of Coleoptera indicated his strong interest in botany and he worked closely with Hincks in organizing the herbarium of the Department of Botany, which led to the establishment of a biological museum. Despite his impressive background in chemistry, Croft showed only minimal initative or curiosity for further investigation.

Hincks' articles were on the ferns, molluscs, Canadian fauna and the classification of vegetables and animals. He was succeeded by Alleyne Nicholson, M.D. who published a *Manual of Palaeontology, An Introduction to the Study of Biology* and numerous studies on the geology of various areas of Canada. Although he had broad interests, he did little to fire up any eagerness to learn about the chemistry of the human body.

Croft was followed on his retirement in 1878 by H.W. Pike who had studied at Oxford and in chemical laboratories in Berlin. He introduced the use of the balance and quantative experimentation into chemical instruction which replaced the traditional "test-tubing." W.H. Ellis who also followed Croft from 1878 to 1882 analyzed specimens of water, milk and the adulteration of food. He also wrote papers on tannin. His contributions began to bridge the up-grading of elementary chemistry teaching to the higher level by the 1890's.

Although each of these teachers authored numerous publications, the quality of their demands on students was not high – simple organic chemistry, botany and primitive physiology. There was little attempt, or capability, of relating these teachings to any morbid process and the basis of disease continued to be on anatomical abnormalities, with concomitant emphasis in the timetable. For example, in 1866, Croft's examination for second year Chemistry asked for the general properties of a magnet and explain the meaning of specific heat and account for the formation of dew.

This changed with the appointment of Robert Ramsay Wright as Professor of Natural History at University College in 1874. Prior to that he had held posts in the Department of Zoology at the University of Edinburgh and had been a member of the Challenger Deep Sea Expedition, from which he published several papers. He was successful in Toronto and rapidly rose to the rank of the foremost teachers, resulting in his appointment as curator of the Museum of Natural History in 1876 and Professor of Biology in 1887. His publications were in anthropology, comparative vertebrate anatomy, and parasitology, with only a few papers on exclusively medical matters, but his broad experience enabled him to teach medical students through analogy and comparative morphology. He was described as being able to present lectures in a wonderful manner, superbly illustrated with the newest materials and methods.[8] This skill in communication stood him in good stead when he spoke, not only in the lecture room, but in the meetings of the Medical Society during which he conducted a virtual post-graduate school in medicine.

Wright's appointment was a major turning point in the development of medicine in Toronto. In 1874, the Senate of the University had made laboratory work obligatory in the under-graduate science courses. This led to the erection of the School of Practical Science. Wright lost little time in ensuring that his students had practical experience. According to Dr. W.H. Piersol "The group of students would gather around him and with the specimens in plain view of all would discuss such subjects as the structure and classification, their habits and relation to environment."[9]

In addition to his enthusiasm and skill, Wright had a deep sense of the difficulties some students might have with the course material. The son of a rigid Presbyterian family which lived in dire poverty, his brilliance in zoology qualified him for an appointment with Dr. J.V. Carus, an eminent professor in Leipzig. However, young Wright did not have a microscope, but was expected to preside over practical classes in microscopy. He wrote to a wealthy relative, "To render me better qualified for the latter, I must have some considerable amount of private work with a good instrument before May. Such an instrument I could hardly ask from my parents and I have been too much occupied this session with examinations to allow of my having had any tutorial work which might have provided me with the necessary funds ... I therefore hope that you will accommodate me with the sum I require for two years ..." Fortunately he was able to receive the money, and repay it. He, like Foster, was able to build a team of researcher-scientists. One of the most prominent of these was Dr. Archibald B. Macallum, who was appointed a lecturer in the Department of Biology in 1883. He was so enthusiastic about teaching medical students that he qualified as a physician and was appointed the head of a newly created Department of Physiology in 1890. His list of publications included many findings from his work over the next twenty years.[10] Another Wright man was Robert Russell Bensley, a university graduate who became Assistant Demostrator in Biology in 1892. In an 1896 publication he argued that the gastric glands "... is still a foundation of our knowledge of the replenishment of cells in the mucous membrane of the stomach."

James Playfair McMurrich, a graduate of 1879, who later became Professor of Anatomy in 1907, established a reputation for himself in Chicago, before returning to Toronto. There he was joined by Dr. John McCrae, (later author of "In Flanders Fields") who had been lecturing and demonstrating in anatomy. This cadre of a new type of lecturer, were specialists in a particular subject, rather than being physicians who lectured on some aspect. This took the teaching of medicine away from "structure for its own sake" to Wright's goal that the importance of physiology was equal to that of morphology.

Wilson, during the formal opening of the Biology Building on December 19th, 1889, said "these buildings furnish somewhat adequate accommodation for the Biological and Physiological sections of university training." The building was lime-lighted from gases stored in the basement. Fortunately, there was a good water supply which enabled the use of a large Zeiss projection microscope and epidiascope, the lens of which was guarded carefully by Wright. R.R. Bensley recorded, when he was a student in 1885, that the "Department of Biology possessed a dozen simple Hartnack microscopes with coarse alignments by a draw tube and fine adjustment by a screw." By 1891 all of these had been replaced by Leitz microscopes.

Alexander Pride, who did the preliminary dissection and preparation of teaching models, occupied the top floor of the Biology Building. Among his many feats was the dissection of an elephant which had died while being exhibited by a traveling circus, and was kept in the quadrangle of the Biology Building during the hot summer months. There was clear, palpable olfactory evidence that there was work in progress. Pride was also notorious as being the man who inadvertently set fire to University College, when he fell while carrying kerosene lamps at a reception.

During the opening ceremonies of the Biology Building, there were four distinguished platform presentations: Dr. William H. Welch who spoke on "Pathology and Its Relation to General Biology"; C.S. Minot on "The Use of the Microscope and the Value of Embryology" and Dr. V.C. Vaughan on "The Necessity of Encouraging Scientific Work." Wright gave a paper on the "Pathogenic Sporozoa," and Osler on "The Etiology of Malaria." The audience noted, some with approval, that there was a strong medical slant in all of these papers.

The malaria presentation was the cutting edge of knowledge of this troublesome problem. Osler, like many other researchers, had vainly sought the cause of the fevers which appeared to have a specific rhythm which could now be tracked, with the modern thermometer. A French army surgeon stationed in Algiers, Charles Louis Alphonse Laveran, had reported seeing certain pigmented cells in the blood of cases of malaria in the *Bull. Soc. Med. Hop.*, Paris in 1881. However, Osler, who examined the blood of six cases could not confirm the findings. Nevertheless, his colleagues urged that there might be some truth in the announcements. There was further persuasion to continue the quest by the appearance, in *Popular Science Monthly* in 1882, of an argument that malaria was transmitted by mosquitoes. This conjecture, plus the memory of the work of Osler's veterinary friend Griffith Evans, may have catalyzed Osler into a renewed activity. Evans had been an artillery surgeon in Toronto during Osler's time with Bovell and frequently helped in the preparation of specimens. On being posted to India he discovered and published, in the *Veterinary Journal*, the finding of blood parasites in infected horses. With renewed vigour, during the sweltering Philadelphia summer of 1886, Osler examined many specimens and finally on July 14 saw the plasmodium in abundance.[12] By September he published in the *Medical News* his acceptance of the "Germ of Laveran" but could not accept a chain of causality. That had to await the publication in *Lancet* by Donald Ross of, "The Role of the Mosquitoe in the Evolution of the Malarial Parasite."[13] Ross was awarded the Nobel Prize for Medicine in 1902.

Although the TSM did not have an examination in Zoology, it was necessary that candidates for the University degree should have knowledge of the subject, which was taught by Wright, who succeeded Nicholson.

• • • • • •

Possibly because of the rumour that they might enter the University in the near future, the students of Aikins' school made preparations to upgrade their level of culture. The boorishness of medsmen was common talk and this may have been a factor in the formation of the Literary and Debating Society of the Toronto School of Medicine (L&D) in 1878.

The level and tone of the presentations clearly contradicted the criticism and disparaging sneers about the medical profession, which were gleefully abetted in part through the continuous sniping by colleagues in the various colleges. Rolph's, for instance, had been attacked publically as,

> "a grinding shop for the manufacture of medicos." The students were described as "lank-haired, seedy-looking customers, embellished with white chokers and shocking bad hats ... who shouldered their creechy bundles and sloped chanting in chorus,
>> There is a good time coming quacks,
>> There's a good time coming!
>> For bloody law, who'd care a straw
>> Since Rolph has checked its fuming!"[14]

Even at the end of the century medical students had an unsavoury reputation, which frequently led to heavy-handed policing after the boys had a night out. *The Varsity* would duly protest these incidents in their editiorials. While many of the student japes were simply high spirits, the incident of suspending a cadaver in a butcher's shop in 1895, shocked the whole city. The general suspicion that it was the work of Trinity students was never proven.

About the time of the opening of the Medical Faculty, a new custom called hustling appeared on the campus. This consisted of "a violent and disorderly struggle between large bodies of students within the University buildings." These disturbances not only completely terminated academic work, but frequently resulted in damage to building and furniture, students' clothing and occasionally in serious injuries. In the autumn of 1891 the hustling took place between Arts and Medical students attending the lectures in Physics, which were completely stopped and the room occupied by a struggling mob of students, who partially wrecked the area. Both Wilson and the Instructor in Physics were powerless to stop the riot, until the engineer turned a hose on the students. This expedient doused the trouble for the day. Subsequently, reports reached the President that the students were organizing for a general hustle. This assumed such alarming proportions that Wilson decided to close the building, and the whole body of students remained outside during the day, watched by a squad of 20 policemen. At the next lecture there was considerable excitement, but no hustling. In anticipation of trouble the engineer was ordered to stand with hose and, if necessary, to apply this form of hydrotherapy. In spite of high water, hustling continued and C. Aess and W.J. Weaver, medical students of the second year, were reported to the Council as guilty of disorderly conduct in the Biology Building. C.G. Thompson, a medical student of the second year, was also reported as having taken part in the organization of the disorder. It was moved by Primrose, seconded by Cameron, that the penalty for participation in the first occurrence of disorderly conduct within the University precinct be a public reprimand, for the second occurrence a fine of $10 and for the third incident, a suspension from the College.

The Constitution of the L&D stated that members were former and present students and that intellectual pursuits by discussions, essays and readings were to be encouraged. "No discussions upon party politics or controversial points in religion shall be allowed."

One of the first subjects for debate was, "Is it advisable that the stan-

dards of the matriculation of the College of Physicians and Surgeons of
Ontario shall be raised?" The fine hand of the Dean was apparent. The
flag for the affirmative was carried by John Ferguson and George Bingham, eventually Professor of Surgery, who won the debate. Other subjects included current issues and one of the early matters was "That the
use of tobacco should be discountenanced by the medical profession."
This resolution was carried by the majority, although on a moral rather
than a medical basis.

The future of Canada and a description of The Battle of Waterloo
were well received and a contentious question, "That the present curriculum in Medicine of Toronto University is calculated to advance the
best interest of Medical Science", was won by a yes vote. One program
discussed, "Resolved that ladies should enter the medical profession."
Messrs. G.L. Milne and P.H. Bryce, later secretary of the Board of
Health, upheld the resolution which, after considerable to-and-froing,
was decided in favour. At the next meeting a fairly grave presentation
was given by J.A. Duncan on "Ancient Literature of the Hindus." At
another the members argued, "Resolved that the Canadian independence is preferable to the British connection."

Early in its history the L & D decided, in order to present medicine in
its best light, that it would be wise to approach the public and hold a
Conversazione "to which both students and public be invited." But it
was not an uncommon happening that because of the press of administration and other matters, the cultural aspects of the evening were postponed. This set a pattern for future medical meetings when minutiae
would dominate more important general matters. Not all the evenings
were devoted to serious pursuits. L.M. Sweetnam who later followed
C. von Rokitansky and preceded Norman Bethune by dying of septicemia acquired at an operation, obliged at one time with a recitation of
"Tell it to his native hills." This was supplemented by the singing of,
"Gathering up the shells from the shore" and for an encore, "Three
thousand miles away." Many of the evenings were filled with song,
either by a soloist or by the entire membership.

But the group, in spite of the sweet sound of music, expressed doubts
over the value of continuing the meetings because there was no priority
given to medicine. On December 7th 1881, "on the advice of the Faculty" the Medical Society (MS) was formed with 20 members. Adam

Wright was elected as president with J.R. Elliot and Aikins as councillors. At this time the L & D was terminated. One of the first things the MS considered was to press for a recommendation of the L&D that there should be a reading room for students. The MS was connected directly to the Faculty and required its permission to adopt a Constitution.

The meeting in January 1882 had an exhaustive presentation on the cause of the current epidemic of typhoid fever in Toronto. Members, who had studied Sanitary Science, had no difficulty in locating the problem in the Parkdale area, where a new sewer had been urged, but had not been approved by the municipality.

The storm caused by the accusation made to the City of Toronto was not as great as the next crisis. On January 27 Miss Gussie Stowe, the daughter of the redoubtable Emily, was proposed for membership amidst 20 male nominees. The slate was accepted provisionally. However at the next meeting the president announced that all the members who had been nominated were accepted with the exception of Miss Stowe, for whom a ballot had been called. The result was 16 against her admission, 11 for. But a sympathetic member pointed out that she was a student at Aikins' school and should, by the Constitution, enjoy all of the privileges. Therefore an invitation to use the Reading Room and attendance at all regular meetings was to be extended to this female medico. An objection was raised to the words "attendance at all regular meetings" and this was carried.

The Reading Room, which opened in February 1882, rapidly became a source not only of medical information but also of worldly matters. There were available *The Globe, Mail, World, Grip, Varsity, Acta Victoriana, Canadian Illustrated*, and *Canadian Monthly*, all at a cost of about $10.50 a month. It was agreed that there should be subscriptions to *Popular Science Monthly* and *The Philadelphia Medical Journal*. *The Practitioner, Canada Lancet* and *Canada Medical Record* were already on the shelves, along with ten other journals.

A paper "Bacteria and the relation to disease" was proposed to be read. The school was using Dr. T. Henry Green's *Introduction to Pathology and Morbid Anatomy* wherein bacteria or Schizomycetes were "believed to produce the infective diseases." Julius Cohn had classified bacteria morphologically in 1876, but a direct connection to infection was still hazy, and the School did not have a specialist in bacteriology until J.A. Amyot in 1905.

Following this lecture it was proposed that Richardson should give a paper on "Science, so falsely called." He was an excellent choice for the subject as he had studied the enumeration type of science as proposed by Louis and had then read of the refutation of that concept by L.D. Jules Gavarret in 1840. His approach to diagnosis and treatment, based on the objectivity of mathematical concepts, was contradicted by W.P. Alison at the British Association for the Advancement of Science in 1855. By that time, Richardson was teaching and took great interest in D.W. Cheever's Boylston Prize Essay in 1861, when he proclaimed that figures were not brains and tables not perceptions. He plumped for the observational powers of the practising physician, and a de-emphasis of mathematical medicine.

Nevertheless the manifest destiny to make medicine into a science, like astronomy, was not to be denied and when Bernard announced his studies in 1865, a new avenue opened. Medicine was not to be a passive observational science, as proposed by the school of Louis, but an active discipline which, on the basis of laboratory investigation, could intervene to change the course of disease. Following the revolutionary findings of Bernard, I.P. Semmelweiss and Lister, medical practice had begun to become a more deterministic activity, reluctantly shedding the mantle of empiricism, and awaiting only the means to be more acute in its observations, which became possible with the work of Carl Wunderlich. He restored the balance between the laboratory branch of medicine and the clinical bedside approach by emphasizing new tools of observations such as the thermometer.

Richardson was able, by his first-hand acquaintance with the workings and history of the profession, to lead a stimulating discussion. It was not an unusual evening as the MS was evolving into a post-graduate school with more of the teaching staff taking great pains to present up-to-date data, well above that taught to undergraduates.

It was a timely topic as the war of words escalated between scientific naturalism and, "those who, while accepting to the full of the methods and results of Science, will not surrender the ancient hopes of our race."[15] Although science as preached and practiced by Ramsay Wright and the Departments of Biology and Chemistry had been given precedence in medical teaching, there remained misgivings. John Dalton's publication of *A New System of Chemical Philosophy* in the 1830s; Darwin's and Wallace's shattering pronouncements on evolution in the 1850's and 60's, with the work of the physicists on the conservation of energy incremented a philosophical force which imbued thinkers like Spencer, Tyndall and Galton. They stormed the walls of accepted Christian faith calling up defenders of a somewhat tattered belief, such as Samuel Butler, James Ward and Henry Sidgwick. This struggle in England between titans was reflected in the small pool at Toronto – and Aikins had need to read again Paley's *Views of the Evidence of Christianity,* which he had bought almost half a century previously.

Ramsay Wright played a key role in this debate. In the lectures, he updated the group on research in cerebral localization, from the morbidity standpoint, using a "magic lantern" for his slides. One month later he gave another talk on Mesmerism, and at that time a group from the "Ladies Medical College" was invited. On various occasions he spoke on histology and pathology with the physiological factors associated with many diseases. Using his biology background he was able to inter-relate human and animal factors, frequently with specimens from the Museum of Natural History which he had developed. Although he favoured laboratory instruction, rather than traditional lectures, he was able to illustrate his points most effectively by drawing on the blackboard simultaneously with each hand. He acknowledged this was a "parlour trick", but he was able to catch the interest and imagination of the audience. He also spoke on the loss of heat from the body surfaces and conditions affecting it, and the evolution of medical education in Europe.

Medical ethics, diphtheria, hip diseases, examination of the viscera in cases of suspected poisoning, experiences in the North West with the Red Cross Corps, all served to engage the group's attention. The minute book provides an interesting insight into the current culture of medicine when it states, "Dr. Adam Wright supplied the humorous portion of the program by a paper on Impotence."

Alexander Primrose, who later became Professor of Medicine, gave a paper on tracheotomy and its indication in the treatment of diphtheria. J.F.W. Ferguson spoke on the advances and failures of scientific knowledge where he claimed that "accuracy is the only true brilliancy." Clark addressed on the "Borderline of Insanity" and Dr. Olmstead, superintendant of the Hamilton General, as a guest lecturer, spoke on the cure of epilepsy by operation.

He also spoke about the prevention of masturbation, which he felt was the direct result of cramming education into the young at public school. His advice to parents was circumcision and hygienic measures, plus general health improvement, outdoor occupation and strict watch over the patient. Mechanical appliances such as mitts or leather muff or a silver wire in the prepuce were suggested, but blistering of the part was deprecated. This attitude towards the "solitary vice" continued until the middle years of World War I when the medical advice to the British Army was that in order to control venereal diseases, it was allowable to engage in masturbation to relieve sexual tension, provided it was neither enjoyed nor habitual.

By 1891 there were more surgical papers and in particular discussions of abdominal surgery, especially with regard to the practices of Robert Lawson Tait, who published frequently in the *British Medical Journal*.

Although he was under considerable stress with the building of the new medical school, plus the Park Hospital and the Biology Building and the affairs in the CPSO, Aikins continued to be an active member of the Ontario Medical Association. At the annual meeting in June of 1889, he presented a paper on "The General Management of the Patient and Sick Room in Surgical Cases." In particular he stressed the necessity for pure air in the sick room and maintained that this branch of treatment was frequently neglected. He suggested that there should be filtration of air, particularly in the cities. This could be accomplished by two sheets of mosquito netting with cotton batten between each sheet. He strongly recommended that "pure air" was the greatest single remedy for consumption, and that patients should be cared for outdoors.

Several other papers at the congress included H.H. Wright, who spoke on puerperal septicaemia. He believed it could be prevented through absolute cleanliness on the part of the accoucheur. He did not believe in antiseptics, but did use hot water, soap and plenty of washing to sterilize the hands. He objected to vaginal and intrauterine douches, "because they are unpleasant for the patient, because they interfere with the physiological rest needed for the torn and bruised parts and because septic matter or air may be introduced and brought in contact with rents in the cervix, vagina or vulva and, finally, because they are unnecessary."

Workman, speaking as an "old fogie", asked members for their opinion on the use of whiskey in fever cases. Geikie replied, while believing that whiskey was of little use in many cases, it was often used as an antipyretic.

In addition to his teaching and lecturing on surgery and anatomy, Aikins filled in as a lecturer on medical psychology for the year 1888-89. For this he received $180.00. All teaching staff received a proportional pay on the basis of school income and Aikins' portion was set at 0.0591, while other members of the staff received 0.0236. This stipend was re-imbursement for some of the administrative problems that frequently surfaced in his duties as Dean. Generally full professors received $619.00 per annum and lecturers $250.00.

By 1892 Primrose was a lecturer in topographical anatomy. Richardson and M.H. Aikins were professors, but it was the junior man who had to bear the brunt of a series of charges made by Dr. Darby Bergin, who had been President of the CPSO. As he lived in Cornwall, he took his medical training in McGill, but returned to Ontario and was elected to Parliament as well as operating a very successful medical practice. During the 1885 Rebellion, he was Surgeon General to the Expeditionary Force. The CPSO required that every candidate for licensure prove that he had carefully dissected the whole human body. Bergin interviewed some students, and found that only one half of the human body was available. When quizzed on this matter, Primrose pointed out that there had been a scarcity of subjects during the last session. In addition, his estimation of how much of the cadaver was available per student disagreed with Bergin's, who was adamant that the dissection of one half of the human body was insufficient. Primrose, in summing up his explanation to Blake, wrote, "you cannot over-estimate the harm which will be done if the Council forces us to meet those requirements. I cannot imagine anything which would hamper me more in reaching efficient teaching in my department." After reconsideration, the CPSO concluded that the two halves were very much alike, sufficiently so as to render the other half unnecessary. Somehow Bergin and the CPSO had failed to grasp that this had been laid clearly in the 1891 calendar which stated:

> The body is divided into Head and Neck, Thorax, Abdomen, each of which is dissected by four students - two Upper Extremities and two Lower Extremities which are to be dissected by two students.

Primrose, who had graduated under the tutelage of Aikins, had learned his lessons well.

The changing of the standards in Anatomy did not pass quietly. Queen's University entered strong objections on the basis that it was necessary that one student dissect a whole cadaver as the duplication was required in order to ensure a thorough grounding.

A.B. Macallum became upset at what he saw as a watering down of qualifications in other areas. By 1888 students could qualify as long as they had obtained 33% on each single subject if their aggregate of marks was pulled up by higher grades in other areas. He argued that in 1891 the 50% aggregate condition was weakened and it was possible to obtain a passing grade even though a student had grasped only $^1/_3$ of a course. These decisions had been made by the Senate "a high University official interfering in affairs which belonged to the examiners alone." However, as long as the student could pass the supplementary examination in the following September, he was qualified. In addition, the Examining Board had lowered standards by relaxing the qualifications necessary for ad eundum status which was made by an appointed committee of the Medical Faculty. This group was able to grant a degree to candidates from other provinces or other universities without authorization by the Senate. In particular, Macallum felt that Wright and McFarland were key figures in this laxness and acted so on advice from on high. "It is well known that Drs. Wright and McFarland always had the ear of Mr. Mulock, and his confidential advisors. Mr. Mulock was from 1887 to 1891 the most important, the most active member of the committee on the Medical Faculty ... ." Macallum's strong protests resulted in an appointment to the Senate where he was able to insist on a more creditable examination procedure. At the same time he was able to present his case more strongly to Loudon on a pressing domestic matter. Mrs. Macallum thought that the quarters which they were occupying in the old Wycliffe building were, "not exactly suitable ... it would be inconvenient to have any laundry clothes hung outside unless indeed a somewhat high enclosure was put up."

Of course, medical linen was never washed in public, but a simmering discontent with Mulock continued over many years. In spite of the fact that he had paid personally for a special visit by Ramsay Wright to Koch's laboratory in Germany in 1890 to discuss the new anti-tubercular find, (Mulock accompanied Wright) he was never able to convince the majority of the medical professors of his sincerity. Unabashed, Mulock continued his theme of the necessity to develop preventive medicine and at a public meeting in 1890 stated, "any scheme of medical education which deals simply with curative, neglecting the preventive aspects of medical science is radically defective." He praised the microscope as the supreme instrument of research and that there were "reasonable grounds for believing that the darkness which had hitherto enveloped the scientific researcher after truth ... was about to pass away." His prodding on this matter was undoubtedly a factor leading to the decision of the Medical Faculty on February 5th 1892 to request the purchase of Ludwig's kymograph; DuBois Raymond's induction coil, manometer, Knowlton's Perfusion cannula; rabbit holders, glass tubing and other items for experimental laboratory work. This was to be funded from surplus funds of the Medical Faculty and represented a rapid gearing up of the school's research facilities. At the same meeting, it was urged that a Museum of Hygiene should be established in connection with the University in order to instruct the general public in sanitary manners. There were to be models, diagrams and examples of apparatus "connected with plumbing, drainage, disposal and refuse, heating, ventilation, climatology, water supplies, fire escapes and protection against fire, furnishings for schools and gymnasia, food supplies, antiseptic preparations." It was also intended that there should be diagrams of defective plumbing and appliances. This was not "research" nor "science," but it put preventive medicine in the public mind and satisfied Mulock's urging.

This was reflected in the 1894 examination in *Sanitary Science* which asked:

Give the dimensions of a hospital ward for 30 patients. Provide for its proper ventilation. What are the principal requirements of a good housedrain in a city where there is a system of sewage. What disinfectants would you use in a case of scarlet fever, a. during the disease, b. in the house after the disease is over.

In spite of this strong stand for prevention, several years were to elapse before it was adopted enthusiastically. R.W. Bruce Smith of Hamilton, the President of the O.M.A. in 1895, gave a lick of lip service to prevention. His major theme was the subject of auto-intoxication and the putrefaction processes in the intestinal canal which caused disease. However, he placed the future of care in serum-therapy which was on the point of demonstrating its usefulness in many conditions. He mentioned another item of interest which had occurred the previous year when the science of bacteriology had such a great impact "... perhaps none too soon are we able to detect, as we most assuredly are, the strong conservatism in the surgery of female pelvic organs. Man's pelvic extremity is now perhaps in greater danger than women's."

REFERENCES

1. Huxley, T.H. Collected Essays, 1:41.
2. U of T Monthly, IV, May 8, 1908; p 22.
3. The University of Toronto and Its Colleges, 1827–1906. The University Library, 1906; p 238.
4. Ontario, Report of the Minister of Education, 1882; p 89.
5. Canadian Journal of Science. Literature and History, July 1866; p 236.
6. Gelison, Gerald L. Social and Institutional Factors in the Stagnancy of English Physiology, 1840–1870.
7. Nature February 19, 1874; p 297.
8. Huntsman, A. G. Proceedings of the Royal Society of Canada, IV-V 1934, Ser. 3, 28.
9. Craigie, E. Horne. A History of the Department of Zoology of the University of Toronto up to 1962; p 80.
10. The University of Toronto and Its Colleges. Ibid; pp 242–243.

11. Craigie, E. Horne. ibid.
12. Cushing, Harvey. The Life of Sir William Osler 1925; p 272.
13. Lancet 1898, 2; pp 488–89.
14. Bull, U. Perkins. From Medicine Man to Medical Man, 1934, quoted from Streetsville Review May 13 '54.
15. Myers, F. Science and Future Life with Other Essays, London, MacMillan and Company 1893; p 192.

Chapter Nine

The Problems

There was never any written game plan, but it was obvious that Aikins constructed and pursued tactics over a number of years to achieve his goal of elevating the level of medical education and improving the quality of graduates of the system. As early as the 1850s he had advocated one central school of medicine for the province. On several occasions, he had suggested that the University Medical Faculty should be reconstituted. Frequently, particularly in his speeches, he urged that the government should give more funds to the Toronto General Hospital, with the aim of improving teaching facilities for the students. At the first annual dinner of the TSM at the Walker House on November 10th, 1874, Aikins responded to the toast to the school with a concise history of the institution and reminded the students that this institution had taken an active part for many years in endeavoring to bring about the incorporation of the profession in Ontario. "Now the profession was incorporated, but the work was not done; medical education in Ontario was not yet what it might be, nor what, in his belief, it would be before long ... He hoped to see annual examinations as in the Arts in the University with a curriculum for each year," the *Globe* reported. The evening had been arranged with a view to promote harmony and good feeling among those most immediately interested in medical education, and the entertainment for the evening was conducted in "temperance principles by the unanimous wishes of the gentlemen composing the school."

His appointment to the Council of the CPSO meant that he had become a major figure in judging a candidate's application to practice.

While through the Education Committee he was able to set higher standards, there remained the problem that he could not influence schools other than the TSM, of the necessity of including in their curriculum subjects which he held dearly, namely the science of medicine. To close the circle – that is the high level of instruction leading to a candidate who would write a tough, realistic examination set by the CPSO – it was necessary that he implace himself on the curriculum committees of those who set the examinations for the degree of M.B. or M.D. Unfortunately, his presence on the Senate of the University of Toronto, although it carried some weight, was not sufficient to convince his fellows to raise the hurdle into the practice of medicine. In 1864, while a member of the Senate, Aikins introduced and had passed a statute for increasing the requirements for the degree of M.B. At the same time he urged that the examinations should be divided into two parts. Again, in 1865, he made several recommendations with regard to the examinations in Medicine, while giving his annual report.

The opportunity to complete his plan came when William Mulock was appointed to the Senate.

Mulock was born at Bond Head, Canada West in 1844. He was a brilliant student who recalled writing his matriculation examination in Moss Hall, one of the first anatomy laboratories. He enjoyed recounting on numerous occasions how it felt to be sitting at a dissection table, which was normally occupied by cadavers. He graduated in 1863 with a gold medal in Modern Languages, following which he sat his Bar examinations and rose rapidly to pre-eminence. In addition he entered politics and, joining the Liberal party, was elected to the Federal Government to represent North York. With his social standing, (the Mulocks were a force in the province and wielded political prestige,) he was appointed to the Senate of the University and was named Vice Chancellor (V.C.) in January of 1881. At that time, *The Varsity* described him as one of the "young, practical and energetic men of the world, who, though young are not inexperienced, though practical, are not devoid of enthusiasm ... It is recognized that his essay for his matriculation had been on the subject, 'That examinations are more of a bugbear in anticipation than in reality. ...'" Mulock accepted this as a credo for his life. When he took his place on the Senate, he found that Edward Blake, Chancellor since 1873, and leader of the Liberal party, was frequently in the House at Ottawa rather than in the Senate chamber. The newcomer astutely observed that the Senate was spending a great deal of time in discussing minutiae of expenses and other picayune matters. By declaring that this was not the best use of that body, he was able to persuade it to appoint a Board of Trustees which looked at financial matters, in particular with regard to the endowment of the University, thus leaving the Senate more time for weighty matters. He became Chairman.

Blake had been on the Senate for 30 years and although he had numerous other duties, he supervised the preparation of a massive report in 1882 which detailed a plan to enlarge the library, construct a gymnasium and a Mineralogy and Geology building as well as a new Convocation Hall. All these were graded in time to constrain expenditures within endowment revenues, so avoiding asking the Government for money. Mineralogy and Geology were a prime interest of the legislature as the young province began to develop its natural resources. Those courses might lead to government grants.

Blake and Mulock, though members of the same political party, clashed on many occasions particularly in matters of tariff relationships with the U.S. Blake felt strongly that there could not be a Commercial Union with the Americans, while other members of his caucus, including Wilfred Laurier and Mulock, were in favour of such an attempt to improve Canada's trade position. Mulock voted that reciprocity with the States was a better approach, but Blake argued that this was a slow journey to annexation.

This combativeness carried into the Senate, but in that chamber Blake had powerful allies in Daniel Wilson, President of University College, James Loudon, Physics Professor and H.H. Langton, Assistant Registrar. Loudon was a late convert who had entered the Senate with Mulock. For a number of years he had benefitted from apparatus for his physics laboratory and other perks which were steered his way through Mulock's influence. But in the late eighties he became disenchanted with the V.C.'s rough-shod tactics and turned to Wilson, Blake noted in his journal," like a sun-flower turns to the sun." Such inconstancy of loyalties and friendships was not uncommon in the halls of academe, as evidenced by frequent re-alignments of friends and foes.

Each of these felt that Mulock was in too much of a rush. He proposed an orchestrated campaign to obtain provincial grants, which Blake and the others opposed because it threatened the University's autonomy. Mulock proposed a College of Technology for the teaching of some sciences. Initially, Blake and Loudon were against the concept as it was to be built separate from the University. However, in 1878 Mulock, displaying an unusual tact, changed his course and the School for Practical Sciences was inaugurated as part of the University of Toronto. This followed the model which was being established at Cambridge.

Mulock pushed for ever-increasing expansion and on November 11th, 1882, at a Trinity Medical dinner, he suggested that Trinity and the TSM should amalgamate: "... with two medical schools in affiliation with the University of Toronto, that Institution will endeavour and I believe with some degree of success, to strengthen the hands of those teaching bodies in their effort to promote medical education in Ontario; and I have it upon the authority of a distinguished professor in a London hospital ... while Canadian students are not highly prepared in the practical knowledge of the healing art, their theoretical attachment is quite equal to those of English trained students ..."

He continued his advocacy, limning the Aikins text, on being appointed V.C., when the initial part of his address was on the admission of females to the University (he was in favour, preferably in a separate annex to the College.) He left that subject and discussed the TSM, declaring, "... public opinion has agreed that it is the duty of the State to place the means of State education within the reach of those who elect to accept from the State ..." and ended with a strong plea that the University should fund medical school teaching. It was not specified where there was such an expression by the vox populi as claimed by the speaker. The print media never called for government funding, either in the popular or professional press. And Geikie was ever alert to one penny passing from the province to the profession.

Just why Mulock and Aikins established a common work plan is not apparent. It is possible that the former, in his ambitious drive to become Chancellor, took up the cause of medicine as one whose day had come, given the recent scientific discoveries in Europe, which promised to provide a text-book opportunity to demonstrate his leadership and organizational skills. Medicine could provide a venue to justify the School of Practical Science and restructure the University away from

Wilson's cadre of metaphysical speculative scholars, to the inductive methodology of Francis Bacon. Alternatively, it is believable that Mulock was fired with a zeal to improve medical practice, and enlisted Aikins because of his knowledge and experience of medical education. Naturally, as the TSM was the largest and most modern of the proprietary schools, Aikins stood well alongside Mulock. But whether Aikins chose Mulock or was used by him is a matter for conjecture. For almost 15 years the pair had a community of interest and a congruence of aspirations that telegraphed a joint strategy. Together they rose, and together they lost their clout, although some of their principles endured.

With the momentous discoveries by Louis Pasteur in the 1860s, medicine began to change from practising an art, to being a science. Repeatedly in the curriculum of the medical schools, there was emphasis on scientific teaching. However, the goal of the new philosophy was frequently barred by mundane matters. In 1879 the medical students petitioned the Senate of the University of Toronto to remove practical physiology from the examination schedule as "no apparatus in the School of Practical Science (is available) for instruction". Professor Wright agreed. About the same time a petition was received to remove practical chemistry, for the same reason. At Mulock's urging, the Senate did not agree and Oldright gave the practical chemistry examination, in particular with its application to forensic medicine and hygiene.

Preparations for examinations was not simply a matter of instructing in a subject, as it was necessary to provide proper examination rooms. On several instances students objected to inadequate facilities and, because of the importance of graduation, on one occasion rioted. In 1880 the Senate recognized this pressing need for sufficient space and made application to the Lieutenant Governor for $30,000.00 for the erection of a new building in which examination, museums and classrooms would be located. Part of the quid pro quo was that the government was attempting to build Parliament Buildings which necessitated the University giving up rights to an existing stone building, Moss Hall, which occupied the site. "No one will be sorry when the large cut stone building in the Queen's Park, Toronto used not long since as a receptacle for female lunatics, shall be utterly demolished and its materials conveyed away ... in the west wing was the laboratory of the professor of chemistry, Mr. Croft and a lecture room for the medical professors, Drs. Wynne, King, Herrick, Beaumount and Nichol and the anatomical demonstrator, Dr. Henry Sullivan."[1]

This matter of adequate space for the students recurred continually in the Senate meetings. Finally, in 1885, Mulock took the matter in his own hands with an approach to the government and said that he was going to raise the money for purchasing and erecting a suitable building, in or near the hospital grounds. This pleased Aikins, who had been on the Senate since 1873 and frequently pushed for more workable examination centres. He already had the experience with the CPSO of inadequate facilities, which had been remedied only recently.

At the same time, Wilson presented to the Senate a report on a proposed medical faculty. He referred to a Committee, chaired by Mulock, which had been working on a proposition to improve the efficiency of medical education with the University of Toronto: "It is desirable to establish a medical college to be known as the University of Toronto Medical College which would be the medical faculty of the University. The College shall have a governing body. There shall be no college council". More importantly, the Committee suggested that if the faculties of the TSM or Trinity decided to leave those schools, they would be welcome at the U of T Medical College. The proposal, wisely, outlined a remuneration schedule which would be "as far as possible the same position for the new college as a whole as professors or lectures to the present schools". To accomplish this the committee proposed to take the scale of the Trinity Medical College as a basis and at the same time another provision was made for the retirement allowance for professors. Following this Senate decision, the proposals were distributed to various medical schools, and the Trustees of the General Hospital.

There followed a rapid series of events. By May 11th, the Senate resolved that the University of Toronto should establish a teaching faculty of medicine. It was agreed "... that no persons other than the demonstrator of anatomy shall be appointed to such a staff for a longer term than five years, but shall be eligible for re-appointment from time to time. However no person at the age of 60 could be appointed or reappointed".

By July 4th Trinity had refused to join, but Aikins said "... that in the interest of medical science and therefore the general public, it is a duty that the provincial university, at the earliest possible moment establish a teaching faculty of medicine". The Senate Committee responded with:

> ... instead of permitting the important branch of medicine to remain almost exclusively in the hands of joint stock companies, liable to be managed with a view to pecuniary oriented proprietors rather than the cause of medical science. Your committee does not desire to be understood as expressing an opinion that such has been the policy of any medical school, but the circumstances of the efforts of this University extending over a long period of years to encourage a higher standard of medical education, appear not to have been practically secconded by any medical school ... such an arrangement, having no private gain but the general interest of the people, is best calculated to promote the highest interest of medical science, and in order to reach the attainment of that goal, this committee desires to place on record their appreciation of the assistance in that behalf rendered by members of the staff at the Toronto School of Medicine.

The Committee then recommended that the Professor of Practical Surgery should be Aikins and the rest of members of the TSM teaching staff received a similar invitation.

One of the most important clauses of the foundation of the new school was that "University staff would be paid each year out of the tuition fees, collected from the medical students in such a year. From the gross amount of fees collected, each teacher was to receive a percentage based on a formula which considered teaching status, length of time, etc. Aikins was to receive 0.0591 of the gross. H.H. Wright, Odgen, Thorburn and M.H. Aikins received 0.0236.

The Committee recommended leasing the Toronto School of Medicine for $1,200. a year and this was signed by Mulock, Committee chairman. Aikins had no difficulty in accepting this windfall.[2]

While the Dean and all members of the TSM were delighted with the formation of the new Medical Faculty, Geikie fired off a hot missile to the Honourable Mr. Ross, Minister of Education, on April 13th 1887: "We, as a body, (Trinity Medical School) will feel much aggrieved if the power to create a new teaching medical faculty be given in the Act ... it will lead to constant intriguing and planning for everlasting hot water – beside destroying our affiliation". He asserted that this move was "... contrary to the policy of the Provincial University as it was established in 1853, and would practically destroy its character as a provincial university so far as regards medical education, and would reduce it to the rank of one, among several, competing universities". He also warned that this was opposed to the recently announced government scheme to have college federation and to carefully preserve the identities of various colleges by not amalgamating them.

His other arguments were that the proposed scheme had no satisfactory financial basis. "Medical professors require to be adequately remunerated, if they are expected to devote their chief energies to the duties of their respective Chairs, and this would not be the case under the proposed plan, such as it does not contemplate any provision for professors' salaries beyond the fees obtained from the students". He hammered on this point continually over the next few years, insisting, as had happened with Johns Hopkins, that professors should be paid adequately. It was his contention that if medical education was dependent upon the support of fees alone, then the best system was the current one as it had been eminently successful for many years.

It was remarkable that Geikie and Aikins, both of whom had trained at the TSM in the 50s and who had espoused the tenet that the education of physicians should not be a charge on the taxpayer, had now arrived at diametrically opposite views.

Geikie's refusal to retreat from his self-proclaimed high ground was understandable because of the credo he had held since his undergraduate years. However, if he had read the sentiments of the Legislature and sensed the force behind the decision, his Celtic wisdom would have counselled that he should "lie down and bleed awhile," and then arise to take a leading role in the new faculty. But his principles were not as flexible as Aikins'.

His cup of bitterness overflowed when Aikins was elected Dean.

The new Dean, like many other University scene observers, was aware of some of the nuances of academic politics. His experiences with Rolph, Victoria and the shift in loyalties of his staff, served as a template on which he could place the protracted squabbles of the various Faculty members as they jockeyed for standing-room at the endowment trough. But it required a seasoned sage to follow the labyrinthine activities of the various religious schools. One of the most vexing problems was to establish the mission of the University of Toronto. It's college constituents were the agents of denominational religions and stressed piety and deference to their creed. But by the middle of the century, the siren call of "science" was luring some students, which led to a questioning of the validity of certain beliefs. While the cultivation of character and the inculcation of social discipline had been the general hallmark of the overall curriculum, there was a new element which stressed that nothing could be taken on faith. This had already appeared in medical studies as a result of the Parisian teaching and the lecturing of Bowditch, Holmes and others. It paralleled the shattering publications of Darwin and other European savants.

Added to this dilemma was the matter of "nativism". Under Wilson's suzerainty, staff appointments, which were made by Parliament, went to British or European candidates. But opposition to this appeared with the Canada First Movement which urged employment of local candidates and was backed by Blake, Mulock, Loudon and many alumnae. This group eventually won the ear of Government, but not before Wilson's death.

Aikins' birth, education and practice were unique qualifications for his Deanship, and when the time came for an appointment, there was no question of his professional ability (which satisfied Mulock), his nativism (which gratified Loudon), or his piety (which mollified Wilson). Behind the aspiration of each of these three was the leitmotiv of the titanic struggle over the primacy of scientific research at the University. Research required money for apparatus and personnel, but Ross could not provide it. Science was a catalyst that advanced knowledge and eroded the pillars of conventional structures. While Aikins had faced money problems at the TSM, he had never been required to consider any reconciliation of the content of his medical courses with metaphysical or religious opinion. It took consummate skill to ride these two chargers in the academic arena. The decade following the initiation of the Faculty of Medicine into the University of Toronto promised great opportunity for success – or failure.

In spite of the constant rebuffs that he received from the Medical Council and from the Government, Geikie persisted. Cassandra-like, he

issued warnings and predictions, "... such a faculty would not do anything to raise the standard of medical education, which very properly is
the work of the Medical Council". He drew attention to his opinion that
affiliation with the Provincial University over the past thirty years had
been a privilege enjoyed by every medical school and they had come to
regard it in the light of a vested right. "If the teaching faculty was established, that affiliation of all medical schools is virtually at an end. The
new teaching facility would do its best to attract as many students as
possible and would exert every influence in its power to belittle, to
deplete and, if possible, cripple other medical schools". It was not fair.
After many years of ill-remunerated toil, things were improving in the
existing medical schools with higher attendance and better equipment.
"The members of the Faculty of Trinity Medical School alone had spent
out of their own pockets, $10,000.00 within a short time to increase the
efficiency of their school." This memorandum to Ross on April 14, 1887
prompted a letter to the Honourable Oliver Mowat on the 24th of July
1887 which deprecated anything in Geikie's correspondence that,
"would influence the action of the Senate of the University in the establishment of the teaching faculty as provided by the Act of the last Session. The only statement in the memorandum to which we ought, I
think, to attach importance is ... we must take special care to prevent
the Medical Faculty being a charge upon university funds. Neither
directly or indirectly should we be responsible for the salary of a single
professor, or a contiguity of any sort". In essence the University of Toronto was setting up a proprietary school within its own domain, and all
expenses were to be born by the students' fees. Nothing was to flow
from the University itself. This was an unusual accommodation, which
was not applied to any other college or course in the University.

The Senate meeting on March 26, 1887 was a moment of exultation
for Aikins. The committee which had been set up to report on the establishment of a re-born medical faculty, delivered the most important
decision of his life. Daniel Wilson, the chairman, announced: "It is
desirable to establish a Medical College to be known as the University
Medical College ... The College shall have a governing board which
shall consist of six members elected by the Senate of the University and
the Chairman and one other member of the Hospital Trust. There shall
be a College Council, which shall consist of the professors of the Medi-

cal College, including such professors in the School of Practical Science as are giving instruction in the subjects of the medical curriculum ... if the faculty or the faculties of the Toronto School of Medicine or Trinity Medical School decide to suspend their charter or charters and are acceptable to the proposed scheme, the members of such faculty or faculties shall hold as far as possible the same positions in the new schools. The present salaries of professors shall be maintained pro rata ... present existing in Trinity Medical School shall be taken as a basis ... the governing body shall seek from the Ontario government the power to raise the sum of x dollars for the purpose of purchasing or erecting suitable buildings in or near the hospital grounds". Vice Chancellor Mulock, Mr. Falconbridge and Wilson were appointed to communicate with the representatives of the medical schools and the Trustees of the General Hospital.

The editor of *The Varsity*, picked out the clause that "the Faculty of Medicine shall conduct the medical examination and such examination as from time to time be associated with them by appointment of the Senate." This gave medical students the advantage of a course in liberal or arts studies, "We are sure that the profession and public will join us in hearing with delight the advent of some such provision. Under the present system, the only training other than strictly professional which the medical schools receive is that obtained previous to matriculation. This is usually of a proprietary and limited character and should not be the only adjunct to the mental furnishings of the future physician's mind".

The final act in the establishment of the Faculty was on June 24th 1887 when Mulock signed the Statute announcing the session would begin on the 1st of October.

The new faculty lost no time in setting a mark for the students. Professor W.R. Wright stated in his inaugural address: "... We felt in the past that many of our medical graduates exhibited little sympathy with an institution, whose halls they only entered to be subjected to rigorous examinations, where no opportunity was offered them of becoming penetrated by the genius loci, and no chance of meeting so as to develop any corporate spirit or to have intellectual fellowship with students of other faculties. We proposed by our present action to remedy these great defects in the future and congratulate ourselves that while London is still clamouring for a 'teaching university', we have advanced a step further and secured ours."[3] He then reported that the German universities had achieved their highest function as a result of money spent liberally by the government with that object. Their government contributed 72% of the annual cost of the universities, 44% of which was devoted to the equipment and maintenance of the institutions, which served for investigation as well as for teaching in the various sciences. In addition the German universities were peculiar in the "large number of young teachers".

The school was an overnight success. In 1887 there were 30 medical graduates, but by the spring of 1890 there had been an increase to 53. In this process the medsmen became an active part of the University and established stronger bonds than had been evident when they were simply in the TSM. Aikins supervised many innovations. While microscopy had been taught in a superficial manner, now first year students learned the use of the instrument. Instruction in physiology and chemistry, previously lectured in a theoretical manner, was now taught in a laboratory and the students were required to perform experiments, under the enthusiastic direction of Ramsay Wright. There was a beginning of an attempt to relate these activities to pathology. Similar changes took place in the dissecting room. The methods used in schools in Great Britain, which emphasized morbid anatomy, were incorporated into the Toronto course by Richardson and his staff. Clinical instruction doubled over the first three years and included more teaching in pathology and demonstrations of biopsies and their relation to the sick patient.

The Calendar for the year included advertisements for the first time. Life insurance; medical books; Hammand the Hatter; Johnson and Larmour, Merchant Tailors; Dixon, the photographer; and J. Stevens and Son, established 1830, surgical instrument makers, 40 Wellington Street East were publicized. A physician's Day and Cash book, 200 pages, sold for $2.00. Clinical charts, "as used in the General Hospital," were 60 cents per 100. Davis Brothers, Jewellers, invited the reader to "call and inspect our physician's watch." Prior to this the Calendar for Aikins' school might have a picture of the building, but no advertisements.

The preamble to course descriptions read:

"During recent years it has been argued that a scheme might be matured which would give the University a teaching faculty in medicine and thus extend to a large degree the usefulness of the University Professoriate, without any extra expense to the Government. The only objection on the part of the public being thus removed, the Government of Ontario embodied in the Federation Act of the Session 1887, a clause which gave to the Senate of the University, the power to establish such a faculty."

The Calendar continued that "biology, physiology, normal histology and chemistry will be taught in the mornings at the University classrooms and laboratory. Anatomy, the practice of medicine, surgery, obstetrics, gynecology, materia medica and therapeutics, medical jurisprudence, sanitary science, pathology, ophthalmology and otology, laryngology and rhinology will be taught in the building formerly occupied by the Toronto School of Medicine on the corner of Gerrard and Sackville streets. Clinical instruction will be given in the Toronto General Hospital and will consist of regular clinical lectures in the theatre, bedside teaching in the wards, clinical teaching and outdoor department in general medical and surgical diseases, skin diseases, disease of women, disease of eye, ear, nose and throat and bedside teaching in the Burnside-Lying-In Hospital. The teaching of anatomy in all the final subjects including clinical instruction will be given between 11 a.m. and 6:30 p.m."

Under Sanitary Science by Professor Oldright, the discussion would include, "air impurities and effects, how it is caused and how obviated, modes of examination, ventilation, disinfection, sewage disposal and utilization, dry, wet and air methods, contagion and infection, climatology, soils, winds, vegetation, hygienic architecture, clothing, baths, water sources; varying composition and impurities, their effects; how removed and prevented." The curriculum also included foods, comparative values, impurities and their effects; sleep, exercise, occupation, mode of life; and sanitary legislation present and its perception in various countries.

Pathological histology by Dr. John Cavan embraced "the examination of urine and such other fluids normal and pathological as can be obtained from the post mortem; the demonstration of phenomena, the results of information; the microscropic appearance of tissues in the various diseased states; the growth and structure of the neoplasms and demonstration of parasites."

Two separate courses in physiology were offered, one for the first year students, which" will aim at imparting a thorough knowledge of the elements of physiology and a more advanced course for the second year students in which special attention will be given to the relations of physiology to medicine."

"In the second year, there will be a demonstration of histology, each student will be instructed in the methods in preparing and mounting histological specimens."

"A three month course of lectures on botany will be held for students of the first year. This will be illustrated by specimens and models in the University collection. Practical class of instruction in the use of the microscope will be arranged."

The University offered instruction in biology, including zoology and botany, and it was quite practicable for students to study similar disease processes in the lower animals as in man. A.B. Macallum felt so strongly that biology should be of practical use that he took the course in medicine and qualified as M.B. in 1889, while still a member of the teaching staff.

Not all these changes were accompanied by the well-wishes of the academic community, in which the cash shortage was so acute that by 1895 the Senate sent a Report to the legislature protesting the "poverty of means". The Arts departments were envious of the new opportunities that were made available to medical students. The continuous rhetoric that "the medical school did not receive any support from the government and was entirely self-supported from frees paid by students" irked many. Access to apparatus for experiments in chemistry and physiology was not possible for Trinity students, and gave Aikins' students special knowledge.

This aggrandizement, as some suggested, of the role of science in medical teaching was given further support by Huxley. In a letter to the *London Times* on the subject of medical education, he wrote:" ... almost a self-evident position that the education training for persons who propose to enter to the medical profession should be largely scientific; not merely, or even principally because an acquaintance with the elements of physical and biological science is absolutely essential to the comprehension of human physiology and pathology, but still more because of the value of the discipline afforded by the practical work in these departments ... it is the delusion to suppose that listening to lectures for two or three hours a week can confer a scientific training .... ." His senti-ments were echoed by the younger Faculty members in Toronto. How-ever this resonance became asynchronous when Geikie and others wrote letters and made presentations to the Minister of Education. Their position was supported in part by Mr. Lawson Tait who, while addressing the British Medical Association in 1889, emphasized that those who entered the craft of Surgery should be taught how to use their hands, in the same way a village carpenter is trained to a saw and plane. At the same time, he criticized as inappropriate, the teaching of physiology and anatomy at the University of Edinburgh, Ramsay Wright's school. The opposition to loading the curriculum with scien-tific subjects, rather than clinical teaching continued in the United Kingdom until well into the twentieth century. Some of this philosophy stemmed from the fact that medical teaching was done in hospitals, and not in universities.

Part of Geikie's remarks deplored the pressure on students to absorb too much knowledge in such a short time. This matter occupied a good part of Dean Aikins' thoughts. In 1889, the winter session in Toronto was six months duration with 2½ weeks of Christmas holidays. Each student was required by the CPSO to attend six sessions. Each session contained approximately 100 lectures on every main subject, plus prac-tical work in the laboratories and attendance at the hospital. A normal day ended at 6 p.m. Aikins, addressing a Convocation for medical degrees explained that this gave little time to the student for physical activities aside from walking from his boarding house to and from the college and hospital. He urged that six months were far too short and should be of nine month duration, so as to do away with the need for cramming. It was his contention that the current timetable, which had been inflated by science subjects, meant that students gradually with-drew from classes by the middle of February to prepare for examina-tions. However, his suggestion to the Minister of Education and the President of University College was not taken up, although it was agreed that summer sessions might be a wise move.

The overloading in the course evoked comment from a number of sources. The *Canada Lancet* in February, 1890 carried a derisive editorial on "so-called modern medicine" which it claimed did not permit the trainee to see small pox or scarlet fever. "We only ask those anxious to thrust into the Medical Course every newly discovered science or scientific apparatus, is it necessary? Is it not possible to appropriate and apply results? Is there a danger of converting the Medical Course into a Science Course? In this age of clamourers for Practical Courses, may not the medical students of the present become practical scientists rather than practical physicians?" The editorial continued that Canada was a young country and possessed some excellent medical men who had not familiarized themselves with the science of medicine, yet were regarded as abreast of any in the world. This attitude was bolstered by a Letter to the Editor asserting that Aikins' old school was now practically a government medical school and this was unjust to the proprietary schools. The writer maintained that the public had not asked for this action, nor had the medical profession nor did the interest of medical education call for it. "The doctor must be eminently practical ... the medical student may be very scientific when he is feeling a tuning fork and trying to determine the number of its vibrations per second, but he would achieve more useful medical knowledge if he spent that time in the dissecting room. In crowding the medical course with unapplied sciences, the tendency is to neglect those of more importance and the more will be the case, where those not in touch with the requirements of the medical profession, are allowed to set courses." These sentiments echoed those expressed in London, where the president of the Royal College of Surgeons, as late as 1910, warned that such "training is very theoretical and scientific and not a preparation fitting a man to go at once into practice."[4]

Of course, it was not unusual nor atypical for Aikins to be unhappy with medical courses, and by the 1880's his voice was joining others in expressing discontent. Dr. John Shaw Billings, who founded the Surgeon General's library, later the National Library of Medicine, and was responsible for the design of the Johns Hopkins Hospital, had words of caution in his address to the International Medical Congress in 1881. Aikins heard him acknowledge that physiology was important, but it was distinct from practical medicine. Although the separation was good for "science" it was not a sound idea to neglect human pathology. Billings bowed to the work of Michael Foster, who insisted that pathology and physiology could not be separated any more than could the science of good weather and the science of bad weather, but Billings held that laboratory physiology could not replicate the diseased body. The only place where the real physiological studies could take place, was the bedside, where "... nature is continually performing experiments."[5]

It was a difficult course for the Dean of a new University school. While Aikins' School of Medicine busied itself with work-a-day subjects such as Anatomy and Materia Medica, there was no pressure to have a broad scholastic philosophy. But as the University of Toronto Medical School, there was a mission to promote speculative, philosophical disciplines – such as physiology. But absorbing as the study of bodily functions might be to some, others felt that it did not merit any higher importance than "interesting phenomena." To most physicians, the art of medicine was encompassed by what knowledge was held and by whom. Since that momentous day in 1847 when the American Medical Association was formed there had been no doubt of the "whom." Men who had qualified to practice medicine, after a rigorous course and who were of unassailable moral character, were physicians. Each of these two components was vital.

Others, although they claimed to be doctors were not acknowledged, as was quite patent in Ontario by the constant wrangling over the status of homeopaths. Although they were licensed to practice, there was a bitter censure of working with other than those who qualified with an M.D. or M.B. This stand was questioned upon occasion, however the CPSO stood firmly against any incursion by other groups. Some practitioners considered that the "physiological therapeutics", which had been born of the science disciplines, seriously threatened this convention. The xenophobic emotion to honour long-held mores facilitated grouping the non-traditionalists with all the others who were outside the pale. This determination reflected a major identity crisis in the U.S. where the findings of science were seen as the new arbiter of practice patterns. Several prominent physicians argued that the principles laid down in 1847 were no longer applicable and a revised Code of Ethics based on new knowledge should be proclaimed, which would permit consultations with homeopaths. The resulting storm by Dr. Austin Flint showed the depth of a division between the two groups. The traditionalists argued that the so-called "scientific medicine" was inexact and varied from patient to patient. In 1886, Dr. Alfred Stille, the Dean of the University of Pennslyvania, gave an address "Truth in Medicine and Truth in Life Inseparable," in which he warned of the dangers of physiological therapeutics. If the findings of science were accepted, they would give a moral sanction to practitioners who were outside the guidelines laid down for the practice of medicine by traditional custom. This intrusion of another set of rules was unacceptable, and resulted in a severe disruption of the AMA.

Throughout his life, Aikins had added to his knowledge, while maintaining and expanding his Christian ethos. To surrender his priesthood in medicine to "science" as embodied in physiology, which would threaten God's place in the temporal world, was precipitating a betrayal of belief. This dilemma was amplified daily by Mulock's unholy alliance with faculty members such as Ramsay Wright, A.B. Macallum and others. Thus, it became necessary for the Dean to straddle the razor-sharp edge division between science and accepted practice.

The problem of accommodation for teaching remained. In February of 1888, Ross, who was still Minister of Education, received a request from the University for assistance to construct a new building for classrooms. The estimated cost was $45,200.00. As the Board of Trustees had $15,500.00, another $30,000.00 was requested, preferably from the University capital fund.

On the one hand, the University was putting up funds for the teaching of medicine, but on the other, it was retreating from the principle of University funds not being used for the Faculty of Medicine. This paradoxical situation was further clouded by Ross when he gave a speech to the Ontario Medical Association and said "the Government was prepared to aid in the direction of higher medical education". The statement immediately triggered a response from Geikie, who cried that physiological and chemical apparatus was very expensive and that when the University was thinking of providing some of these to the University (ie. TSM), Trinity Medical College had similar needs and wants. Ross replied, "I am glad that you appreciate my efforts to promote the higher education of the medical profession; and I am glad also to know that we have in Trinity University a valuable co-adjutor". However Ross avoided any mention of money.

Mulock's connection with the cabinet and his Senate position bore fruit and he proposed an addition to the Biological laboratory which was approved by the Board of Trustees of the University in October of '89. The architect estimated the work would cost about $68,000.00 and sent the plans to J.E.B. Smith, the Bursar.

Two weeks later Premier Ross was able to report to Mulock that the expansion of the Biological Department had been approved, and the Lieutenant Governor, by Order-in-Council, appointed Archibald B. Macallum, McKay, and Alexander McPhedran to the staff. Ross also sent a personal letter of commendation to R. Ramsay Wright, who was being sent to Berlin as a representative of the University of Toronto to observe the work of Professor Koch. "I am extremely anxious that our universities should keep abreast of those discoveries of medical science for which we are largely indebted to European investigators", wrote the Premier.

Wright was not the only University representative. Mulock accompanied the professor when Koch announced his treatment for tuberculosis. Wright's expenses, paid by Mulock was an unusual event for the University of Toronto, which usually received funding only from the government. This was quite unlike the situation in Quebec where McGill rarely received significant support from government sources. The feeling in the francophone Quebec Assembly was that the main responsibility was for primary schools in public education. A McGill petition of 1886 to the government quoted all the monies received by the college from public sources. Beginning in 1854, this did not amount to one fourth of the annual revenues of the University of Toronto or one tenth of the value of Mr. McGill's bequest. In 1870 the school Board of Governors, facing one of their recurring financial crises, appealed to the Montreal anglophone community and raised a very gratifying $52,000. It was proposed that this might be used for the admission of women, however, the amount was insufficient for co-education and, in addition, there was a preference for a separate college. A request to Donald Smith resulted in a further $50,000 on condition that women's classes be entirely separate from those of men. He gave another $70,000 in 1885. In addition some money was raised from selling parts of the James McGill estate. A fund-raising program based on the proposition that a strong University was good for the country resulted in a series of donors including John Henry Robinson Molson and William Christopher Macdonald. The latter contributed over a twenty year period, $800,000.00 in endowments and special grants. Smith made a special donation in 1905 of $50,000.00 to cover the added costs of extending the medical course from four to five years.[6]

In Ontario even the proprietary schools received money from government, so there was little need perceived by the public or business for additional support. Trinity resented the fact that the University of Toronto, after it absorbed the TSM, was supported fully by the government while Trinity was "forgotten". Geikie conveniently ignored the fact that his school, like others, had received considerable assistance for many years. Fortunately, the practice of private donations, from individuals or industry, became more attractive in the twentieth century following a thrust by Mulock to encourage the University to be more oriented to wooing business men by the quality of its graduates.

••••••

Although there was now a Medical Faculty in the University, the level of examinations had been raised to CPSO's standards and there had been a partial solution of the problem of insufficient classrooms, one vital factor was absent from the curriculum. Aikins had argued for many years that a hospital should be available for clinical teaching and the furtherance of scientific medicine, which should be supported by the government. His experiences with the General Hospital, with its many feuds and factions, had convinced him that a "University" hospital would be the solution to this last problem. Fortunately Mulock agreed.

When Mulock had proposed to the Toronto Senate that Victoria University should come into an alliance with Toronto, he approached Senator John Macdonald, a member of the Senate of both universities. Macdonald, the "Merchant Prince", owned the largest dry goods business in Canada, with a gothic five storey warehouse. He employed more than a 100 clerks with annual sales of over a million dollars (and gave Timothy Eaton his start). Macdonald was well acquainted with Aikins, after the accident to his wife some years earlier. In addition Macdonald was a devout and generous Methodist, who preached almost every Sunday. He laid the corner-stone of the Metropolitan Church for which Aikins had campaigned and donated so generously, and each sat on the Board of Trustees.

Macdonald was in favour of the union of Victoria and Toronto, but it was unsuccessful at this time.

A close relationship continued to exist between the three Senate members and after the establishment of the Medical Faculty in 1887, Macdonald expressed his desire to found and fund a hospital which "will in an eminent degree prove a blessing for all time to come to the afflicted classes of this great city, and which was the earnest wish of my child, but will also materially contribute to the advancement of medical science in connection with the University of Toronto". Amy Macdonald had died some years previously and her father had promised on her deathbed that her inheritance would go to establishing a hospital. Aikins, in his new Professorship was excited that new and better facilities would be available for the teaching of surgery. Mulock took the proposition to the Trustees of the University who were delighted with the proposal and undertook to secure the additional $110,000.00, which would be necessary for building and equipping the hospital.

Originally Macdonald had requested that the institution would be called "The Amy Macdonald Hospital", however this smacked of a private institution and an alternate name "The Park Hospital" was accepted, because of the proposed site in Queen's Park. A draft agreement and necessary letters were circulated in the Senate and the Board of Trustees, which agreed that the project should proceed. Mulock was voted permanent chairman of The Park Hospital Board of Trustees.

Word spread quickly through the press and led to an outcry by some residents close to the park that this was a wrong site. The hospital was seen as a nuisance to their properties, and should "not be in my backyard". To allay these sentiments and sell the idea of the proposed building, Mulock, Ramsay Wright and several other members of the Board visited hospitals in Boston, New York, Baltimore and other cities and came to the conclusion that there was no substantial ground for objecting to a hospital being located close to a residential area.

In addition, Aikins and Mulock were aware of another militating factor. The Arts Faculties, always jealous of their budgets, suspected that the hospital, which was to be controlled directly by the Senate of the University, would require both operating and capital funds. But, in spite of the arguments of the opponents, none of the proponents were to be swayed. The University had recently re-established a Faculty of Law, with appointments being a charge on the general resources of the University, and this was seen as setting a course for any medical innovation. Mulock's sturdy advocacy for the venture was a decisive factor. In a letter to the Toronto Senate on the 31st of May 1892, he wrote, "There are those whose opinions are of value, who think that a hospital forms a necessary part of the equipment of every efficient medical faculty, and in proof of this, it is only necessary to remind the Senate that the great medical schools of Great Britain, United States and Germany have control of hospitals". He added that opposition to the hospital amounted to "... an assault ... aimed at our Medical Faculty".

By good fortune, two lots of land were available next to Wycliffe College, which had been leased to that institution, if needed. The Hospital Trustees, in an adroit land assembly deal, proposed to use these and discovered alternate property for Wycliffe. The sale figure was $60,000.00. The V.C. persuaded (or, as was charged later, misled) Ross to give a 999 year lease for the two College Street lots on Mulock's statement that an additional donation from Macdonald hinged on the availability of the property.

But the price, plus the vehement opposition from members of other Faculties, slowed the process. The delay was ended abruptly when Mulock, in a whirlwind of action because Macdonald was dying, persuaded the Hospital Trustees to press Wycliffe to accept an offer of $40,000.00. Mulock did not report this action to the Board of Management of the University because of "the urgency of the imminent demise." However he did advise that $60,000 more was to be left by Macdonald which might be a lever to convince Wycliffe. The College took the offer but the deal was never closed. The will was contested, and as the money was not forthcoming, Wilson wrote the epitaph to the Park Hospital:

> But in this case, as in all else connected with the Medical Faculty, I have had no say. The V.C. (Vice Chancellor) was resolved to have all the honours and glory – and also such political and other influence as his assumed services would carry with them. So now he has to bear the burden of blame of a mismanaged affair.

The President's bitterness was not concealed and revealed the enmity between the classicist and the entrepreneurial Mulock clique. Eventually, the plan was abandoned – much to the chagrin of the two remaining chief architects. Mulock blamed the University community and lamented the state of affairs when he wrote: "If the literary side of the University arms itself against the scientific, the Arts Faculty against the Medical, we shall soon see counter-movements that will not be confined to these limits". This was an ingenuous overview of what had been an established activity for many years.

The sadly-mismanaged affair was a prelude to a chorus of objection and discontent by the Faculty. Aikins had to be content with the newly-opened operating rooms at the General. Wilson revealed the deep chasm that separated some University leaders from Mulock and his allies and there was a whiff of the future of the first Dean of Medicine.

The head of steam and ebullience which had been generated during the first years of the new Faculty resulted in a rapid expansion of the course. Realizing that there may have been over-combustion in some areas, a committee of the Medical Faculty was formed in 1891 to consider re-engineering. It looked at several facets of the school and made recommendations to a committee of the Senate, chaired by Blake, who then added many other clauses for a new look at medical education.

One of these matters concerned lecturers' fees. When Aikins headed his proprietary school, each faculty member was a shareholder and took a share of the profits of the school. But in the University in 1891, each professors' share reflected the amount of teaching he had done and he was entitled to a retirement allowance which was 70% of the salary he received for the year immediately preceding his resignation, payable at the end of the first year. Sixty percent was payable at the end of the second year, 50% of the third and so on, until the fifth year after retirement, when he was still receiving 30% of his annual pay. The prospect of a more generous retirement package was one of the incentives to form the new Faculty, and enjoy University perks. The usual and fixed salary for lecturers was $250.00 per annum. This was raised slightly if he held the rank of associate or professor. Until that level, there were no full time appointees and each was expected to get their main income from private practice. Due to the amount of time required, it was recommended that one professor and a demonstrator in the Department of Anatomy should be full time and should not be dependant on other income. This was the beginning of the geographical full-time appointment, which became the structure of the Department of Medicine in the following century.

In order to qualify for the per annum, Aikins was required to deliver fifty lectures. By an elaborate formula he was one of the highest paid group in the Faculty. He also received other compensation for lectures given during summer sessions which were not approved by the Senate or the Bursar, and did not pass through the University. But his rate of pay was reduced, compared with the TSM, and it was freely agreed that Aikins and the members who had joined the University, had willingly given up some income in return for other benefits.

In the new school, student payments were put into a special Medical Faculty Surplus account, which had been set up by Mulock, from which the staff drew their pay and other expenses for material. Although there was some fuzziness of bookkeeping, it could be shown that the Faculty did not receive any money from the general funds of the University. This special fund provided for retirement allowances, which became a major expense, given the fact that many of the Faculty were approaching the end of their teaching days.

Having received the committee report, the Senate performed some surgery. With the thoughts and recommendations of Blake at hand, Drs. M.H. Aikins, J. Ferguson and W.W. Ogden were retired. No provisions were made for a retirement payment. It was argued by the Senate that they had not resigned and, therefore, because of their age were not eligible for retirement funding.

At the same time, the chop was applied to other areas. W.T. Aikins, MacFarlane and Richardson were all reduced in pay to the level of junior members of the staff and in addition had an extension of their lecture hours. The Dean had received $920.00 in 1888, $1001.92 the next year and then successively $1091.04 and $1152.45 in 1891 was reduced to $835.70 for 1892. Meanwhile Drs. Cameron, Peters, McPhedran, Cavan and Primrose were elevated to the status of professor which entitled them to receive more per lecture. A.H. Wright, who had served as a secretary to the Faculty lost this position and was replaced by Cavan and Primrose.

These changes caused an immediate uproar in the Faculty and the profession. The *Ontario Medical Journal* in September 1892, felt forcefully that justice had not been done, based on the fact that the Senate Committee was made up of non-medical persons. Their decisions, according to the Journal, were made in private and "some aspiring individuals, forgetting their oft-repeated friendships, would get the ear of another friend or relative near a committee man for the furtherance of their own selfish ends." The article continued, that it had to be remembered that there were vested rights by members of the old TSM which had not received fitting consideration. This was an important item as the University of Toronto was occupying buildings of the old Toronto School of Medicine and it was not until 1893 that there was a talk of a renewal of the lease. At that time, the property was valued at $18,000, which if divided between the proprietors, yielded a good sum.

But aside from financial matters, the major target of the report was on the quality of teaching. In preparation for the recommendations Blake made a note on possible appointments for the following years:

> Useless
> Dr. W.T. Aikins, Dr. Richardson, Dr. W.W. Ogden, Dr. M.H. Aikins.
>
> Indifferent or Worse
> Dr. MacFarlane, Dr. D. Clark
>
> As Yet Undetermined Position
> Dr. A.H. Wright
>
> Dangerous
> Dr. John Ferguson[7]

This devastating list was enlarged by individual assessments.

> W.T. Aikins – a good practical surgeon one who was 10 or 12 years ago, head of his profession in the province ... he has not kept pace with the advance of surgical knowledge and methods. This fault so far as the interests of the Faculty are concerned is not a very grievous one, but he is very careless in preparing his lectures and as a result these are what might be "talks" which are of little value to

the students and following no system. The field of surgery has wid-
ened universally in the last few years, yet Dr. Aikins rarely in his
lectures touches on subjects outside of what was considered surgery 15 years ago. In fact he doesn't cover the ground of his subjects
and into what he enters he doesn't go deeply enough to make it
worth the while to the students to attend his lectures. I heard one of
his old colleagues say that Dr. Aikins never did his duty in the lecture room and that it never was his habit to prepare himself for
duty there. The students speak disrespectfully of his lectures and
will not attend them any more than the minimum number of times
sufficient to get their tickets signed ... Indeed there would not be a
loss but a gain if he were to give up lecturing, thereby allowing
somebody else more ambitious and more desirous of doing his
duties to take his place. Hence the suggestions (one of expediency
largely) which I made as to the Deanship.[8]

This summarized his thoughts on Aikins, who had been a prime participant in the Park Hospital farrago, the Biology Building deception and had
always backed-up Mulock. Whether Blake was ignorant of, or ignored, the
honours conferred on the Dean from his peers was not clear, nor was there
recognition of the setting up of the Medical Science Society by Aikins.[9] His
pioneering work in tourniguets for preserving blood by "blood savers"
during an operation; the invention of a fracture bed; the continuous application of cold to a wound by circulating water through coiled rubber tubing, and his use of elevation to control haemmorhage were all forgotten -
or ignored.

MacFarlane, Professor of Clinical Surgery, was described as, "not a
capable teacher in his subject – never having had the ground work even
passively prepared, he brings to his duties knowledge neither right nor
accurate and what is more serious he is too old to unlearn and learn."

Blake felt that I.H. Cameron and Peters were excellent, but Cameron's practice was so great that he could not give time for lectures and
consequently was not at all anxious to continue on the staff. "Dr. Peters
is a first class teacher and his qualifications as a Fellow of the Royal
College of Surgeons, by examination, is a distinction much coveted, but
of which he is only the bearer as yet, I believe, in Canada."

"Dr. W.W. Ogden is exceedingly poor timber. His opinions in the
lines of medical jurisprudence are worthless. He lectures also on toxi-

cology, of which he knows nothing practically, excites ridicule, not only amongst the students, but amongst the Faculty and in the profession.

However, his brother Dr. Uzziel Ogden, is one of the most careful and painstaking teachers on the staff. He conscientiously and carefully prepares his lectures and the students appreciate them for the attendance is good. According to Cameron, Ogden is the best surgeon in this line in the city. Ogden does not stint his reading or his efforts to keep abreast."

But Adam H. Wright was not judged a success as a teacher in Obstetrics: "He is not good speaker, his want of preparation sometimes barely shows itself – it may be that his duties as secretary, which he performs almost equally badly, interfere with his 'duties' as lecturer. His conduct in the position of secretary has resulted in the formation of two factions in the Faculty – factions were apparent at the Faculty meets where one group supported the Dean, but the other leaned to U. Ogden and Cameron. Dr. James M. Macallum is a splendid teacher in pharmacology and therapeutics. Dr. John Cavan is a splendid teacher in pathology."

But the Chancellor had other targets. He had received a letter from Dr. John Ferguson, Professor of Anatomy, earlier in the year, who wrote that during the past five years, he had been responsible for a number of activities in the department of Anatomy. "If you had been with me on some of the hot summer days, you would have formed some idea of the nature of my ideas." He ended with a series of endorsements from some of the more famous neurologists in North America and pointed out that it would be his intention, if appointed, to give five lectures to the second year students in the anatomy and structure of the nervous system; five lectures to the third year students on methods of study and diagnosis of nervous diseases and ten lectures on the general treatment of nervous disorders to the fourth year students, making a course of 20 lectures of each year.[10]

This proposal earned no kudos and caused extreme hostility as Blake felt that he was "dangerous." Blake diarized "... the old style of teaching anatomy (in the lecture room) had its day and must now give place to a method which will give the student ... practical dissection in the dissection room ..."

There remained three other contentious staffing issues. When H.H. Wright retired from the Chair of Clinical Medicine, the Faculty urged that the duties should be divided and proposed McPhedran as Professor of Medicine and Graham for Professor of Dermatology. McPhedran was incensed and denied any Chair to Graham as, "he would rather the Faculty went to pieces than he should not get what he wants." The solution was a win-win appointment of McPhedran to head Medicine and Graham to the Chair of Clinical Medicine, thus permitting the latter to compete against his rival for consulting practice.[11]

The fact that he was able to complete an assessment of the Faculty of Medicine in approximately six weeks was typical of how Blake worked. He had driven the staff mercilessly in order to complete the 1892 organization report. Now he used the same method to turn an objective eye on medicine. His forthright, candid appraisals were based largely on his own observations, made first hand in the class and meeting rooms. It was not easy to make recommendations that the Dean of Medicine, who had been his personal physicians, should not continue. Others, whom he downgraded, were in many cases friends. But there still remained one position – lecturer in Medical Psychology.

Daniel Clark, who had worked in the goldfields of California and Central America before graduating from Aikins' school in 1858, had taken further studies in Edinburgh, London and Paris. Subsequently, he had served as a surgeon with the Union Army along the Potomac. In addition to his studies, he had written numerous monographs on various subjects. After being appointed to be Medical Superintendent of the Asylum in Toronto in 1875 he was active in the Toronto Medical Association and lecturer at the TSM in Medical Psychology.

Blake wrote that "... is a fair teacher on the purely clinical portion of his subject (medical psychology). He is very much behind however in the knowledge of the researches that have been carried out over the last 15 years on the psychology of the brain and consequently his knowledge of physiological psychology, the kindred subject, sadly lacking. – will not unlearn what was thought safe views of 20 years ago. I believe it is well to abolish the professorship in order that the University may, if the situation warrants it, have a freedom to alter the teaching, or its character in this subject ..." However, the Faculty was well aware of Clark's competence. His essay written in 1878 on, "An Animated Molecule," was a masterful analysis of normal and abnormal mental activities. He had quoted many authorities in the field of psychology (or as it was called metaphysics), and in explaining mental processes instanced the French vitalist P.J. Cabanis who wrote, "that as the liver secretes bile, so does the brain secrete thought." Clark was convinced that much thought, normal and abnormal, was on the basis of a physiological process.

Blake's recommendations were made while sitting in the eye of a hurricane. On the death of Professor George Paxton Young, who held the chair in Logic, Metaphysics and Ethics, there had been great controversy about his successor. Until that time the Chair had also been responsible for philosophy and psychology. But by 1889, there was a strong sentiment that the responsibility for the Chair should be broken up in the same manner that other Chairs had been divided. Wilson and the Presidents of Knox and Wycliffe were in favour of a Dr. James Baldwin, an international applicant, who had studied in the school of Scottish realism which had preached "common sense." He had also worked in the German laboratory of Wilhelm Wundt, who founded the school of experimental psychology. Loudon and Mulock favoured Dr. James Gibson Hume, who had been a student of Young and subsequently studied at Johns Hopkins and Harvard. More importantly he was a native son. This schism in the University personnel was reflected in Parliament, where the decision was made in typical fashion with Baldwin taking the Chair in Logic and Metaphysics and History of Philosophy and Ethics to Hume.

When Blake, acting through the Senate Committee, decided to retire Ogden, M.H. Aikins and J. Ferguson, he uncovered several financial problems which had not been anticipated when the TSM joined the University of Toronto. A number of comments had been made recently by Geikie and others that it was foolhardy of the University to have embarked upon this union, without having a clear understanding of the financing which would be necessary to maintain the facade that the University was not supporting the training of physicians. Mulock had directed that any fees from medical students should be kept in a separate account, with interest at 5%. However, there was a failure to realize that each of the staff were a member of the Corporation and had a share in the funds and real estate of the TSM. In addition to the equity in the buildings, many of the staff had loaned money for expansion of science facilities. In 1881, Aikins had contributed $663.28 to the "1st Building Fund" and received 10% interest per annum. He also received 8% on a loan to the "2nd Building Fund" of $201.82.[12] Part of this stake was used for retirement income. In previous years, when H.H. Wright and Thorburn retired, they were granted an allowance. However

Ogden, Aikins and Ferguson, who had served at least five years with the University and had been with the TSM previously, were told that there were to be no retirement payments.

This matter was complicated even further by the fact that the University of Toronto was paying TSM $1200. yearly rental. By 1892, there was a surplus in the Medical Faculty Surplus account of approximately $2,500.00 and the Faculty members sent a special petition to the Senate Committee, urging that the three should receive retirement allowances.

Following his reorganization recommendations, Blake resigned as Chancellor and moved to Ireland. Loudon, President of University College following Wilson's death in 1892, reluctantly, agreed, after considerable pressure by the Medical Faculty to the payment of the allowances. But he was aware that there were problems with assigning fees collected to the proper source. Somehow, medical students taking lectures in physiology and other science subjects at SPS were never shown as an income to the University. In addition some Arts students who took anatomy courses, paid their fees into the Medical Surplus Account.

In spite of the moneys that seemed to be available for various special projects for the Medical School, there were still major shortages. Ramsay Wright, in his continuing efforts to improve the course of instruction, in 1891 offered to give a special course in bacteriology without any extra remuneration. Other oddities of bookkeeping were that Clark, who lectured in Medical Psychology, received $5.00 from each Trinity Medical School student who took his course. One of the goals of the reorganization of the Faculty was to bring uniformity to the revenue and disbursements.

Undaunted by this creative bookkeeping, Mulock in addressing the Sixth Annual Banquet of the University Medical School in December 1892 still claimed that, "whilst no University money is now being expended or is intended to be expended on medical science, still the public interest demands that medical science received due recognition at the hands of the State ..." He stressed that until a very recent period, medicine was regarded almost wholly as curative art, which led to a multiplication of medical schools, all cast in the same mold, "imparting education but not aspiring to advance the science." He urged that a wholly different principle must be involved which emphasized preventive medicine and as this would constitute a vast benefit to society, a

wholly different principle of funding should be involved. "The maintenance of public health is not only legitimate and proper, but an imperative duty on the part of the State."

Although he had been only recently re-elected as Vice Chancellor of
the University, Mulock was still under considerable fire from a variety
of sources because of his involvement in the Biology Building imbro-
glio. The *Toronto Mail* in June of that year recorded his statements in
defense of his action not only with the Anatomy Department but also in
regard to the Park Hospital. "What is particularly disappointing in this
part of the defense is the absence of any expression of regret for having
attempted to effect an important change in University policy by resort-
ing to such an unheard of succession of concealments" stated the
paper, attempting to chastize the V.C.

But regardless of the problems associated with finance, which were
interwoven with the politicking which went on between the Arts and
Science Faculties, the business of medical education continued. By 1893
there was a new emphasis on bedside and clinical experience as shown
by the timetable.

LECTURES AND DEMONSTRATIONS
In Gerrard Street Building

	M	Tu	W	Th	F	S	
Clinical Chemistry	8:30		8:30				Dr. Gamble
Minor Surgery		8:30		8:30			Dr. H.W. Aikins
Operative Obstetrics			9:30				Dr. A.H. Wright
Physical Diagnosis		9:30				9:30	Dr. Starr
Dietetics	9:30				9:30		Dr. Gordon
Mental Diseases					8:30	8:30	Dr. Cane
Pathology (Gross Demonstrations)			9:30				Dr. Amyot

Clinical Lectures and Demonstrations
In General Hospital

		M	Tu	W	Th	F	S	
Dr. Graham	Clinical Lect	2:30						1st five weeks
	Bedside		3:30	3:30	3:30	3:30		1st five weeks
	Out-door Skin			2:30				1st five weeks
Dr. McPhedran	Bedside	3:30						1st five weeks
	Out-door Skin			2:30				2nd five weeks
	Bedside		3:30	3:30	3:30	3:30		2nd five weeks
	Clinical Lect.	2:30						2nd five weeks
Dr.W.P. Cavan	Out-door				1:30			
	Special classes	3:30			3:30			
Dr. McFarlane	Clinical Lect.		2:30					1st five weeks
	Bedside	3:30		3:30	3:30	3:30		1st five weeks
	Bedside				3:30			2nd five weeks
Dr. Cameron	Clinical Lect.				2:30			
	Bedside		3:30					1st five weeks
	Bedside	3:30	3:30	3:30		3:30		2nd five weeks
Dr. Peters	Out-door				1:30			
	Special classes	3:30			3:30			
Dr. Primrose	Out-door	1:30						
	Special classes			3:30		3:30		
Dr. A. Wright	Special classes	4:30						
Dr. J.M. Mac-allum	Outdoor		1:30					
	Special classes		3:30		3:30			
Dr. B. Spencer	Out-door				1:30			
	Special classes		3:30		3:30			
Dr. Reeve	Out-door		3:00					
Dr. Burnham	Out-door			3:30				
Dr. McDonagh	Out-door					3:30		

Victoria Hospital for Sick Children

	M	Tu	W	Th	F	S
Dr. Thistle	11:00	11:00	11:00	11:00		11:00
	M	Tu	W	Th	F	S

• • • • • •

To the naive bystander, the new Faculty of Medicine was an out-standing success. There was a serene sense at University Convocation as graduates were inducted into the service of mankind. Aikins was admired universally. He had recruited a first-class teaching staff. Enrollment had increased. There was no visible or audible dissent. But beneath the mill pond surface, pressure was increasing on the dam, and the lynch pin which precipitated an academic deluge was Medicine.

One of the reforms Blake had introduced was that fifteen of the Senate were to be elected from graduates. In 1892, a letter was addressed to all members of the Convocation, "of special importance to enable members to decide whether the new policy of reform," brought in by Blake during the past two years should continue or whether "the danger of a reversion to the old policy which was responsible, among other things, for the Anatomical Building and the Park Hospital schemes – a danger not to be ignored in the present crisis". Blake's monumental study of the administration had brought in many changes, some of which gave more equity to the junior staff. The letter was a direct challenge to Mulock and his faction by Loudon. It stated that the function of the Senate, was "initiating, debating and determining the education policy of the University." But the Board of Trustees had usurped these functions with the result that the Biological Building addition "was erected without the knowledge and sanction of the Board of Trustees or the Government and was in contravention of a clear understanding that the amount of $60,000. appropriated would be expended on a building for the science department of the University and not for a medical building."

This document was signed by more than 200 alumnae and staff and stated: "the time has come for an inquiry into the merits of the scheme, and for a conference with regard to the complications of the aforesaid". The discontent, frustration and anger of the Arts Faculty and, interestingly, several of the medical staff including A.B. Macallum, was apparent. This was only one of a number of publications or briefs on the same theme, to which was added a charge, that "a full investigation of these matters was successfully resisted in the Senate by the Vice Chancellor and his friends".

In addition to the general charges, there were specifics. For the first time Mulock's Medical Faculty Fund was revealed. The Ministry had uncovered this "misappropriation of fees" and had clawed back a portion as rent for the medical faculty and directed that a percentage of the registration fees should go into the general funds of the University.

But not all the pressure was being built from inside the University. From the initial announcement that there would be a Faculty of Medicine, opposition was expressed in explicit, explosive terms in several forums. Geikie was the foremost gladiator. Trinity had refused to join on several bases, one of which was that the goal of the Government in the College Federation proposal was not to extinguish, but rather to carefully preserve the identities of the affiliating bodies. It was obvious that TSM had lost its identity and Geikie refused to go down the same path. Serious questions were raised as to the financial stability of the institution because, if professors "were expected to devote their chief energies to the duties of their respective chairs," it would be impossible to pay their salaries from fees generated, unless the University contributed over and above the students' fees. But it had been announced and it could be read on the lips of the Minister, that no public money could be used for the new venture.

Trinity also argued that the new school would increase the number of medical schools and break down the "healthy rivalry between schools" which existed. Geikie did not skulk in his tent, as befitted a defeated Scottish chieftain, nor let the matter rest. He continued a series of public statements, Letters to Editors and brochures outlining Trinity's objection to the Government action. A letter to *The Globe* praised "two medical schools co-working in a spirit of a not unfriendly rivalry ... the classes in which two schools are good in point of number, yet not so large as to be unmanageable." He urged that the University should stick to the business of examining in medicine. Even after the school had been functioning, he continued his campaign and in March of 1890 he had fresh amunition.

> It is well known to you and to everyone, that the new lecture rooms and laboratories in the building are very largely used for medical teaching purposes ... all the instruction these medical men get in this department is given by teachers, who are paid entirely by salaries drawn, as in the case of all other Arts professors, from the latter source. Thus, certain Arts professors earn a large amount of medical students fees, which go not to the University ... but to be distrib-

AIKINS OF THE U OF T MEDICAL FACULTY

uted in a proportion fixed by the University statute to various members of the Medical Faculty.

He supported these allegations with hard figures that showed $4,260. was paid into the Medical Faculty Fund each year from 1st and 2nd year men alone.

He bolstered his claims by drawing attention to the Medical Calendar of the University which advertised that those who taught in the Biological Building were members of the "Medical Faculty." For example, courses given by teachers such as Ramsay Wright and Macallum closely followed the requirements of the College of Physicians and Surgeons. Geikie ended his charges with "Physiology, Bacteriology and Pathology and other medical studies are taught in the expensive building (and none but medical students take these subjects), is it not contrary to the fact, and most misleading, to speak of the new Biological Building as for Arts only?" He growled that, in contradistinction to the University; "Trinity Medical College and other strong colleges elsewhere have provided their own Biological, Bacteriological, Physiological and other laboratories, but altogether at their own expense."

Geikie's dedication to exposing the University's "malfeasance" was remarkable and he dug into his position deeply, never retreating from his post, even after Trinity had joined the University in 1896, over his objection.

His stand was applauded by many practitioners. Dr. William T. Harris in a Letter to the Editor of *Canadian Practitioner* in January 1890 detailed, "his anxiety, if not alarm, at the movement which has made the old Toronto School of Medicine practically a government medical school ... thereby excluding the possibility of other medical colleges deriving any benefit from any of those advantages which have been and are now being secured to the provincial university at the expense of the Province."

In spite of a spirited defense of the activities of the previous years by Mulock, whose tongue was acknowledged not only to be adroit, but also coarse, there were too many questions being asked on all sides. The precipitating factor was a resolution by the Alumnae Association to the Senate asking for a strict accounting of what had happened in the matter of the Park Hospital. Serious questions had been raised as to whether the transfer of properties was void or valid under the Mortmain Law. The Government could no longer shield Mulock with the result that the Senate nominated a committee "to inquire into and report upon any or all matters connected with the erection of the Biological Building and the establishment of the Park Hospital."

Never before had there been such a searching inquiry into the affairs of the University. Although the report was delivered to the Legislature, the process was under the charge of the Senate. So momentous was the occasion and so portentous was the outcome that it was incumbent on all the members of the Committee to seek the truth. But truth was sometimes obscured by the smoke and sparks coming from the grinding of political axes.

To ensure the credibility of the proceedings, a prestigious chairman was appointed. William Glenholme Falconbridge, a University graduate, had been called to the Bar in 1871 and became Queen's Counsel in 1885. He had been Registrar of the University, but at this time was a judge of the Queen's Bench of the Supreme Court of Ontario. Later he became Chief Justice of this court and was created a Knight Bachelor in 1908. He ruled the proceedings with an iron gavel. One of the first testimonies was given by Mulock who, in a masterful summing up of the history of both the Biology Building and the Park Hospital, stated that he was carrying out "what I believe to be the policy of the University to place the Medical Faculty on such a footing as would enable it to fulfill the object which the Senate had in view when establishing it. It never occurred to me that there existed, and I do not think that there did exist in University circles any opposition to such a policy." In his submission several events were highlighted. Although the Biology Building had been authorized and funded by the University, it was to be for a combination of Biology, Mines and Geology. However, Mulock maintained that in conversation with Ross, he was given the information that a separate School of Mines was to be established, therefore the demand for floor space was considerably reduced. Mulock pointed out that if this action was taken the University would lose $3,000.00 a year for the endowment of a Chair, which it received from the City of Toronto for Mineralogy. But, according to the testimony, the Minister responded that he was making other arrangements. When pressed for any paper trail of these statements, Mulock was forced to admit that it was solely his recollection.

During the planning and building of the eastern wing of the Biology Building, which eventually became occupied by the Faculty of Medicine, the key person was Ramsay Wright, who had raised the level of instruction in physiology while in the School of Science and later the School of Practical Science. In general, this subject was not taken by all medical students and indeed, in some cases, had not been offered in specific years. However, Wright was appointed by Mulock to be his point man in the building and negotiations. He was instructed to liaise with Professor W.H. Pyke of Chemistry, but had to admit that he had never been able to make any headway. Pyke had refused to play the game when he was presented with what appeared to be a fait accompli as far as the planning of the building was concerned. His stand was based on an extensive report that he had sent to Blake, who had asked if the chemistry required for medicine could be taught by Pyke's staff. The reply was that this would require a minimum of one extra staff member, the provision of an additional lecture room and extra money for supplies. He also added that the presence of medical students in the classroom was not desirable, as they took the lectures only because they were mandatory; had little or no interest in the subject and, in general, were a noisy, obstreperous lot. This sentiment, added to the fact that Pyke had not been involved in the planning stage, meant not only non-co-operation but outright obduracy.

But much more importantly, Wright was instructed by Mulock to direct the University architect, David B. Dick. This was one of the most pertinent points turned up by the Committee. The crux of the matter was that the plans were drawn by the architect, but according to instructions given by Wright, certain names were not to appear on some rooms - in particular the Anatomy and Dissection Room, which occupied the entire top floor of the building. Wright maintained, and Mulock agreed, that these names had been left off (as a matter of fact, they had been erased from the first draft) because of the fear of public reaction to a near-by anatomy room full of diseased bodies. Geikie's name was brought forward on several occasions as someone who was "busying himself" about the University involvement in medical education. The Dean of Trinity had already been active in lobbying against the Park Hospital, and on one occasion had even approached Macdonald for a one-on-one discussion.

When Dick testified, he admitted that he had kept secret the allocation of rooms, but he added, if anyone on the Senate had asked for a more specific description, it would have been provided. The catch with this facile excuse was it appeared that the Senate had never seen the plans, or if it had, it was only for a cursory peek. According to Mulock, Wright had shown the plans to Ross. According to Wright, Ross had barely glanced at the plans and had not asked any specific questions and, inasmuch as the rooms were nameless, was not in a position to comment on the appropriateness of the floor plan.

However, all agreed that the Senate had made some modifications to the plan. The original drawing had called for sky-lights with an elaborate cornice on the top floor to provide ideal lighting conditions for dissection. But Senator Colonel Gzowski, ignorant of why so much light was required, suggested that expenses could be pared if the sky-lights and the stonework were reduced. This was the only change that was ever minuted. Of course, the Senate was not fully informed of the week-to-week activities or arrangements, although the Board of Trustees was more in the picture. But, they too were not aware of the full import of the structure.

Houston asked: "Did anybody else other than the Vice Chancellor ever suggest that this information should be kept from persons not in sympathy with the University, members of the Faculty, etc?"

Dick replied: "I have no recollection of such."

Dr. McLaren asked: "How are the wishes of the Trustees conveyed to you as to changes?"

Dick answered: "My knowledge on that point is not clear."

A follow-up question was, "Were you at any meeting of the Board of Trustees where the plans were discussed?"

Dick: "No sir."

"Did you receive any letter from the Bursar on this subject?"

"I cannot find any excepting that authorizing the acceptance of tenders. Had no communication with Colonel Gzowski as far as I can recollect."

"How do the suggestions of the Board as to the sky-lights, etc. come to you?"

Dick: "I have no recollection how the information came from the Senate."

Wright tried to backstop some of the answers and stated that the only remark that was made with regard to the plans was one by Colonel Gzowski. Mulock explained that he was not present at that meeting.

Loudon now entered the pursuit. "At the Board meeting was any question asked as to any room being a dissecting room?"

Wright answered that no questions were asked and no hints given as to the use of the building.

Loudon: "Could this Order-in-Council be given by the Board without them knowing that it was for a dissecting room?"

Wright: "They would likely know something as to the uses of the room."

Loudon: "Could the suggestions have been given by the Board without any knowledge of the real object of the room?"

The chairman disallowed the question. However, Aikins added, "It was a very wise suggestion if they had known it was to be used as a dissecting room ..."

It was becoming repetitive and obvious that the Senate, and most likely the Government, had not been informed or had not bothered to ask the purpose of the addition. A deposition from Ross said that he had been informed by J.E.B. Smith, the Bursar of the University in October of 1889, that plans for the proposed Biological Building had been approved by the Board. But Ross had not seen the proposed plan. However, early in November he informed Mulock that an Order-in-Council had been passed approving the extension of the Biological Department.

The Bursar was called. He was quizzed whether the extracts of the minutes of the Board of Trustees beginning in February, 1888 and ending in February, 1889 contained all the references to the erection of the Biological Building?

"Yes."

"Are you aware, or did you communicate with the Senate?"

"I think not", answered the Bursar.

Loudon testily asked: "Were there any letters or explanation offered by you in sending the plans to the Government?"

"No, I do not recollect that I sent the plans to the Government."

Ramsay Wright was called. He explained: "As I was asked to keep the matter a secret I did so."

He was then asked when did Mr. Ross express any surprise that the building was to be used for the convenience of medical students?

Wright hesitated and swallowed: "I was in Germany and not in Toronto when the building was going on."

Mulock came to his rescue with the statement that it was at his request that Wright assisted the architect and was in no way responsible for any question of policy. "I would advise those who seek to make a point against the development of the science side of the University, that the University must keep the faith of those who endorse Confederation. Nor need I remind you how easy is the work of destruction ... I never imagined that the grounds would be taken that no assistance was to be given to medical science and certainly in University circles such an attitude was never assumed until after the completion of the building in question. I felt were Dr. Geikie to be aware that it was in contemplation to provide any accommodation for the Medical Faculty, he would seize hold of the dissecting room feature and use it with the public with increased effect".

The tactic was out in the open and clear. Although Mulock had praised Trinity when a guest speaker at their annual dinner just the previous year, and emphasized the training of practical physicians, now he had doubled back and was pushing "frogology". This was a pejorative label used by those who did not have the advantage of biological lectures. It was part of an anti-science wave which had become apparent particularly outside University circles. Several medical journal editorials and newspaper articles had queried whether the University should be training doctors for scientific laboratories or whether they should be taught to take care of the sick.

Mulock, although he admitted some culpability, excused himself due to the fact that for the best part of the year he had been discharging his duties in Ottawa. "While I do not wish to avoid responsibility, I do not wish, in a like manner, to be made responsible for a thing for which I am not responsible. The sketch plans were no way finality, but merely sketches ... in fact, I was very largely absent from Toronto more than being present for several years". Houston, always irrepressible, always hurrying, rushed a question. "Nothing of all of this was communicated to the Senate?"

"Nothing, as far as I know."

"Was provision for the dissection room a part of the original sketch plans?"

"My instructions were that. I suppose I was voicing the entire University opinion and perhaps in helping it by not asking too many of our friends to keep a secret."

Loudon interjected: "Did you submit the final plans to the Government?"

Muloch fudged the answer by saying that they went to the Board, but Loudon was not to be refused.

"Were the plans explained by Professor Wright in your presence?"

"I do not remember any conversation between the Minister and Professor Wright."

Loudon recalled Wright and asked, "Are you aware that during the building of the extension that Mr. Ross denied in the House that the public moneys were being spent for medical teaching?"

"I think I heard something of that sort: yes."

"Had you any reason for believing that Mr. Ross did not know the dissecting room feature?"

"I do not know that I had any reasons. I cannot answer that question."

In truth a number of the witnesses were having memory problems. The Bursar: "I do not remember particularly, I don't think medicine was ever mentioned. I cannot say ... I cannot say ... I cannot say ... you will have to ask him."

Dick was recalled and even though questioned closely he had nothing further to add. Loudon now called Archibald Macallum: "What was the object of the Minister of Education in sending for you before the completion of the building?" Question disallowed.

"What did the Minister say to you?" Question disallowed.

"Are you aware that Mr. Ross was not cognizant of the existence of a dissecting room about this time?" Question disallowed. The gavel was becoming impatient.

"Did I tell you that the Government had come to me in regard to the matter?" Question disallowed.

"Did I not tell you that I was astounded to learn that the Government did not know that there was a dissection room there?"

Loudon moved that Blake should be invited to attend the Committee to discuss his statement that he had "no cognizance of the details of the Biological Building." The motion was defeated with Aikins in the nays. Houston moved to obtain testimony from members of the Executive Council. His motion was defeated.

It was obvious that the inquiry was quickly coming to an end. Sufficient blood had been let and the conservative members of the committee began staunching measures. It was then moved by Houston that the proceedings be adjourned pending a statement from the Minister of Education as to his relation to the scheme in its various stages. More to the point did Minister become aware that provision was to be made in the building for the dissection of human bodies and the teaching of primary anatomy for medical purposes? This was lost on a division; the ayes, Loudon and Houston, the nays Burwash, Hoyles, Aikins, Wilmott, Father Teefy and Maclaren.

The chairman led a majority of members in declaring that the actions of all concerned had been with the best intentions and that there had been no attempt to mislead any parties.

At the same time, "the Committee is not to be held as expressing approval of any secrecy practiced in regard to any of the purposes of the building". It was an unctuous resolution. The draft report, incorporating all the evidence to date was moved by Aikins and approved. It neither condemned nor praised. It revealed nothing new. It was the perfect political document. It passed.

REFERENCES

1. The Varsity June 9, 1886; p 2.
2. Number 52, First Session, Sixth Legislature, 50 Vic, 1887.
3. The Varsity October 29, 1887.
4. Royal Commission on University Education in London, 5 Vols., London, HMSO, 1910–1912, Vol. 5; pp 21–25.
5. The Lancet. Our Medical Literature August 13, 1881; pp 265–270.
6. Frost, Stanley B. McGill University 1801–1895, McGill-Queen's University Press; p. 255
7. Blake Papers, University of Toronto Archives, B72-013/3 B55- 1892.
8. Ibid
9. The Varsity October 21, 1890.
10. James Loudon Papers B720031/06, U of T Archives.
11. Blake op. cit.
12. Toronto School of Medicine. Acount Book. Robarts Library, University of Toronto, Robarts Library.

Chapter Ten

The Faculty

A further problem that weighed on the Dean's pate was the re-organi-
zation plan of 1892, complete with Blakes' recommendation. Charges of
"injustice, unfairness and aggravations" filled the columns of the
Ontario Medical Journal;

> When the TSM entered the University Confederation and became
> its teaching Faculty, it was fully believed that the vested rights of
> all who had laboured so long and faithfully to build up the TSM,
> would be fully respected and honourably rewarded.

The Journal continued to report that some members of the Faculty
had been dismissed with retiring allowances, others without and some
dismissed with a "status" appointment. Some were downgraded in
pay, some were promoted and some were underpaid, compared with
others.

> ... some of the ablest members of the staff received less pay than
> some of the youngest members ... in the case of Dr. W.W. Ogden, it
> is evident that an injustice was done by breaking up his department
> into two lectureships ... was retired with the status of Professor
> Emeritus but without any retiring allowance granted.
>   M.H. Aikins laboured efficiently on the staff of the TSM for
> twelve years ... has been relieved of his professorship without retir-
> ing allowance.

The case of Dr. J. Ferguson is especially aggravating. He served in the TSM for six years and during that period gave an enormous amount of time, both winter and summer, to the advancement of the college ... his diligent work was paid in the full by dismissal from the Faculty without either status or retiring allowance.

Drs. Ogden, M.H. Aikins and J. Ferguson, who served for five years without a retiring allowance is unfair discrimination ... it is hoped that every member of the Senate will hasten to remedy and wipe from the records a proceeding so glaringly ... unjust to three of the staff.

However Aikins and the others held their fire and, in effect, continued to hold their appointments with lower pay.[1]

The Dean's accountabilities also included Geikie.

Aikins was never wary of making enemies. He had alienated himself from Beaumount and Hodder during the Toronto General Hospital investigation of cruelty to patients. At that time his reward was a temporary excommunication from the Cathedral of Healing. Then he infuriated Rolph by resigning and taking the TSM, with some of the faculty, away from Victoria. In 1876, when Geikie claimed his seat on the Ontario Medical Council as representative of the newly incorporated Trinity Medical School, Council refused to let him sit. The *Canada Lancet* had no doubt as to who was behind this move "... the Council as at present constituted is ruled by a few individuals, who in this instance had made it the cat's paw to subserve their own private feelings and interests". The result of this action was that Geikie sued and after a legal hearing was permitted to sit. A similar action had been taken against Covernton, when he accepted the chair in Trinity College Medical School in 1871. He was ruled inadmissible as the representative of Gore and Thames division, which had nominated him previously under the territorial formula.

Of all the opponents Aikins had in his many years in medicine, none was so doughty as Geikie. There was never open warfare between the two, but there was no doubt that when Geikie launched his bombardments against the University of Toronto, the target of choice was Aikins. But Aikins never became involved. He remained distant, or bunkered behind the University president or Mulock.

In spite of his contant rebuffs Geikie was once again pounding a familiar note in 1892. He charged the University with "gross abuse and shameful misappropriation of University funds ... the Legislature of Ontario, which hastened to vote $160,000.00 to aid in repairing the damage done by fire (to University College), had no idea that most of the sum so promptly and liberally voted, would be spent in a way which is never for a moment intended on dissecting rooms, etc." Wilson objected to this reckless statement and claimed not a single dollar of money voted by the Legislature had been spent for such services. However Geikie continued that the Biological Buildings of the University were really an addition for the accommodation for the Medical Faculty, "they were to all intents and purposes a medical school building." Wilson was able to show that the Medical Faculty was paying rental for the facilities, a price which had been set by Mulock, and this was paid out of the special Medical Trust Fund. "An abuse worthy of Ottawa" replied Geikie who showed that the fees which were collected from University students for physiology, chemistry and biology were deposited in the Medical Faculty Fund. He continued his crusade against the public funding of medical education until well after it was a dead issue, and not likely to be revisited for another century.

In addition to those general problems, there were the recurring incidents with which Aikins had been battling for many years.

In 1894 the *Canadian Practitioner* highlighted what it considered to be another threat to the regular doctors. Christian Science doctors were reported as performing miracles and it was noted that many of these occurred in Quebec. However the journal highlighted a specific obstetrical disaster "with regards to parturition, the CS held a notion that it is (when normal) a phenomenon unaccompanied by pain ... practitioner and patient reach this end, jointly, by mentally asserting with endless iteration, that there is no pain, or whatever manifests itself in the focus of the patient's field of sensation".

"This patient however met with less degree of success and, while agreeing the pains of bearing down were an illusion, found they caused her to groan audibly. Knowing nothing of such superfluous details as pelvic anatomy, or the physiology of labour, the medical attendants had probably never heard of breech presentation either. A rather facile way of getting over certain facts is to refuse to admit that they exist, and in this rhetorical accomplishment the school in question is pre-eminent".

Finally a physician was called who delivered a stillborn child "markedly hydrocephalic". The physician could "hardly understand the noises of a frightful dispute which emanated from the next room, where the incensed CS were pushing the husband from hand to hand, endeavouring to incense him to the point of entering the lying-in chamber, to forcibly drive the physician out of the house ... a faint smell of carbolic acid reached the nostrils of the CS and intoxicated them with anger over such heinous pollution." One member saw the physician administer morphine hypodermically and thus further profane the situtation.

Quackery and self-puffery continued to lure the consumer:

> The first three months free of charge. The staff of eminent physicians and surgeons are in Toronto and have permanently located at the residence # 272 Jarvis Street, (near Gerrard). All invalids who visit these eminent doctors before January 1st will receive services for the first three months free of charge. The only favour desired is a recommendation from those whom they cure bear the object in pursuing this course is to become rapidly and permanently acquainted with the sick and the afflicted.

> The doctors treat every variety of diseases and deformities and will perform all surgical operations free this month viz the removal of the cancers, tumours, cataracts, polypi, etc. All diseases of the eye, ear, throat, lungs, heart, stomach, liver, kidney, bladder and all female difficulties arising from whatever causes. All nervous prostrations, feeling of vituality and diseases originating from impure blood, treated with the greatest success ... invalids will please not take offence if they are rejected and incurable. The physicians will examine you thoroughly, free of charge, and if incurable, they will positively tell you so. Also caution against spending your money on useless medicine. Remember the date and go early as their offices are crowded daily. Hours are from 9 a.m. to 5 p.m. and from 7 p.m. to 8 p.m. and Sundays 2 to 4.

This advertisment was placed in Toronto papers and decorated wooden poles.

The physical problems of the school were a constant nuisance. Lectures were given at the TSM which was a good distance away from the Biology Building where dissection was performed and the SPS science lectures were given. Medical students divided their time between the University campus and the old school of medicine. The University arranged for a streetcar line to link the two sites and paid hundreds of dollars in fares, but it was still estimated that the first and second year students spent at least an hour and a half each day commuting between their lectures.[2] The students had other resentments, which they expressed by a decline in attendance at Richardson's lectures. They complained of the unsatisfactory character of his talks and stated that the dissection, as they carried it out, was of more importance and that the lectures and demonstrations were not up to the standards of those in the dissection room. They felt that they could get better information out of their textbooks, alongside the cadavers.

And they had other vexations. A Letter to the Editor of *The Varsity*, December 2, 1890, complained that the honoured professors have a "delightful habit of neglecting to give the lectures at the hour stated on the timetable." In addition, the lecturers frequently talked more than a hour, which denied students the opportunity to get their next class. "There is one professor in particular, who persists in sitting at his chair in the Faculty room", rather than in the lecture room. This was one of a series of faults which had been present over the previous years and centered on the fact that there were too many students and too few patients. The Faculty also laid their complaints at the Dean's door. Dr. Cavan, in the Faculty meeting of February 26, 1892 stated that if he were to take charge of the Pathology Department, it must be at a salary of $1500.00 per annum, because of the increased amount of work necessary to be of any use to the University. He would be forced to completely forego his practice and income. Although the calendar stated that the course was six hours per week, there was preparation necessary and there were post mortems at the Toronto General Hospital. In order to do the job properly, he had to give up the lectures which he had been giving at the Veterinary College, with loss of those fees.

Pressure on the Head of the Medical Faculty was also felt from the

CPSO. Bergin, acting on the complaints of many of the country doctors, criticized the University, and Trinity, for producing too many physicians, a recurrent dissatisfaction of the large body of country doctors who blamed over-crowding for lowering incomes. There was some justification. A surfeit of medical services caused hardship and there was no social net to give assistance. A notice in the *The Canada Lancet* read:

> A medical man, resident in Toronto, and having a large family, has, through no fault of his own, become very much embarrassed pecuniarily. In England it has been customary in such cases to show, in a practical manner, a feeling of professional brotherhood by sending contributions through the agency of some of the medical journals ... we can say that the dishonored paper which he had endorsed, and not any dissipation or other extravagance, has caused the misfortune, which he hopes to surmount by timely aid, and were it not for physical infirmity, which has kept him back, he might have been able to meet his friend's (?) liability without making this appeal. We shall be happy to receive, acknowledge and forward all contributions sent to us.

Of course, there was always Mulock, who could be counted on to behave like an unshackled howitzer. He was brilliant, imaginative, pushy and provocative, but vital to the progress of the University. The V.C. used the University as an extension of his career. He continually urged expansion, but Blake resisted because he felt that the endowment was insufficient. Aikins, as Dean of the school which was growing rapidly, was frequently between these titans. The open and hidden warfare resulting from the Biology Building garboil caused several stormy meetings of the Senate, centred on the status of the Medical Faculty. In June of 1892, with Blake in the Chair as Chancellor, the record of attendees was the highest of the previous forty years. Mulock had written a letter in which he confessed that he directed Ramsay Wright to instruct the architect. Although this took the weight from Wright, Mulock's letter was challenged. A motion was put by one of the Senators which censured the Vice Chancellor for his policy. Loudon stated, "then followed the most bitter debate ever staged in the University

Senate." Mulock defended himself by explaining that this had been done for the "progress and prosperity of the University, not in part, but as a whole." Although the debate was heated, when the matter was put to a vote, it was defeated and Mulock's actions were not censured.

By 1892, there were 280 students enrolled over the four years, and this number continued at approximately the same level until 1895, when occasional students were included which raised the number of registered students to 334. By 1901 a fifth year was added to the course and registration was around the 500 level, increasing to 700 by 1903.

The teaching staff of the Faculty took great pride in the quality of their work and in particular the high standards they saw in their graduates. It was obvious that things had improved considerably over the past twenty years. However J.E. Graham, when addressing the Fourth Session of the restored Medical Faculty, highlighted some home truths. He used as his yardstick, Membership in the Royal College of Physicians and Fellowship in the Royal College of Surgeons in the United Kingdom. Only one Canadian had been successful in the Membership category – William Osler.

Seven Canadians had attempted the Fellowship over the previous twenty years. Two had passed. "Can it then be said with truthfulness that Canadian graduates have easily carried off the highest honours in England?", he asked. Graham, although an enthusiast for the new school, was a forthright realist. This action-type orientation may have stemmed from the fact he had studied in Paris in the late 1860s.

The pressure to raise the level of teaching and the calibre of the graduates prompted Uzziel Ogden to write to Blake in May,1892 urging that the younger staff members of the Faculty be given more money and better arrangements as they were receiving offers from other schools. "It would be very unfortunate if any of the older members of the Faculty, who having discharged their duties with efficiency and satisfaction, should have their subjects or positions cut down or changed ..." however he urged that there should be a bigger pie that should include an upgrading of junior teachers. He admitted that he was impressed with the quality of the new school, although he had objected strongly at that time to the five year term which had been given to Aikins: "I am free to confess that it would have been well if a five year appointment had always prevailed for the older school." In truth, Aikins had virtually dominated the old school, even though different members assumed the chairmanship on various occasions.

Ogden's comments may have had some bearing on the Medical Faculty. The usual practice was to elect a Dean in the month of April for the ensuing year. Although Aikins had been given a contract for five years in 1887, he was still elected each year in order to maintain the tradition of the proprietary schools, in particular the TSM. On April 11th 1893, with an attendance of 18 members, the election took place "without nomination, of the Dean of the Faculty of Medicine." Ogden received 9 votes. Aikins received 6, and three vital voters abstained!

There are difficulties in reconstructing Aikins' final years. "My father married a second time and he married a tidy woman. Every scrap that my father ever wrote was burned," said his son Henry Wilberforce.[3] There is no doubt that when he lost the Deanship, there was profound disappointment. It was a close vote and, in effect, Odgen's policies did not differ that much from his own. This blow came on top of the death of Wilson the previous year. Loudon, who took over the Presidency of University College, was not unfriendly to Aikins, although it was obvious that they had tangled during the Biology Building inquiry.

There were other causes for despondency. The anguish associated with his practice and the inevitable deaths, took its toll. He had lost his mentor, Egerton Ryerson and the post-partum haemmorhage that took the wife of his dear friend, the Reverend William Punshon, was a shock. This barely preceded Punshon's own death, which was a great blow to the members of the Metropolitan Church, including Aikins, which he had led in bringing the towering temple of Methodism to Toronto. Then too, his friends were disappearing; Langstaff, who had been his support in his political campaign, went to his grave. John Bethune, an old colleague from the days when the TSM broke from Victoria passed on and Joseph Workman was dead as well as Michael Barrett.

William's financial status was also depressing. In his obituary the *Christian Scientist* spoke of many worries connected with business which had affected him during his last years, as evidenced by leaving the house he had built in the fashionable area on Jarvis Street at Gerrard where he had lived from 1878 until 1894. The property was not mentioned in his will and it is likely that it was sold to solve a cash problem. In addition, his real estate investments resulted in heavy losses. Part of this problem was relieved by a $400 loan from his brother, J.C. Aikins, which William acknowledged with gratitude. The census of 1871 showed he employed four servants and a nurse. By 1891 there were no servants, but a much smaller family. While he had never lived as a wealthy man, although so reputed, he was distressed at the fact that he had to reduce his donations to his church. Prior to 1890, the Missionary Society had been receiving $500 yearly, which declined to $100 in 1891 and 1892. Subsequently there were no donations. He was no longer able to lend money to the Metropolitan Church, as he had done frequently in the past. The only money received by the church was the pew rental. In addition to a downsizing of his capital, his salary was reduced and by 1895 he received only $385 per annum.

Though he had experienced more than his share of family disasters – three children died in infancy and one after scalding in hot water, possibly the most severe blow was the death of his son, William Heber, whom his father described as his "wandering first born." Whether he was an "alcoholic" as was whispered[4] or not, his dying at the age of 40 weighed heavily on his father. His estate was $24 cash, plus a $1,000 insurance policy.

In addition to William's mental state, he sustained a hemiparesis as the result of a cerebro-vascular accident in 1894. Though partially disabled and unable to operate, he continued to occupy a place on the Faculty and was elected as Treasurer of the CPSO once again. "I think it is in the recollection of every one of the old members here of the amount he has sometimes undertaken to carry for this Council; and I feel in reappointing him now, we are simply offering him a very slight reward for the work he has done in the past; and as he is now ill, it would be a compliment to him to reappoint without any amendment being submitted ... he had a great deal to do with the incorporation of the profession, and has had a great deal since to do in the way of keeping this Council out of difficulties on many occasions. Dr. Aikins is recovering from his illness rapidly and with further rest, in say about six months, his physician has the fullest expectation of a satisfactory restoration to his health," stated Bergin. (Bergin died two years later, an impecunious bachelor.) However Sangster objected that Aikins had been incapacitated for some time and this could continue for many months. But the Bergin motion was passed and Aikins continued with the formal assistance of his son.[5]

When he was still a few months short of three score and ten, the Board of the Metropolitan Church sent a note on May 4th 1897;

> Dear Doctor and Mrs. Aikins:
> We cannot allow ourselves to pass over the 25th anniversary of the Metropolitan Church without remembering the absent ones - more specifically yourselves.
>
> We greet you with loving affection and pray that grace, mercy and peace from our Lord and Saviour Jesus Christ may be abundantly bestowed upon you until He shall call you to His Presence with the glad message, "Well and faithfully done, enter into My Joy and sit down on My Throne."

It was a prescient letter as Aikins, ever a Victorian gentleman, died three weeks later, on the Queen's birthday.

A sombre group attended a special meeting in the Biology Building of the Medical Faculty on May 31, 1897 and passed the following:

> Resolved that in the death of the senior Professor of Surgery and the first Dean, the Faculty of Medicine has been deprived of a member held in the highest esteem for his personal work, and one whose varied and great experience, unusual ability and prolonged service as a medical teacher placed him in the front rank if not in the leading position amongst educationists. The Profession has lost one whose keen and intelligent foresight, broad views of medical polity, sincerity, steadfastness and purpose led him to take a very prominent part in securing the present high unexcelled professional standard and status in Ontario. The laity will also miss one who, in season and out of season, for many years, with an unselfish charity that never failed, ceased not to enforce the great importance of sound hygienic rules.
>
> And that this resolution be conveyed to the members of the Faculty of their lamented confrere with the expression of the warm sympathy of the Faculty in the bereavement which has taken a good husband and a kind Father.

The secretary was instructed to have the Resolution engrossed and forwarded to the Faculty.

REFERENCES

1. Ontario Medical Journal, Volume 1, no. 2, September 1892; pp. 82–4.
2. Gallie, W.E. Medical Graduates. 3:2, 1956; pp. 6–13.
3. Keane, D.R. Personal Communication.
4. Personal communication.
5. CPSO Minutes 1894.

Chapter Eleven

A Summary

The dwarf sees farther than the giant, when he has the giant's shoulder to mount on, wrote Samuel Taylor Coleridge in *The Friends, Essay 8,* as he paraphrased Newton's famous self-effacement. But after the dwarf descends and looks at the giants of the early days of the University of Toronto, he realizes how tall they stood. When the uninformed observer hears tales of medical practice of a century ago, he may be bemused, horrified or outraged. With further deliberation it is realized that egocentricity is not limited to any one person, profession or nation, because those who practiced and taught medicine in the 19th century stand shoulder-to-shoulder with their counterparts of the end of the 20th century. And in Toronto, there was no cause for self-denigration or kow-towing.

Aikins' professional life spanned an explosive, turbulent, revolutionary period in medicine. He and his colleagues responded forthrightly to the challenges put forward at that time, just as physicians respond today. Of course the questions put were of a different order, yet the gravity of the queries commanded equally weighty answers.

No apology is necessary, or asked for, to describe the University of Toronto Medical Faculty in the nineties. By that time bedside teaching had commenced, well in advance of many other North American schools and in step with leaders such as Johns Hopkins. Part of this may have been due to the influence of Bovell, who had been a student of Robert J. Graves and William Stokes in Dublin, where they had insisted on patient contact. Some resulted from the urging of Osler, who asked that on his epitaph should be written the credo "I taught medical students in the wards."[1]

The Aikins school appreciated and reacted to the changes in the concepts of disease, from G. Morgagni's organ pathology, through Xavier Bichat's tissue pathology and finally to Rudolph Virchow's cellular pathology. The final advance was met by providing microscope courses, with each student having the opportunity to observe the cell changes. The shift in the paradigm of sickness from restoring balance to the patient to correcting the abnormal state of the body was accomplished in the teaching and practice of medicine. A challenge by the sanitarians that prevention by a change in the style of living was adopted, but did not overwhelm the conventional curative therapies.

Another important evolution was the qualifications of the teachers of medicine. In the early 20th century Ph.D.'s gradually displaced physicians in many countries, particularly in the basic sciences. However, Toronto with Ramsay Wright, Macallum and Pike had already made this improvement. In addition a trail-blazing step was the full time appointment of the Chair of Anatomy, a pattern which was to become the desired arrangement for other Chairs in the first quarter of the 20th century. The anatomy situation posed an interesting problem. In the early 1890's Blake, Loudon, and Mulock were on the point of approaching the Senate to declare that anatomy was as a separate discipline and thus should be taken over by the University. This implied that it was not necessarily subservient to medicine, but rather was a science in its own self. Although there was an element of scholasticsm in this recommendation, the fact that the cost of the department would be transferred from medicine, and would be hidden in the budget of University College, was a major attraction to Mulock. However the course in anatomy in Toronto developed with the philosophy that descended from Edinburgh and Hopkins with less emphasis on formal lectures and more on the morphological changes, demonstrated by dissection, and stayed within Medicine. Part of this was due to pressure from the students who stated that they preferred the anatomy laboratory rather, than lectures.

Possibly in the teaching of physiology, Toronto led, more than followed, many other establishments. Dunglison, Aikins' teacher at Jefferson, had published *Human Physiology* in 1832. This was a standard text when Aikins was in his post-graduate years and by 1858 thousands of the volume had been sold. Although Dunglison and S. Weir Mitchell lectured in the didactic manner, the latter pioneered the demonstration-type lecture, necessitated both because of the increased number of students in classes and the impossibility of providing physiological apparatus to each student. The University of Pennsylvania established a physiology laboratory about 1874 and Ramsay Wright, at the School for Practical Science followed this in 1878. His strongest teaching point was that students should perform the experiments themselves, in order to grasp the principles behind morbidity. When Abraham Flexner made a survey of Toronto in 1910, he was able to compliment the school on the excellence of "the central discipline of the medical school."[2] The same report accepted that Toronto had emplaced bacteriology but ignored a lost opportunity. When Ramsay Wright visited Koch in 1891, he failed to grasp the offer for a U of T man to take Koch's first course in bacteriology. This introduced the technique of agar-plating to identify bacterial colonies and became an effective means of strain identification. McGill took advantage of the course and sent George Adami, thus establishing a scientific basis for disease identification. Toronto did not have a qualified bacteriologist until 1905 with J.A. Amyot, and failed to take part in the major controversies over immunity and specificity in the first part of the twentieth century.

Toronto qualified with high marks in the fact that it had developed a teaching hospital. While the Park Hospital had never proceeded, relations with the Toronto General, and cross representation between the University and Hospital Board, ensured that the students had opportunities for clinical teaching. The full scale development of out-patient clinics meant that students saw not only the severe problems requiring hospitalization, but had contact with a large number of ambulatory patients, whose disorders were the type seen in general practice By this development, the dilemma of too many students seeing too few in-patients was avoided. In addition it completed the evolution of the grand walking round, through the amphitheatre presentations with the ultimate situation where students actually touched patients. This contact meant that the embryo doctors could use the kymograph, developed by Carl Wunderlich to chart temperatures; the ophthalmoscope perfected by H.L.F. von Helmholtz, the reflex hammer and finally the inflatable bladder sphygmomanometer. These instruments ensured that by the turn of the century the student could do a quantifiable physical examination.

However even with the skills of auscultation, etc. there was still a serious lack of understanding of the causes of diseases. The textbooks, even though they spoke of the science of medicine, remained short of precise, accurate explanations of disease processes. Although the bacterial theory of disease vectors was being accepted, even the great Osler, in his early editions, failed to appreciate the microbial pathogenesis until the latter part of the 1890's. This was not surprising as it had been accepted that a knowledge of bacteria did not cure a patient. "Let the bacilli take care of themselves, let us take care of our patients", was expressed by many leading physicians.

But given that the facts of chemistry and physiology were primitive, compared with what was known fifteen years later, physicians were able to be more effective in clinical medicine and at the same time build a bank of scientific knowledge and techniques, which acted as a springboard for the great advances of medicine in the first quarter of the 20th century. It was a slow process, delayed, in part, by the general climate in which the doctor studied science:

> Education – It may embrace, as in the case of medical men who
> must have a certain amount of scientific instruction; but what it
> lacks is the true scientific grasp of life as a whole ... all sciences
> are but parts of one great science, and the highest function of
> the universal science is to teach us how to live.[3]

This opinion could cause a student to reflect that others might have rejected the scientific method. Arthur Conan Doyle, who seized the imagination of a generation, wrote in *The Physiologist's Wife*, a satire on the man of science. His protagonist, a Professor Ainslie Grey, constantly disparaged his wife by answering her concerns in physiological terms. Minor house-hold problems were answered with patho-physiological aphorisms. When she worried about his moral value system, he replied that she was suffering from "congestion of the medullary pons ... your vasomotor system is excited ... your arterioles have contracted ...". In effect, this man who had been portrayed as the hero-figure of twentieth century medicine, was revealed to have traded his compassion for a set of scientific shibboleths. The story underlined the tension between the facts of science and the beliefs of the humanist which constantly plagued the physician who had difficulty in finding God at the bottom of a test-tube.

The reluctance to accept fully the scientific basis of medicine, with all its implications, stemmed from the British ethic that the clinical approach, at the bedside, was more important than the laboratory venue. The result of this was that Britain lagged in scientific development as was highlighted by Flexner, (and Osler), when he made his testimony to the Haldane Commission.[4] These events reflected on Toronto as most post-graduates went to the U.K. rather than Germany, and did not receive the emphasis on the theoretical and scientific basis of medicine.

By the end of his Deanship, many of the philosophical controversies, which affected medicine, had been resolved. The evolution of man, as proposed by Darwin and popularized by Huxley, had been discounted by questioning of the mechanism of natural selection as the basis for evolution. Huxley, himself, had been humbled by the Marquis of Salisbury in 1894 at the meeting of the British Association for the Advancement of Science. Wilson, now dead, would have rushed to re-assert his faith in the creation of man as a unique act of God and would have quoted from his *Prehistoric Man* (1863) that "Christianity lifts for us the veil of Isis ...". Even the *Christian Guardian*, Aikins' secular bible, which had countenanced some Darwinism in its early stages, reversed itself with the appearance of *The Descent of Man* and recanted, "... in our effort to be liberal towards the theories and speculations of scientists, we may have surrendered too much".[5]

Aikins was a born broker. He sensed early in the game that the Toronto School of Medicine was under attack, which could be withstood if it was affiliated with an academic institution, and so notified Rolph. He then brokered the amalgamation with Victoria and later cannily picked up the remnants of Victoria's Medical department. By a combination of persuasion, flattery and knowing the likely men to approach, he assembled an excellent faculty. Through constancy and steadiness in pursuit of a higher level of teaching he achieved key positions in the CPSO, the OMA and the CMA. His close relationships with his brother in the Legislature and other political figures, including Mulock, resulted in legislation which gave the physicians of Ontario form and forum. Undoubtedly he was in the foreground of the takeover of the TSM by the University of Toronto – truly a University Dean incarnate.

To the general public and to many of his colleagues, Aikins' life was a constant upward progression, rarely impeded by criticism and usually charged with Christian equanimity. But there were many occasions on which this Garden of Eden was scented with brimstone. In 1876 a movement was made in the Senate of the University to cancel the affiliations of all existing medical schools with a view to re-affiliation on a different basis. This powerplay, which was engineered by the TSM to create itself as a monopoly and close out other medical teaching centres, was recognized by the *Canada Lancet*.[6] as a threat to Trinity College. The journal outlined the TSM tactic over the previous two years which had been to secure a larger number of representatives on the Senate. "They endeavoured in a hole and corner manner to manipulate the legally attended meetings of that body, and only too easily succeeded in the object they had in view". And what was the purpose of this conspiracy? To prevent the students of Trinity from taking prizes away from TSM students. "The most peculiar thing of all, and that which shows the moral obliquity of the whole proceeding in its full light, is the fact that at the very time this scheme of theirs had been urged on the Senate, the Toronto School of Medicine itself occupied the most intimate relation to Victoria University, Cobourg". It appeared that Aikins was chairman of the Board of Examiners for Victoria University and medical degrees were conferred by that University. Thus Aikins and his TSM colleagues could gather up the Senate seats which would be occupied by Victoria members.

This arrangement between Victoria and the TSM was a matter of convenience for each side. The Victoria calendar for 1877 announced that "students intending to graduate in Victoria University are recommended to attend lectures at the Toronto School of Medicine from which school certificates of attendance, will be accepted by the Examiners of this University". This bare-faced relationship between the two schools was pinpointed by M.B. in a letter to the editor of the *Canada Lancet*[7] when he questioned:

> How a pious Methodist, like Dr. Aikins, could say in the face of this, in his letter to the Lieutenant-Governor-in-Council asking for the dis-affiliation of all medical schools connected with the Toronto University with a view to re-arrangement, and "that the students of the Toronto School of Medicine can avail themselves of the degree of the Toronto University only" is a mystery.

Not only was Aikins a target of opprobium in the matter of dis-affiliation, he was also seen frequently as a blot on the page of the *Canada Lancet* and by many of the general practitioners throughout the province. The main contention was who should examine students for the CPSO. By the structure which had been set up by Parliament for the Ontario Medical Council and the CPSO, representatives of medical schools were automatically on the Council. These members, with some territorial representatives, comprised the examining Boards. In a sense this was a re-play of the longstanding complaint about professors examining their own students. If Aikins was on the Examing Board, it was natural that he would sit in judgement on some of his students. Of course, this was contrary to his previously held position, widely publicized through articles and presentations, from which he had derived much notoriety and kudos from the general profession. But somehow, he was now able by a convoluted process of illogic, to justify his position. Despite several efforts by the territorial representatives, he was able to hold his status.

One of the plans to overcome this disproportion of schoolmen was to enlarge the representation on the CPSO by increasing the number of territorials. Initially the make-up of the twenty-five members was eight from medical schools, five homeopaths and twelve from across the province. This expansion was presented on several occasions, but was invariably voted down by the sitting members. The *Canadian Journal of Medical Science*[8] felt that there were already too many members and editorialized against expanding the number, citing the current Council as being "characterized by puerility, incapacity, and unseemly wrangling. To an impartial on-looker the proceedings of the Council are simply disgusting. The log rolling, the wire pulling, the open interference by outsiders, and the mutual recriminations freely and incessantly indulged in by members, might perhaps be tolerated in a County Council or even a Local Legislature; but, when rampant and running riot in an assembly supposed to be composed exclusively of professional gentlemen, the unedifying spectacle cannot fail to fill one with ineffable disgust". While the *CJMS* was against the proposition, the *Canada Lancet* was in favour and noted the vote had been defeated by a small majority made up from schoolmen and the homeopaths. "... who stood shoulder-to-shoulder in the interest of the monopolies, against the claims of the general profession". Geikie's vote was for expansion. *Canada Lancet* argued that having more territorial representatives would break the "ring" which was leading the territorial members "... by the nose at the insistence of a few manipulators".

The only recourse to Council's decision centered on Aikins and was led by Geikie and Berryman. They introduced a motion that a permanent officer of the Council should not be connected with any of the schools. This, of course, had special reference to the Treasurer, who had held his position since the inaugurration of the Council. The *CJMS* gave Aikins an accolade when it said "... we may safely leave that gentlemen (Aikins) to take care of himself, ... although Dr. Berryman was put forward to entrap the Council into an implied censure, those who spoke bore ample testimony to the faithfulness and impartiality with which he discharges the duties of his office". However Aikins pleasure at being supported was tempered by a letter in the 1880 *Canada Lancet* which stated that a gentleman accepts office always for reasons of, one from philanthropy or charity; second because he is forced to do so, and third for gain as honour, influence or money:

> It would be absurd to say that either charity, philanthropy or force was the reason or the whole of them combined for Aikins to remain as Treasurer ... the profession does not need the first, and Dr. Aikins would not submit to the last. Then it must be for gain. Gain of what? Not of honour, surely, for it would bring dishonour to his name when he knows that so many of the profession oppose his appointment. It surely cannot be that a wealthy surgeon would wish to hold the emolument from so many of the more needy practitioners when it is so paltry in comparison with the immense profits of his profession. No, we do not think he is so penurious. Then it must be for gain of influence. Influence over whom? The suggestion of new students comes at once, and then our minds say: "if the Toronto of School of Medicine needs such questionable means of support to hold its own, it must be weak, and the party who uses the means can be neither fair minded nor honourable".

The letter was signed by Medicus from Beeton.

Great Deans and teachers are recognized by the institutions they have built, and by their pupils. While Aikins could not be held responsible for all the fine students who graduated from the TSM, there is no doubt that he was a major factor in their success. Certainly by his constancy from 1851 to 1895, he was able to influence many great physicians. While others such as Uzziel Ogden or Richardson had approximately the same tenure, they were neither in control of the programs, nor did they remain as movers within the school.

James Elliott Graham, who qualified in 1869, became a renowned surgeon. After completing a residency in the Brooklyn City Hospital, he went to Europe for further training and then served in the Franco-Prussia war of 1870-71. He was honoured by the Emperor of Germany for his treatment of wounded soldiers and presented with a medal forged from a captured cannon. Although the award read "With God, for Emperor, King and Fatherland," Graham was a staunch Canadian and returned to a practice in Toronto and married the daughter of Aikins' brother. One of his early tasks was to demonstrate microscopy and he also spent some years lecturing in chemistry. With the formation of the Medical Faculty at the U of T, he was appointed Professor of Clinical Medicine and Medical Pathology, and developed an interest in dermatology.

George Armstrong Peters was another brilliant graduate from the TSM in 1886. His major work was in the University and the Toronto General Hospital. Following a visit to the United Kingdom, he qualified as a Fellow of the Royal College of Surgeons of England. Although he was not an enthusiast for Listerism, he used an aseptic technique and avoided bruising and tearing tissues. He was an excellent physician as well as surgeon and identified the "Peter's sign" – breath sounds heard in the abdomen to indicate a peritonitis. He also pioneered the extra peritoneal transplantation of the ureters into the rectum. While dying of "angina pectoris" he dictated to his stenographer a description of the radiating pains to his left arm and remarked how they differed from accepted ideas of angina.

Abraham Groves who graduated from the TSM in 1871 was a daring and clever surgeon. Within weeks of beginning practice, he transfused blood to a "bled-out woman" using a rubber syringe. She lived. After performing his first ovariotomy, (also his first abdominal incision,) he flushed out the abdomen with gallons of boiled water. This was done before Lister's influence, and even preceded the work of Lawson Tait of Birmingham, a critic and competitor of Lister. "I boils me tools" the Canadian recalled, on his deathbed. He operated for many conditions including depressed fractures of the skull, prostate disease and bladder calculae. He innovated the suprapubic route for bladder procedures in Canada. Most noteworthy was his removal of a diseased appendix in 1883, when a 12 year old boy was suffering from pain and tenderness in the right iliac region. Groves opened the abdomen, identified and removed the inflamed appendix He reported that on a return visit to the boy three days later, that the father was "very much dissatisfied." A neighbour, apparently suffering from the same condition, had been treated successfully by poulticing. The father told Groves that, "If I had known how to treat the case properly, no operation would have been necessary, and if the child did not recover, it would not be well for me."[9]

When he reported the procedure to a medical meeting, there was strong opposition and it was prophesized that if the surgical procedure became common, the "death rate would be appalling." In his will, he left the hospital which he had founded to the town of Fergus. He was daring and innovative and was a strong believer in positive action to relieve certain surgical conditions.

An outstanding faculty member was Irving Heward Cameron, a graduate in 1871, who spent some time in England and Scotland in post graduate work. According to his biographer, he revered Aikins from whom he learned his surgery. Like Aikins, Cameron was able to assemble a prestigious group about him, including F.N.G. Starr, George Bingham, John Malloch, C.V. Shuttleworth and George Wilson. Norman Shenstone acknowledged Cameron's virtuosity, even though he refused to wear gloves because of the loss of sensitivity of his fingers, however he prepared his hands in carbolic solution.

Charles Kirk Clarke had worked closely with Workman and, on his retirement, took over responsibilities in the Psychiatric Hospital. He was a strong teacher and eventually became Dean of the Faculty and the first Professor of Psychiatry in Toronto. He worked unceasingly at convincing his colleagues that "an insane person is one suffering from bodily disease, just as much as the patient with typhoid fever ... why not hospitals for persons suffering from insanity?"

Another renowned graduate was Herbert A. Bruce, who became the standard bearer to ensure that Canadian soldiers were cared for by

Canadian health personnel in World War I. On his return to Toronto, he was the head of surgery at the Toronto General and later was appointed Lieutenant-Governor of the province. In addition to his surgical skills, he had a great compassion for the poor and homeless and was the initiator of a giant housing complex in downtown Toronto.

Each of these reflect a splendor on Aikins' life. His son Henry, continued with the CPSO and the OMA, dying in 1942. His widow, Lydia Ann, died in February 1914.

His school, now enriched by the new disciplines which were not dreamed of in the TSM of the 1860's and 1870's, entered the twentieth century with the integrity, skills and enterprise of the leading universities of North Amercia. If he had not been present, with his strong commitment to maintain the standards of the CPSO and the primacy of investigative medicine, it is possible the Medical Faculty would have had a different history. Geikie was a strong, outspoken voice who maintained that the public should not be taxed for the education of doctors. He represented the same hierarchy of power and prestige that had fought the TSM fifty years previously. Geikie lost his struggle and the province embarked on a century long program of the public footing the bill for the education of the professions.

In his presentation to the Canadian Historical Society, historian Professor Michael Bliss spoke of William Osler.[10] He recalled that Osler, the priest's son became a High Priest of Medicine. "Just as his father had devoted a life to saving souls, he devoted his to the salvation of bodies." Aikins was of a different creed, but no less devout. His dedication to succoring the sick and raising the level of his fellow physicians was a calling that countenanced occasions when his congregation might look askance. But in the end his gospel (and John Wesleys'), to minister to the sick, gave blessing to his work. In a time when science threatened the faith of the ages, Aikins managed to steer the first and preserve the second.

Aikins' Faculty prospered and in recognition of its founder, established the W.T. Aikins Awards for Excellence in Undergraduate teaching.

> Faculty members and students are invited to submit nominations for the Faculty of Medicine Awards for Excellence in Undergraduate Teaching. Recognition and form rewarding of outstanding

teachers acknowledges the emphasis that our Faculty assigns to the
importance of high-quality undergraduate teaching.

Faculty of Medicine academic staff who teach undergraduate students. Three awards given annual in each of the three categories.

(1) Course/Program Development and Coordination
(2) Development and Use of Innovative Instructional Methods
(3) Individual Teaching Performance
The winners (see Appendix) carry on the spirit of the first Dean of
Medicine.

REFERENCES

1. Osler, W. Aequanimitas 1904.
2. Flexner, A. Medical Education in the United States and Canada. New York
   1910; p 37.
3. Popular Science Monthly October 31, 1885.
4. Royal Commission on University Education in London. London, HMSO,
   1910-12, Vol. 3; pp 2–6.
5. Christian Guardian July 18, 1871.
6. Canada Lancet v.9. 1876–77; pp. 157–158.
7. Ibid March 13th, 1878.
8. Canadian Journal of Medical Science July 1879.
9. Groves, A. All In a Day's Work: Leaves from a Doctor's Casebook. Macmillan Company, Toronto 1934.
10. Bliss, M. Sir William Osler in the Making of a Secular Priesthood. Cana-
    dian Historical Association, Montreal August 27, 1995.

Appendix I

W.T. Aikins Award Winners

1985 Dr. K.V. Robb, Dr. A. Roberts
1986 Dr. C. Whiteside
1987 Dr. U. Ackermann, Dr. H.S. Himal
1988 Dr. J. Desmond, Dr. D.K. MacFadden
1989 Dr. A. Agur, Dr. C. Chalin
1990 Dr. E.J. Akesson, Dr. H. Ho Ping Kong
1991 Dr. R. Reznick
1992 Dr. R. Hyland, Dr. J. Tenebaum
1993 Dr. J. Keystone
1994 Dr. Dr. A. Gotlieb, Dr. R.K. Murray, Dr. S. Mintz
1995 Dr. M. Goldberg, Dr. J. Butany, Dr. R. Richardson
1996 Dr. C.M. Deber, Dr. D.J. Gare, Dr. P. McKee
1997 Dr. D. Brooks, Dr. D. Panisko, Dr. M. Sarin, Dr. M. Wiley

Course Development and Coordination

1985 Dr. D.W. Chamberlain
1986 Dr. D.L. Shaul, Dr. I.M. Taylor
1987 Dr. P.H. McCleary, Dr. J.L. Provan, Dr. R.M. Shier
1988 Dr. J.R. Ross
1989 Dr. W.J. Weiser
1990 Dr. D.I. Amato, Dr. A. Biringer
1992 Dr. A. Gotlieb

1993   Dr. R. Schneider
1994   Dr. M. Vearncombe, Dr. P. McCleary, Dr. I. Taylor
1995   Dr. P. Brubaker, Dr. D. Gray, Dr. M. Pare
       Group Award:
          Dr. C. Whiteside, Dr. N. Bryne, Ms. D. Alli
1996   Dr. D. Gasner, Dr. D.E. Isenman, Dr. D. Painter, Dr. D.G. White
1997   Dr. D. Reid, Dr. T. Rutledge, Dr. D. Wasylenki

Development and Use of Instructional Media

1985   Dr. N. Ranganathan, Dr. B.E. Stubbs
1987   Dr. M.L. Chipman
1989   Dr. R.A. Buckman, Dr. S. Mintz
1990   Dr. R. Cohen, Dr. C.G. Jamieson, Dr. J.L. Provan
       Group Award
1992   Dr. M. Shier
1993   Dr. I. Silver
1994   Dr. D. Cleave-Hogg, Dr. M. Wallace
1995   Dr. V. Watt
1996   Dr. W.J. Weiser
1997   not awarded

Special Contribution to Teaching

1997   Dr. N. Camerman

Appendix II

The end of the 19th century saw a flurry of new and up-dated medical publications, as authors scrambled to access the latest scientific findings. The Calendars of the course at Toronto listed suggested texts which included:

Principles and Practice of Medicine, Charles H. Fagge and P. Pye-Smith, 1888

A Textbook of Medicine, Adolph Strumpell, 1887

General Pathology or the Signs of the Causes, Nature and Course of the Process of Disease, Ernest Ziegler, 1901

An Introduction to Pathology and Morbid Anatomy, T. Henry Green, 1889

A Textbook of Physiology, Michael Foster, 1877

A Textbook of Medicine, William Osler, 1892

The Science and Art of Surgery, John E. Erichsen, 1853

Anatomy Descriptive and Surgical, Henry Gray, 1858

Disorders of Kidney and Urinary Derangements, W.H. Dickinson, 1875

A Textbook of Pharmacology, Therapeutics and Materia Medica, T.L. Brunton 1885.

The majority of these texts were from England and concentrated around the London Hospitals; Guy's, St. Thomas', St. Barts. The other recommended books were from Germany including University of Leipzig and Freiberg. There were a few American texts on the recommended list.

Not mentioned were:

Cavanagh, F.J.L, 1898: Head Troubles and Their Causes, in which he repeatedly warned that deliberatly wetting one's head led to innumerable ailment.

and:

Simpson, JJ Wesley – A supplement in "The Microcosmic Health Pamphlet" which promoted the merits of frequently flushing the colon with enormous quantities of water, injected by enema. Published in Toronto.

Appendix III

Contributions of W.T. Aikins to the Missionary Society from the Annual Reports of the Missionary Society of the Wesleyan Methodist Church

Year	Donation	Comment
1854	12 pounds	
1855	12 pounds	
1856	5 pounds	
1857	5 pounds	
1858	17 pounds	
1859	10 pounds	
1860	$5.00	
1860		
1861		Aikins listed as member of General Committee for 1862–1863
1862	$20.00	Aikins listed as member of General Committee for 1863–1864
1863	$100.00	most of the donations are less than 5.00
1864	$50.00	Aikins listed for General Committee of 1865–1866
1865	$400.00	Aikins listed for General Committee of 1866–1867
1866		Aikins listed for General Committee of 1867–1868
1867	$229.07	Aikins listed for General Committee of 1868–1869
1868		Aikins listed for General Committee of 1869–1870
1869		
1870	$90.00	
1871	$5.00	
1872	$140.00	for Japan
1873	$180.00	
1874	$100.00	
1875	$100.00	
1876	$265.00	
1877	$500.00	
1878	$1,000.00	
1879	$1,050.00	
1880	$1,200.00	
1881	$1,200.00	
1882	$200.00	
1883	$400.00	
1884	$400.00	
1885	$500.00	
1886	$500.00	
1887	$500.00	
1888	$500.00	
1889	$500.00	
1890	$100.00	
1891	$500.00	
1892	$100.00	
1893		no further mention of Aikin's in contributions

Index